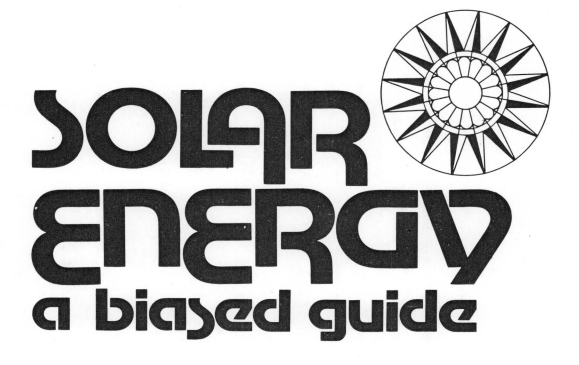

SOLAR ENERGY
a biased guide

by william l. ewers

● DOMUS INTERNATIONAL LIBRARY OF ECOLOGY
NORTHBROOK, ILLINOIS

COVER ILLUSTRATION **ruth guest**

BOOK DESIGN **macdonald-ball studio**

EDITORIAL DIRECTOR **victor margolin**

SOLAR ENERGY CONSULTANT **tony keisner**

Copyright © 1977 William Ewers
Published by
Domus Books
400 Anthony Trail
Northbrook, Illinois 60062

Second Printing 1977

Manufactured in the United States of America

Published simultaneously in Canada by
Gage Publishing
164 Commander Blvd.
Agincourt, Ontario M1S 3C7
Canada

Library of Congress Cataloging in Publication Data

Ewers, William.
    Solar energy.

    Bibliography: p. 93, 94
    Includes index.
    1. Solar energy.   I. Title.
TJ810.E9   1977   621.47   76-55551
ISBN 0-89196-013-9 pbk.

contents

DEDICATION

*To the loves of my life—my grandchildren,
Heather, Lisa, Jeramy and Jesse Lee, in the
fervent hope that the skies of their future will
always be bright, pure and blue.*

foreword

The solar industry is rapidly emerging as one of the greatest industries this nation has seen since the birth of the automobile. The facts support the premise that solar energy must contribute its share to the total energy needs of the world in the reasonably near future, and we must prepare now in order to meet the constantly increasing demands for energy.

The first useful application of solar energy was exhibited over 350 years ago. However, due to the vast supply of cheap alternative fuels such as natural gas, coal and oil, there was no need to immediately adopt the bountiful solar source. With the advent of fossil fuel shortages and increasing economic pressures, the world is now turning to other alternatives—nuclear power, wind, tide and direct solar utilization—to supplement its vast energy requirements.

Education of the public is the greatest tool with which the existing solar industry has to work. The general public must first be made aware of solar energy's potential and the effective utilization of that potential. The economic "dollars and cents" justification for utilizing solar energy for such immediate applications as hot water and space heating and cooling must be convincingly stated to potential users. This book will go a long way in objectively presenting the necessary information regarding solar energy to the public in language which is concise and easily understood.

Without such knowledge, potential users are unable to apply solar energy to their needs, nor can they evaluate the systems presently available to them. Texts and technical reports on the subject are generally composed in a form that overpowers and confuses the average reader. These works are necessary to research and the industry. However, books such as *Solar Energy: A Biased Guide* are needed if the public utilization of solar energy is to become a reality in the decades to come.

I am pleased to review this book, and lend suggestions as to its content. *Solar Energy: A Biased Guide* is one of the most comprehensive works on the state of solar energy technology available today, yet its format is simple and its content clear. Speaking for the Solar Industry, Mr. Ewers has our sincerest gratitude for the time and effort he has devoted to this very worthwhile endeavor.

Don W. Young
Executive Vice-President
CONSOLAR, Inc.
Tucson, Ariz.

introduction

When I began to research this book, my first impression was that the application of solar energy was a utopian ideal, a great topic for discussion but not much more, at least in the foreseeable future. I was determined to remain completely objective and dispassionate about it, but soon found, as so many others have before and since, that once you venture into the solar energy field it's impossible to remain neutral. There is no middle ground. You're either for it or against it, and I'm very definitely for it!

Having completed the book, I still can't understand why the United States has taken so long to get into full-scale solar energy research and development. One fact above all else is true. Sufficient information is NOW available to begin a viable solar energy program in both water and space heating. Space cooling is just around the corner. Although the initial cost factor is high when compared to conventional systems, most solar systems are now within reach of the average American family. There are, of course, variables which can influence a given situation (i.e. location, how elaborate the system is, utility rates, available financing, zoning laws and aesthetics), but the fact remains that solar energy technology is here.

Government involvement is necessary for a widespread application of any solar energy program. When a total government commitment is certain, private industry will join the parade and the success of the program will be assured.

I want to thank the many people who aided and guided me in completing this work. I'm especially appreciative of the assistance given me by Don. W. Young of the University of Arizona's Hydrology Department, who is also Executive Vice-President of Consolar, Inc. Dr. Young was kind enough to write the foreword. His wife Sherry Lawry Young prepared the excellent graphics.

William L. Ewers
Tucson, Ariz.
December, 1976

List of Acronyms

Throughout the book, government agencies are referred to by their acronyms.

ERDA   Energy Research and Development Administration

HEW   Department of Health, Education, and Welfare

HUD   Department of Housing and Urban Development

NASA   National Aeronautics and Space Administration

NSF   National Science Foundation

history of solar energy development

Solar energy is a subject more widely discussed than any other, with the possible exception of sex, as we earthlings head for the year 2000. It is virtually impossible to read any large metropolitan newspaper without noticing at least one article on the subject. The same is true for the broadcast media and weekly news magazines. If one were to believe the countless articles, it would appear that the world is in the midst of a solar energy boom. Unfortunately, it's not true and won't be for some time to come.

There are several reasons why the subject has generated this sudden publicity. Not the least of these was the sudden oil embargo imposed on the rest of the world by the OPEC countries. When the oil cartel suddenly cut off all shipments of crude oil, it made us realize that oil is a precious commodity and that it won't last forever. We had a good look at a fuel-short society and we didn't like what we saw. That experience of things to come might have been the best thing that ever happened to North America, and the rest of the world as well. Now all we have to do is remember those days of long lines at the gas pumps and the curtailment of home heating fuels in parts of the country and turn to a source of energy that is infinite and waiting to be tapped, the sun. The finite status of fossil fuels makes it imperative for us to look for alternate sources of energy.

The sun provides, directly and indirectly, *virtually all* energy used on this planet. All forms of life depend on the sun and it's rays. The sun influences climatic changes and ocean currents. It evaporates water from the earth which returns to us as rain. Millions of years ago, chemical reactions stimulated by sunshine formed all fossil fuels. Without this process we would have no coal, natural gas or petroleum.

Another important partner in this process is the atmosphere. This relatively thin layer that encircles the planet protects us from ultraviolet and infra-red rays by reflecting and scattering them out in space. After the harmful elements of the sunlight have been warded off, the helpful rays continue on to the earth. It is these helpful rays we must capture to supply future energy needs. *Radiation* is the term used to describe the rays which result from on-going reactions on the sun's surface and which come to us as sunlight and infra-red/ultraviolet rays. As an energy source, the sun has many plus factors. It is cost-free, pollution-free, available everywhere, and infinite. But, in terms of energy it is also diffuse and relatively low in temperature. Therein lies the big problem. Sunlight is everywhere in abundance but must be harnessed and stored to be effective as an energy source. The sun is free but the systems required to utilize it are not. In fact, the collection and storage of solar energy is presently very expensive.

In the technical use of the term, solar energy is the electromagnetic radiation produced on the sun and radiated over 93,000,000 miles (149,637,000 km), at a speed of 186,000 miles (299,274 km) per second, to all of us on earth.

Sunlight arriving at the edge of the earth's air space carries energy at an almost constant rate of 428 Btu's (British thermal units) per hour,* for every square foot of area. Considering absorption by the atmosphere, hours of darkness, cloud cover, and geographical location, the average amount of sunlight falling on a square foot of ground in the United States, on a year-round basis, is about 13% or 58.5 Btu's per hour.** This amount of heat, if absorbed and retained by a little less than a cubic foot of water, would raise the water temperature by 1 degree Fahrenheit, in one hour's time.

However, averages can be misleading, and we're dealing here mostly in the abstract. For example, when it's hot enough during the summer to "fry an egg on the sidewalk" there is seven times more solar energy reaching the ground compared to a typical cloudy day in winter. And of course, no solar energy reaches the earth during the night.

According to one estimate, enough solar energy falls on the continental United States every twenty minutes to supply our energy needs for a year. The *approximately* 17 thermal watts per *square foot* mentioned above would be twice the amount required to heat and cool the average home. Other considerations include the efficiency of present solar collectors, collecting methodology utilizing solar cells, and whether the system is for an individual dwelling or for the mass generation of electricity. Based on 1969 total energy usage figures in the United States, scientists estimate, that all the energy consumed in that year could have been supplied by a solar incidence on just 0.14% of the United States land area. To put it simply, if solar collecting equipment were placed on just 0.14% of the continental United States and technology was advanced to the point

*Equivalent to 130 watts in electrical power units.
**Equivalent to 16.4 watts in electrical power units.

**Design for a
passive solar
library, Lake Villa,
Illinois**

where it could be efficiently utilized, the sun could be our sole source of energy and fulfill all our needs.

Unfortunately, this large source of energy must be tapped before it can be put to work. The major problem facing everyone involved with solar energy is how to efficiently collect, utilize and store that power.

Storage methods are the biggest obstacle. Another side to the problem involves heating buildings, since the average amount of sunshine is always less in the sections of the country that require it most, and in times when heat is most needed. Conversely, this is an advantage where a dual system is designed to utilize solar energy for cooling as required in warmer parts of the country during the summer months. Relative to the overall use of solar energy solar cooling has a very bright future to reduce reliance on existing conventional air conditioning systems. I should state, however, that at the present time, the technological development associated with total package systems (i.e. heating and cooling) *is directed to* bringing the costs of the cooling cycle down to a level that is economically feasible. One that the heating cycle now enjoys.

It is a fact of solar energy technology that storage is the big handicap. Until an effective, inexpensive method of storing collected heat overnight or during overcast days is found, solar energy as a viable alternative power source may be a long time coming. Storage systems currently in use include water storage tanks, bins of rocks, a combination of those two, and also the addition of substances such as eutictic salts, which liquefy as they absorb heat and later emit the stored heat as they solidify. The use of solar energy for water and space heating, swimming pool heating, cooking, food drying, and distilling is nothing new. The technology is now available for the widespread use of these systems though many were in use long before fossil fuels were found to be an energy source. In fact, the sun was once the primary energy source, and primitive people built their homes to take full advantage of it's heat.

History tells us that solar furnaces were used in medieval times and that solar energy smelters were used in the late 1700's. The sun was used to separate salt from salt water beds and was very important in commercial salt manufacture.

Solar energy research, especially in the United States, had been plodding along in a rather unexciting manner since the late 19th century until the recent oil embargo again thrust the energy problem into the limelight. Solar energy development has proceeded at a faster pace in such countries as Japan, France, Israel, Australia, South Africa, and the Soviet Union. This development was spurred by a great need for additional energy at a lower cost in those countries, while the United States was enjoying relatively low-cost energy from natural gas, coal and oil. After World War II, advanced American technology harnessed nuclear energy for peacetime purposes, again at a relatively low cost. The wisdom of this program is currently being debated and we may see the end of the expansion of nuclear power plants.

The oil embargo opened our eyes. We were warned for years that domestic fossil fuels were dwindling and would some day run out, but some said we shouldn't worry because we had unlimited oil coming from the Middle East and elsewhere. That was before 1973. We now have high-cost energy, dwindling supplies, and no assurance of backup stock; hardly a solid base on which to build a future.

It's too bad that we didn't follow through on the solar energy research that was started before 1900. There were numerous applications before that time including a solar-powered steam engine for operating newspaper printing presses in Paris, France, and a solar-powered irrigation system which, by 1913, was in full operation in the middle of the Egyptian desert near the city of Meadi.

Meanwhile, in the United States, the solar water heater was gaining in popularity in Florida, California and the Southwest. The industry started in the early 1920's and was in full swing just prior to World War II. This growth lasted until the mid-1950's when low-cost natural gas, which was suddenly very plentiful, became the primary fuel for heating and lighting. This is probably why additional research wasn't undertaken, since it then appeared that we had enough low-cost natural gas to last forever. The timing was indeed unfortunate for the solar water heater industry, at least in the United States.

The fact remains, however, that the United States with its vast technology lags behind such countries as Australia, South Africa, Israel, France, and the Soviet Union in solar energy development. Solar water heaters are manufactured commercially in all of those countries, but are only produced on a limited scale in the United States. The solar water heater is standard equipment in many countries, notably Israel and Australia. Many Australian schools and public buildings are now equipped with solar heating equipment, and the number is growing.

Japan is a leader not only in the development of solar water heaters, but also of solar cells. That country is well into a multi-billion dollar program known as "The Sunshine Project" which is planned to extend over a twenty five year period. Japanese companies well into solar energy research and commercial manufacturing include Nippon, Sharp, and Hitachi, which is already marketing solar system components in the United States on a limited scale.

Solar systems were widely used in Israel after its founding. As the country developed, utility companies produced low-cost energy and for a time solar energy was relegated to a back burner. The on-going Middle East turmoil is changing that situation and the industry is again thriving, especially the manufacture of solar water heaters. A major manufacturer is the Miramit Company, which has been making solar water heaters since 1955.

The Russians use solar cells in their spacecraft program and have been conducting an extensive research and development program in Tashkent for many years. They are experimenting with methods of generating electricity on a massive scale, as well as with simpler systems for general use.

And so it goes around the world. Developing countries, as well as many which are more versed in technology, now realize that some use of solar energy is vital if they are to enjoy levels of energy use to which they've become accustomed. The threat of another oil embargo is always a possibility and the United States discovered, much to its chagrin, that even the very powerful nations are not immune.

The biggest area of research and development in the United States has been the use of solar cells in spacecraft and satellites. Much progress has been made since the Bell system manufactured the first workable solar cells in the mid-1950's. The Early Bird satellite was sent into orbit in 1965 with a life expectancy of less than two years. It operated at an effective level for nearly twice that time. Most spacecraft-satellites now circling the earth are powered by solar energy which is also used to recharge their batteries. The success of all space exploration has been made possible by the solar cell.

Solar energy programs around the world are funded, for the most part, with government money. Until recently most research in the United States was financed with corporate or foundation funds. Therein lies a problem.* Private industry has been, for the most part reluctant to invest

---

* Notable exceptions include National Science Foundation (NSF) funds to companies such as Pittsburgh Plate Glass, Westinghouse, and Olin.

heavily in a field in which the Federal government has been unwilling to advance large sums of money.

The research and development money advanced by NSF and other agencies prior to the passage of the Heating and Cooling Demonstration Act in 1974 was miniscule compared to the overall need. Again, there are exceptions to action by private industry. Companies such as Pittsburgh Plate Glass, Revere Copper, Honeywell, Westinghouse, ARKLA, Olin, Motorola, and Mobil Oil are well into manufacturing solar components or controls.

There are also numerous smaller companies in the solar energy business. Most of these manufacture, fabricate, or erect, components for solar water heaters, solar swimming pool heaters, and collectors for many different applications. There is an increase in the number of manufacturers and builders producing complete packages for home space heating, and to a lesser degree, space cooling. The industry has progressed from the late 1960's when you could count the number of solar heated homes in the United States on both hands. Hopefully, there has been a change in government thinking, and there are indications that the long awaited journey into the area of alternative energy sources is finally underway.

Alternatives under serious consideration at the present time are the use of nuclear energy on a larger scale, solar energy, wind power, methane gas from waste materials, a combination of wind, sun and the sea, and a return to the old standby, coal. The direction we take in relation to any of these programs is contingent upon where and how the government allocates research money. Hopefully, solar energy development will move up from the bottom rung of the ladder.

Government involvement prior to 1974 was practically non-existent, with the exception of some NSF activity and NASA's work in the space program. The Federal budget for solar energy in 1970 was only about $100,000. In fact, the total budget for solar energy research, excluding the space programs, from 1954 to 1971 was about a million dollars. As a basis for comparison, 3 billion dollars were allocated for nuclear research during that same period, a 3,000 to 1 ratio. And it wasn't as if both programs were starting from square one, since solar energy was at that time more advanced than peacetime nuclear research programs. Another bit of information you may find interesting, is that the solar energy program was initially under the direction of the Atomic Energy Commission, which is like letting the fox in with the chickens. The entire area of energy was later lumped together in a new agency, the Energy Research and Development Administration (ERDA).

There are valid reasons why the nuclear program received so much support and funding. Technology was much more advanced due to weapons research and when peacetime research and development started in 1954, there was a solid base from which to grow. Although solar energy research had been around longer—programs had been in existence at M.I.T. and in Florida since the 1930's—there was no single solid base for growth. The amazing part is, however, that this imbalance continued under four different administrations.

In retrospect, it seems equally strange that the strong pro-business Nixon administration apparently had little desire to promote a solar energy program. The concept was right up their alley, since after the initial outlay for research and development, solar energy could have been one of the greatest examples of the free enterprise system ever undertaken, rivaling even the oil and automobile industries.

The strongest fight for solar energy legislation in the Congress has come from Senator Mike Gravel, a liberal from the unlikely state of Alaska. The record must show that Senator Gravel influenced and promoted more solar energy legislation than his peers, and that any large scale government involvement is due in part to his participation. Other senators and congressmen have advocated solar energy development but Senator Gravel has been the driving force. He has made repeated efforts to increase allocations for research and on-site test projects. The big push which started in the early 1970's culminated in the first meaningful legislation known as The Heating & Cooling Demonstration Act of 1974, under the sponsorship of two Democrats, Senator Gravel and Senator Alan Cranston of California. The original appropriation was of 50 million dollars. When that bill passed, solar energy devotees must have thought they had died and gone to heaven. To digress a bit, the minimal funding of prior years was put to good use. One example was the establishment of a Solar Energy Panel jointly organized by the NSF and NASA in January 1972. The panel, under the direction of Dr. Paul Donovan of NSF and Mr. William Woodward of NASA, included approximately 40 scientists and engineers with expertise in solid state physics, chemistry, microbiology, power engineering, architecture, photovoltaics, and the thermal sciences. It also included economists, environmentalists and sociologists.

The panel's job was to assess the potential of solar energy as a national energy resource and determine how far it had progressed to that point, and in which areas. They were also to recommend increased research and development in areas of importance. The scope of the research was to include all applications of direct solar energy, as well as wind power, ocean thermal differences, and useful energy from replenishable organic materials. The conclusions and recommendations of the Solar Energy Panel were as follows:

CONCLUSIONS

1. Solar energy is received in sufficient quantity to make a major contribution to the future United States heat and power requirements.

2. There are numerous conversion methods by which solar energy can be utilized for heat and power; e.g. thermal, photosythesis, bioconversion, photovoltaics, winds and ocean temperature differences.

3. There are no technical barriers to the wide applications of solar energy to meet U.S. needs.

4. The technology of terrestrial solar energy conversion has been developed to its present limited extent through very modest government support and some private funding.

5. For most applications, the cost of converting solar energy to useful forms of energy is now higher than that for conventional sources but, it will become competitive in the near future, due to increasing prices of conventional fuels and increasing constraints on their use.

6. A substantial development program can achieve the necessary technical and economic objectives by the year 2020. Then solar energy could economically provide up to (1) 35% of the total building heating and cooling load; (2) 30% of the nation's gaseous fuel; (3) 10% of the liquid fuel; and (4) 20% of the electric energy requirements.

7. If solar development programs are successful, building heating could reach public use within five years, building cooling within 6 to 10 years, synthetic fuels from organic materials within 5 to 8 years, and electricity production within 10 to 15 years.

8. The large scale use of solar energy as a national resource would have a minimal effect on the environment.

RECOMMENDATIONS

1. The Federal government should take a lead role in developing a research and development program for the practical application of solar energy to the heat and power needs of the U.S.

2. The solar energy research and development program should provide for simultaneous effort towards three main objectives; (1) economical systems for heating and cooling buildings, (2) economical systems for producing and converting organic materials to liquid, solid, and gaseous fuels or to energy directly, (3) economical systems for generating electricity.

3. Research and development of various methods to accomplish the above objectives should proceed and programs with phased decision points should be established for concept appraisal and choice of options at the appropriate times.

4. For those developments which show good technical and economic promise, the Federal government and industry should continue development, pilot plant, and demonstration programs.

5. Environmental, social, and political consequences of solar energy utilization should be continually appraised and the results should be employed in development program planning.

Within a period of two years, annual funding for solar energy programs jumped from one million to 50 million dollars for other than space oriented programs. Despite the size of the increase, this amount fell far short of requested funding. It was also miniscule compared to nuclear energy funding for the same period. Two meaningful laws passed in 1974.* The Heating & Cooling Demonstration Act of 1974, and another research and development energy package bill that included all of the alternative energy sources such as nuclear energy, solar energy, wind power, methane gas, energy from ocean currents, and coal.

The problem with the latter bill was that most of the research money was channeled into nuclear power, even considering the public outcry against nuclear power plants. The other programs, including solar energy, were again relegated to a back seat. Although the solar energy arm of the Atomic Energy Commission constantly pushed for additional funding, it was undercut by the Chairman at that time, Dixy Lee Ray, who is now Governor of the state of Washington. An example of the inequity occured in fiscal 1974 when the recommended funding was 32 million dollars for solar energy programs and 700 million dollars for nuclear energy research. Chairman Ray often stated that solar energy research was a thing of the future with implementation well into the next century. She advocated limited studies during the late 1970's with some implementation to be made during the 1980's. The bias of Chairman Ray was a well known fact and although she is no longer chairman of the AEC, her views haven't changed. In a February 1976 speech to the Southern Arizona Chapter of the Electrical League of Arizona, Ms. Ray stated that there would be no significant impact from solar energy until after the year 2000 and that the economic feasibility of solar energy applications was at least twenty-five years away. Nuclear power was her answer to avoiding dependence on foreign oil.

I can hardly argue with the need for independence, except to state that increased research into solar energy programs could eventually reduce those gigantic costs referred to when talking about the eventual generation of electricity from solar energy. Ms. Ray was, of course, referring to generating electricity on a large scale but her adversary position regarding solar energy was very apparent. She made one point—and validly at that time—that since the sun's rays are diffuse, utilizing solar energy was like trying to harness 100 million fleas and then teaching them all to jump in the same direction at the same time while harnessing nuclear power could be likened to harnessing one elephant.

Many people still believe that more research and development money is needed to solve the problems inherent in the widespread use of solar energy and to gain a parity with existing energy sources. If the same money had been spent on solar energy that has been spent on peacetime nuclear energy research since 1954, we would now be on the threshold of a viable solar energy program. Energy independence by the 1980's, a goal widely proclaimed by the Nixon and Ford administrations, would be a reality. At the time of Ms. Ray's Arizona speech, she was no longer Chairman of the Atomic Energy Commission, so she was not speaking from an official position. But her views are a good example of thinking on that level.

---

*Four solar energy laws were passed during the 93rd Congress.

solar energy systems

For some time to come, solar energy will have its greatest application in the home. However, we can also look for several applications on a larger scale. We need a few more towns like Bridgeton, Texas. When the utility company recently raised the rates in that city, the City Council and the Mayor refused to sign a new contract. The town administrators are now looking to solar energy for power and intend to have it by the time the current utility contract expires in 1978. The technology exists for undertaking such a venture and the townspeople have faith in their ability to make it succeed. Many offers of assistance have poured into Bridgeton from leaders in the solar energy field. It goes without saying that the eyes of the solar energy industry will be on this project.

I will now delve into the utilization of solar energy systems currently available to the average person, and look at how we as individuals can use this power source. In this chapter, I will cover some of the necessary components of a solar energy system and explain their functions. Solar collectors will be covered to a greater degree since they are the most vital component in a solar energy system. For some time to come, the flat plate collector will continue to be most widely used, although this may change when low-cost methods of manufacturing solar cells are developed.

At this time, the most likely application for the average homeowner is the relatively inexpensive method of heating water, followed closely by space heating, in both new and existing homes and offices. Space cooling is still in the early stages of development, but an early breakthrough will lift the entire solar energy program off the launching pad. It is now possible to return to a time, comparable to the period in Florida and the

Southwest from the 1920's to the 1950's—when widespread use of solar water heaters was in vogue.

The construction of a solar water heater is well within the capability of the average person. Dealers can supply complete component packages ready for installation. The costs range from around 550 to 1000 dollars. There are also contractors in most sections of the country who are well qualified to install solar water heaters. This is true in many other countries including Australia, Israel, Japan, and South Africa.

The solar water heater industry in Florida was at one time a full scale operation, but faded away for two basic reasons:

1. The systems, especially water storage tanks, were not constructed to last for long periods of time. Improvements and modifications have since eliminated most of those problems.

2. The sudden availability and low cost of natural gas in the area, especially in Miami. We are all too familiar with the skyrocketing cost of natural gas today, not to mention its relative unavailability. The situation is so critical in some places that utility companies no longer accept new gas hookups. Every winter finds more and more curtailments in industrial plants, and as those shortages continue, homeowners will be next. The marriage between solar energy and swimming pool heating is natural. Several states are preparing legislation barring new gas connections for swimming pool heaters. This is already taking place in California and Arizona. Other states won't be far behind.

Advanced technology, coupled with a desire to re-examine the potential of heating water with the sun, has returned the solar water heater program to some prominence. A system can be installed as a primary heating source, with the conventional fuel-fired system as a backup source. By installing a couple of simple controls, the setup can be reversed. The solar water heater hasn't really changed very much from those early units in Florida. There are modifications and improvements—both in controls and collectors—but the basic system of a flat plate collector with the water storage tank is pretty much the same.

The use of solar energy for space heating and cooling probably has the greatest growth potential. A typical system consists of a collector in which water or, in other systems, air, is heated and then passed either directly through ductwork to the living area or to an insulated storage bin or a combination of both and then to an auxiliary system to back up the solar unit during cloudy days and at night. The cooling cycle is much more complicated and the technology is less advanced than in the heating cycle. It operates similarly to a gas-fired air conditioning system which requires the use of pumps and other controls to convert heat to cooled air before it is circulated to the living area. The big problem is that existing collectors cannot heat the water to the level required for making the cooling cycle operate. (Figure 1 on the following page shows a typical system using heated water.)

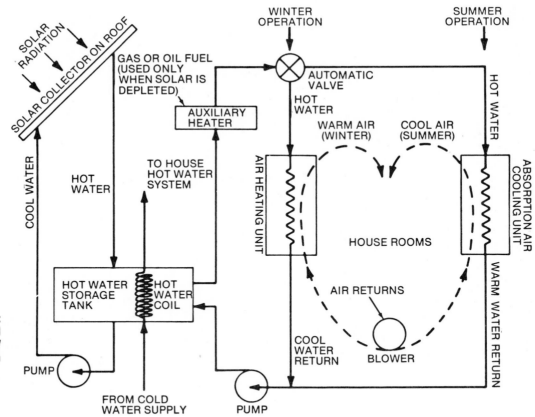

**Figure 1:
Diagram of a typical
space heating/
cooling system**

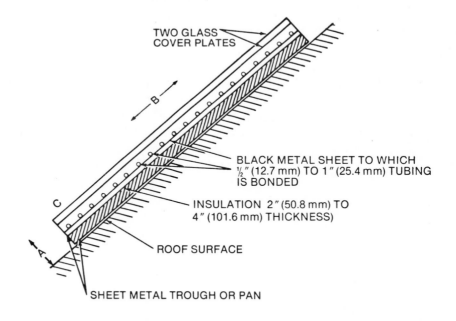

**Cross section of a
typical flat plate
collector**

TWO GLASS
COVER PLATES

BLACK METAL SHEET TO WHICH
½" (12.7 mm) TO 1" (25.4 mm) TUBING
IS BONDED

INSULATION 2" (50.8 mm) TO
4" (101.6 mm) THICKNESS)

ROOF SURFACE

SHEET METAL TROUGH OR PAN

NOTES: ENDS OF TUBES MANIFOLDED TOGETHER
            ONE TO THREE GLASS COVERS DEPENDING
            ON CONDITIONS
DIMENSIONS: THICKNESS (A DIRECTION) 3 IN (76.2 MM)
            TO 6 IN (152.4 MM)
            LENGTH (B DIRECTION) 4 FT (121.92 CM) TO
            20 FT (609.6CM)
            WIDTH (C DIRECTION) 10 FT (304.8 CM) TO
            50 FT (15.24 M)
            SLOPE DEPENDENT ON LOCATION AND ON
            WINTER-SUMMER LOAD COMPARISON

THE SOLAR COLLECTOR

The two most popular solar collectors now available are the flat plate collector (Figure 2) and the parabolic collector (Figure 3).

The typical flat plate collector consists of a frame and coils of tubing soldered either vertically or horizontally on a metal plate with either one or two panes of glass facing the sun. The tubing and plate are painted black to absorb the incoming heat. Most collectors have insulation integrated into the frame which rests between the collector plate and the rooftop. There are variations including plastic plate collectors, black plastic pipe, honeycomb instead of tubing, fins attached to the tubing, and flat metal plates bonded together with channels for water passage. There is also a relatively inexpensive collector constructed of corrugated sheet steel.

**Figure 2:
The flat plate
collector**

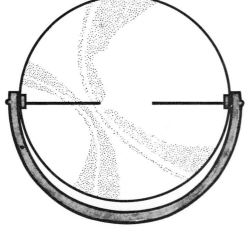

**Figure 3:
The parabolic
collector**

Clear plastic is sometimes used instead of glass, but it loses in efficiency what it makes up for in safety. Although most collectors use window pane glass at this time, the industry standard is almost certain to be tempered glass, at least for the outer pane in a two pane system.

Figure 4 illustrates one of the more popular collectors used in the Florida water heater industry. Note that the tubing runs parallel. Most of the models utilizing tubing today run the tubing horizontally. This requires comment, because the parallel unit has a lower profile when roof-mounted. An average horizontally-oriented unit will stand 7 to 8 feet (2.13 to 2.43 m) in the air, compared to a 24 to 30 inches (60 to 76 cm) for the average parallel unit.

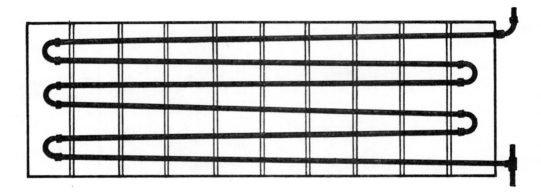

**Figure 4:
Copper tubing
configuration on a
flat plate collector**

A variety of flat plate collectors are being manufactured today; quite a change from the single copper plate with copper tubing in different configurations used in the Florida industry. Some of the available types in metal include:

1. Copper tubing on a copper plate
2. Aluminum tube on an aluminum plate
3. Brass tubing on brass plate
4. Iron pipe on iron plate
5. Steel platecoil
6. Aluminum Roll-Bond
7. Copper Roll-Bond
8. Corrugated steel plate
9. Aluminum honeycomb on an aluminum plate

As you can see, there are several different ways of constructing a flat plate collector, but the two most popular metal absorber plate materials are aluminum and copper. Another material widely used in swimming pool solar systems is black plastic. It is limited to swimming pool heating primarily because the black plastic collector cannot produce sufficient temperatures to operate a space heating system. Heating water for the average home would be a marginal thing unless several collectors were used but that's another story.

Aluminum is popular because of its lower cost. The Fauquier School in Virginia utilized the Aluminum Roll-Bond by Olin Brass because it was less expensive, although delivery time was also a consideration. But aluminum has definite drawbacks, one of which is corrosion. Aluminum must also be used with aluminum since other metals have a chemical reaction when coupled with it. It is less efficient than copper, which is a better heat conductor. The corrosion problem can be neutralized with water treatment, but then the cost factor is also changed. Without the water treatment, the average life of an aluminum collector is five to ten years. When the cost is amortized over that time period, a copper unit with fifteen to twenty years life expectancy, even though it may cost twice as much, suddenly becomes more attractive. Additionally, aluminum is a bit more difficult to work with, especially helioarc welding of the tubing to the absorber plate. But copper tubing must also be carefully welded to the plate for maximum efficiency.

What it boils down to is paying less up front and planning on a regimented program of maintenance to prolong the life of an aluminum unit or paying more up front and enjoying relatively trouble free collection from the copper unit. Another factor involves the black coating on the absorber plate and tubing. If this is painted when needed, it will prolong the life of a unit. Galvanized steel collectors probably fall somewhere between the other two metals vis-a-vis upkeep and length of service.

The Roll-Bond technique doesn't use tubing, but rather two plates of copper or aluminum, with one formed over the other. A special substance is placed on a plate and the other plate is rolled over and adhered by a special process. The substance is placed where the water channels are to be. Then pressure is applied to the plates and the channels bubble out, forming the water passages. This process has several advantages including a uniform water flow throughout the collector and less heat loss which occurs when water in the tubing loses some of the absorber heat during transference. Again, it would appear that the copper plate would be the better of the two because it's a better heat conductor. Consolar Systems, of Tucson, Arizona, uses the copper Roll-Bond plate in its collectors and the plate efficiency is very high.

Plate efficiency is a term you will hear when shopping for comparative flat plate collectors. It can be very misleading since any basis for comparison at this time would be very vague. Most of the charts illustrating plate efficiency show a curve on a two dimensional graph, which is not sufficient to make an accurate measurement. An expert pointed out to me, that the very least requirement for accuracy should be a three-dimensional chart, while a four-dimensional one is required for absolute accuracy. The latter can be obtained only by computer since many variables are involved. It would be wise to take the measurement of plate efficiency with a grain of salt and look very closely at the system before purchasing. You should also remember that efficiency is tied to the collector plate surface regardless of application or type of material. If the collector surface is too small, you will never get the heat required for a hot water system, swimming pool system, or most importantly—space heating. You should also avoid a collector surface which is too large for the system. This is especially important in a hot water system since too many collectors would produce extremely hot water, steam in many cases, and could blow up a system. Most hot water systems in the warmer or temperate climates utilize two collectors. A third may be required in the cooler climates.

Most applications do require more than a single collector, regardless of manageable size. The single collector is but one of a series engineered to handle the requirements of a particular installation. Two or more collectors are joined together by connecting pipes, both ingress and egress, to establish a flow pattern. They are then affixed to the desired location on a permanent basis, generally on a south-facing roof. Figures 5 and 6 show multiple collectors in place on the Timonium Elementary School in Maryland, a good example of how banks of collectors can be installed.

**Figure 5:
Multiple solar
collectors on the
Timonium
Elementary
school,
Timonium, Md.**

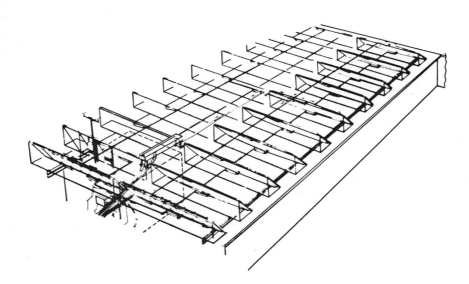

**Figure 6:
Sketch of the solar
collector
installation
at the Timonium
Elementary School**

Rarely would a residence require that amount of collector exposure. Information on how to construct collector modules will be covered in subsequent chapters describing the different types of units—water heaters, swimming pool heaters, and space heating or cooling. All necessary components for building collector modules should be readily available anywhere in the United States.

Another innovation, soldering fins to the tubing, has been added to some collectors to increase heat collection. The theory is that the increased metal surface will collect more heat and transfer it to the tubing and subsequently to the water to be heated. This is undoubtedly true, but it also raises some questions. Firstly, there is another weld or a break in transference because the joint cannot be 100% compatible with the tubing surface; secondly, unless the collector tracks the sun across the sky (and most do not) there must be a shadow factor. To my way of thinking, this would occur during the morning and evening hours when maximum collection is needed. It is entirely possible that any gain in efficiency from the addition of fins may be lost during those crucial periods when they cast shadows.

A parabolic collector is generally constructed of aluminum or another mirror-like material which catches the sun's rays to build up and collect heat. The parabolic collector functions more as a concentrator. The mirrors concentrate collected rays on a receiving component such as a tube, which is painted black and the water is then circulated back into the system. The more sophisticated versions contain a timing device which tracks the sun across the sky, thereby catching a maximum of sunshine. The parabolic collector will probably be used in the solar farm concept since much higher temperatures can be generated with this type of concentrated collection. This collector is also much more effective in areas with large amounts of sunshine.

SOLAR CELLS

Solar cells, also known as photovoltaic cells, are one result of the extensive research and development effort of the space program. There are, or have been, more than six hundred spacecraft equipped with solar cells, man-made solid state-like substances which convert sunlight into direct electric current. Solar cells have contributed greatly to the success of the space program. Without the ability to recharge batteries and power systems in space, the program could never have achieved the level of success it now enjoys. The Russians also employ this form of generating power in their space program.

The solar cell is a unique invention that converts sunlight into DC (direct current) electricity to provide energy. It is a solid-state device formed primarily of silicon, although there are other substances in use. It contains no moving parts. When placed in series, solar cells can supply energy to anything currently powered by battery or electrical power.

The material most used in solar cell manufacture at the present time is silicon, a substance found almost everywhere on earth. And don't worry about stripping the earth of yet another natural resource because silicon is one of the more plentiful elements around. A conservative estimate is that silicon makes up more than one fourth of the earth's crust and is perhaps our second most plentiful element.

Simple solar cells are used to power small transistor radios. They serve as automatic light controls in headlight-activated garage doors and have been used in other similar applications.

More sophisticated solar cells are used for charging batteries, on buoys in harbors and on shorelines, in microwave stations, and as the power source for signal devices and many different machines.

How do solar cells relate to the solar energy program? They could very well be the much needed breakthrough necessary to make solar energy the viable power source we desire. We know that the most expensive component of a solar unit is the flat plate collector. And, of course, this is also true of solar cells, except more so. It would require a vast reduction in present costs to a figure around five hundred dollars per kilowatt which would be competitive with nuclear energy costs. This means a reduction in the cost of manufacturing silicon, or other substances such as cadmium sulfide, to a level where array construction would be feasible. There are signs of significant success in silicon production. Tyco Solar Energy Corporation is perfecting a process for "growing" silicon ribbons as long as 80 feet (24.384m), at a rate of 2 inches per minute (50.8mm p/m). But the cost is still prohibitive for the average homeowner. This means the use of solar cells for space heating or cooling, where the increased energy will be a big boost, or heating water, for the average person is still somewhere in the future.*

Another hurdle to be conquered in solar cell development is the low percentage of effectiveness, currently around 10%. Some scientists feel that a maximum of at least 25% efficiency is possible for the conversion of sunlight to a usable electrical charge in a single semiconductor unit at room temperature. Using a 10% efficiency factor, an average size home equipped with an array of solar cell panels 20 by 30 feet (6.09m x 9.144m) could collect an average of 25 kwh (kilowatt hours) per 24 hour day. This would be sufficient to supply enough daily power requirements for the average family. Larger homes would require larger solar cell arrays since there is direct correlation between collector size and house size, as is the case with flat plate collectors.

The use of solar cells for generating sufficient electricity for individual consumer usage lies somewhere in the future. Some of the concepts currently under study are solar cell arrays on buildings which include integrated convertors for supplying all required energy to the building; central systems erected at ground level with huge arrays of solar cells capable of serving an entire distribution system; and central systems somewhere out in space, which beam power back to central earth stations and into existing distribution systems.

---

*If you are interested in experimenting with solar cells, write to: Edmund Scientific Company, Barrington, New Jersey, 00807, for their latest catalog. They offer solar cells of varying costs and effectiveness for experimental as well as functional purposes.

Although most solar cells are now made of silicon, other substances have been used in limited quantities. These include cadmium sulfide, cadmium telluride, and gallium orsenide.

Cadmium sulfide is being researched and tested on a large scale. The manufacture of this substance will probably be the most feasible due to the relatively inexpensive cost, once some of the bugs associated with it's manufacture are ironed out.

There are indications that mass production of solar cells is just around the corner. And, as is almost always the case, mass production means cost reduction. This, coupled with increased efficiency, should bring solar cell units within reach of most users. Costs should be in the two to four cents per kilowatt hour range which equates them with those of more conventional systems.

Of the three systems mentioned, the installation of solar cell array systems on buildings is probably the nearest to reality at this time.

The big plus factor in that system is the installation of the generator at the place of use. This eliminates the need for an outside delivery system, and matches collected energy with actual need. Since it is virtually impossible to store more than an average day's needs, some type of auxiliary power would be required. As now conceived, the solar cell array would be mounted on, or in some cases integrated into, a building in combination with flat plate thermal collectors. This would complete a package including water heating, space heating, and air conditioning, as well as the direct use of electrical power. Figure 7 shows the cross section of such a collector. Figure 8 illustrates all the components of a complete energy package for a commercial application.

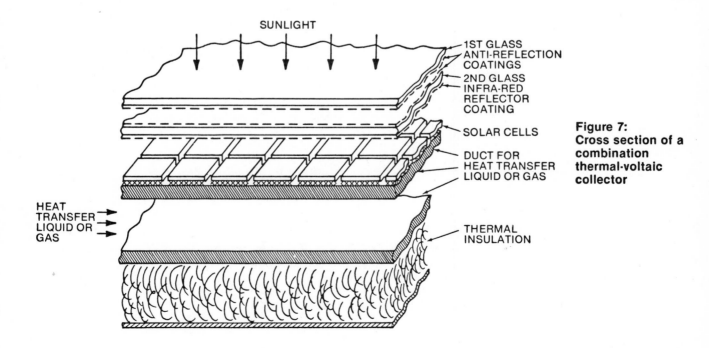

Figure 7:
Cross section of a combination thermal-voltaic collector

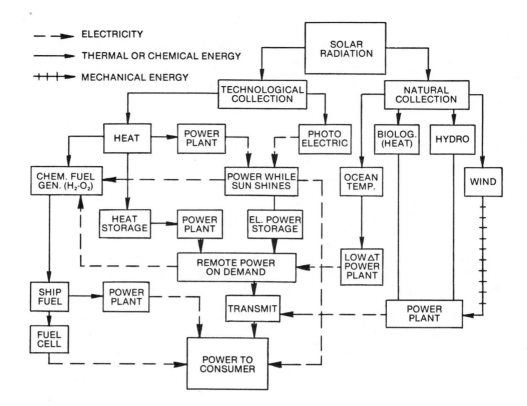

Figure 8: Diagram of a complete alternative energy system

Before you rush out to buy components for a solar system, there are some additional things to consider. Firstly, if you're considering space heating, look at the insulation of the structure. If it is not well insulated, the heat will pour out faster than your solar unit can bring it in and a solar energy package would be a waste of money. This is applicable to retrofit, adding a solar unit to an existing building not built with a solar package in mind, more so than to an O.E.M. (original plan). If you are planning a home specifically for solar energy, make sure it is well insulated. You should also determine whether the structure has a south-facing roof, or ample area for a solar collector array facing south. This is a must for an operable system.

Secondly, make certain that the solar energy plant is large enough to accommodate the house. Since installing a solar package is quite an investment, don't skimp on components. You will save money in the long run. However, as stated before, don't overbuild, especially with a water heater system.

Thirdly, check zoning laws, environmental impact studies for your area, and your legal status regarding potential obstacles, such as a tree, tall building, or similar structure, which might reduce the effectiveness of your system.

Finally, shop carefully. Check components for efficiency and be sure the unit is capable of meeting your requirements.

solar water heaters

Heating water in the family dwelling is one of the most advanced applications of solar energy both here and abroad. Solar water heating had it's beginning in Florida during the early 1920's and gained popularity until it peaked just prior to World War II.

Those early heaters vary only slightly from today's units. A typical system contained a flat plate collector and a galvanized steel tank connected by pipe. It operated on the thermosiphon principle for water circulation in the collector to the tank and return loop. The tank was placed above the collector which permitted the less dense hot water in the collector to rise to the top of the tank. It also prevented reverse cooling circulation during the night.

The big differences between those early models and most of those featured today are an improvement in collector efficiency, and the addition of controls which enables the system to be piped into a conventional fuel-fired water heater. This reduces fuel consumption in the existing water heater. Multiple collectors can increase the rate of efficiency to the point where the conventional unit is rarely activated.

An operable solar water heater can be easily constructed from components by anyone with average mechanical ability. The cost is determined by which components are used. I will discuss a system using copper tubing with copper absorber plate, another with copper Roll-Bond manufactured by Olin Brass, and a relatively inexpensive model using galvanized corrugated sheet steel. As in other applications, the collector is the most expensive component. More efficient collectors cost more money. Other items such as double pane glass, which raises the efficiency level, thicker insulation between the collector and roof, and insulation of connecting pipe and tank also increase the cost.

Another difference between the early Florida models and those of today is that the Florida models were the primary water heater source. It wasn't until the late 1930's and early 1940's that booster units were used to heat the water when the sun didn't shine. Today, many systems tie in with the existing conventional system which acts as the backup unit. When the sun shines, hot water is fed directly into the water heater and as long as the temperature level is high enough, the conventional system is not activated. If that temperature falls during the night, or during ex-

Figure 9: Diagram of a typical roof-mounted solar water heater in Florida

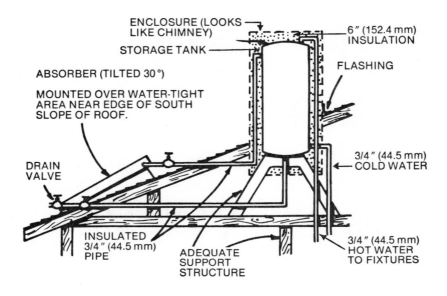

Figure 10: Diagram of a typical ground-mounted solar water heater in Florida

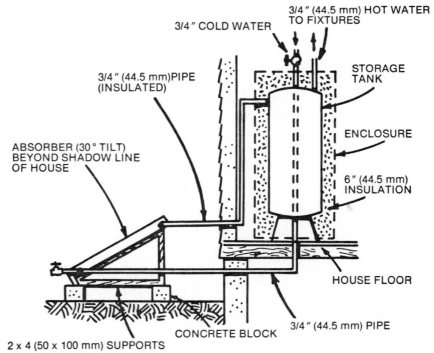

tended periods of overcast days, the conventional system is activated and the user enjoys uninterrupted hot water.

Consolar Inc. of Tucson, Arizona, features a mixer control that I haven't found on other models. This control supplies cool water to the solar-heated water when the temperature of the latter is greater than the setting on the hot water heater. This makes sense because it would be impossible to supply scalding water through the system if some additional control were not employed.

Figures 9 and 10 show different methods of erecting solar water heaters in the Florida industry. It is not widely known, that at one time there were more than sixty thousand solar water heaters in Southern Florida, mostly in the Miami area.

They were installed in new homes and retrofitted on older homes. As is the case today, retrofitting was more expensive and less satisfactory, mostly from an aesthetic point of view, since it is very difficult to avoid that "added-on" look.

There were three basic plans for positioning the collectors and the same is true today. The roof-mounted unit was most popular, followed by the ground-mounted and window awning-mounted units. Figure 9 illustrates a roof-mounted unit. It was a retrofit unit; most systems constructed when the house was built were integrated into the roof construction. Note that the storage tank is placed above the topmost portion of the

Figure 11: Solar collectors as window awnings in Florida. (Top) Collector panel placed over south-facing window functions as awning. (Bottom) Another method of placing collectors to blend in with dwelling appearance.

collector, which allows the circulation of the water by gravity, unassisted by a pump or mechanical means. This is known as the thermosiphon process. The storage tank is well insulated and placed in a specially constructed fixture, generally a metal structure designed to look like a fireplace chimney.

In this system, both water lines from the collector were inclined slightly to speed water circulation, and the line connecting the collector top to the tank was well insulated to prevent reverse circulation during the night. The drain valve was strategically located so it could drain the tank and collectors at the same time. A periodic draining was required to clean the system and get rid of corrosive buildup.

Figure 10 illustrates a ground-mounted unit positioned adjacent to the dwelling with the tank located inside the wall. Although it was less expensive and easier to maintain, the collector was more subject to damage and was probably less effective if trees or shrubs were planted nearby. Note that the same configuration applied when the tank was located above the uppermost portion of the collector. The collector is mounted out beyond the maximum shadow line of the dwelling.

The use of collectors as window awnings, shown in Figure 11, killed two birds with one stone. It didn't change the appearance of the house too much, and it shaded south-facing windows thus reducing heat build-up inside the home. The tank was also located inside. A disadvantage *could be* that the size of the collector is restricted.

Most fabricators in the Florida solar water heater industry used a copper plate absorber with copper tubing. Figure 12 illustrates the three most commonly used layouts. Note that the tubing is placed at a slight angle rather than parallel which helps speed water circulation through the system. The double coil and duplex coil concepts were used to speed recovery time when hot water was drained off rapidly during periods of peak usage.

The duplex coil absorber was manufactured by the Solar Water Heater Company of Miami, Florida, which claimed that the design circulated 20% more water and also produced hot water up to 30% more than absorbers with a single coil design.

The original base material was very light copper. As designs improved, it was increased from six to ten ounce (170g to 283g) stock. Tubing was then, as it is now, mostly ¾ inch (44.45mm) soft copper. The space between tubing rows was about 6 inches (152.4mm). Some manufacturers placed the tubing closer together. All that accomplished was a cost increase, since tests proved that the 6 inches (152.4mm) spacing produced 93% of efficiency gained by the closer spacing. Another interesting statistic was that if a 3 ounce (85g) copper base material was used instead of 6 ounce (l70g) material, the tubing had to be reduced to 4 inches (101.6mm) spacing to attain equal efficiency. Continual soldering of the tubing to the base provided much greater efficiency than spot soldering, which provided less heat flow. However, that heat loss could also be gained by closer spacing of the tubing.

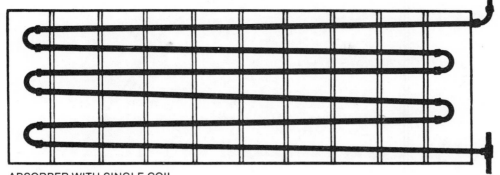

ABSORBER WITH SINGLE COIL

Figure 12: Sample absorber tubing configuration in the Florida industry

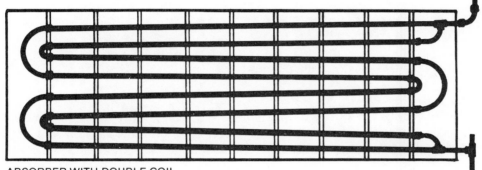

ABSORBER WITH DOUBLE COIL

3/4″ (44.5 mm) COPPER RETURN BENDS

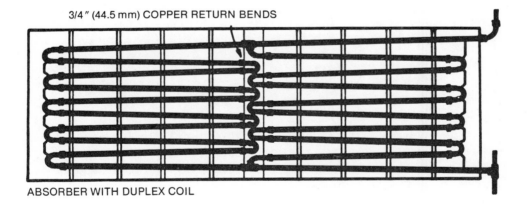

ABSORBER WITH DUPLEX COIL

The actual collector absorber plate was encased in a weathertight frame (Figure 13). The first units made by the Solar Water Heater Company were constructed of 24 gauge (1.19mm) galvanized steel, but when rust became a problem, the company changed to a combination of ⅛ inch (3.l75mm) galvanized angle iron and asbestos. This was also unsatisfactory, so they finally settled on 18 or 20 gauge (1.58mm or 1.98mm) galvanized sheet steel. Thousands of units were made of this material until a unit fabricated of ⅛ inch (3.175mm) galvanized angle iron with aluminum sheeting became standard.

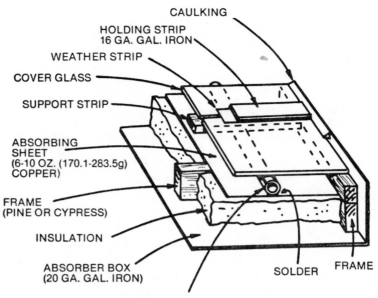

Figure 13: Cross-section of a typical collector

CAULKING

HOLDING STRIP
16 GA. GAL. IRON

WEATHER STRIP

COVER GLASS

SUPPORT STRIP

ABSORBING
SHEET
(6-10 OZ. (170.1-283.5g)
COPPER)

FRAME
(PINE OR CYPRESS)

INSULATION

ABSORBER BOX
(20 GA. GAL. IRON)

SOLDER   FRAME

PIPE COIL (3/4″ (44.5 mm) COPPER)

Refer again to Figure 13, and note the presence of insulation. Various types were used, including mineral wool, regranulated cork or cork board, insulating wall board, sawdust and vermiculite. The insulation served a two-fold purpose; to prevent heat loss through the collector and to protect the roof from collector heat.

The base sheet of copper and the copper tubing were painted with a dull, flat paint which provided adequate absorption of the sun's energy over the life of the unit. Black is the most widely used color today.

The number of glass cover plates varied between one and two, depending upon location. Two glass plates were used in areas subjected to freezing, although the second plate also prevented heat loss and made a more efficient unit. Most systems today utilize two glass plates. The glass type was ordinary window glass, single strength, supported on a wooden strip (See Figure 13). It was weatherstripped at the joints and held in place by a 16 gauge (l.587mm) galvanized iron holding strip. The glass edges were caulked all around to form a tight seal.

Storage tanks were of the standard, commercial type; galvanized steel, with supports of either steel or wood (Figures 9 and 10). The tank was insulated with 5 to 6 inch (127mm to 152.4mm) thick insulation and the entire unit was encased in a chimney-like structure on the roof. This was for roof-mounted units only. If the system was ground-mounted, the tank was installed just inside the nearest wall.

Cold water entered the tank through a line near the bottom, or in some cases through the tank top down to about 6 inches (152.4mm) from the base of the tank (Figure 19). The pipe carrying hot water to the tank exited near the top of the collector (absorber) and was piped to the top of the tank which allowed the hot water to be drawn off the top.

As mentioned previously, these systems operated on the thermosiphon principle. Hot water is less dense and rises to the top of the collector as it heats. It continues on into the tank, as cold water from the tank bottom returns to the base of the collector to start the heating cycle again. The ideal separation between the collector top and tank bottom was found to be 2 feet (60.96cm). The primary reason for this was to stop reverse circulation during the day when the sun wasn't shining and during the night. The addition of insulation to the pipe from the collector top to tank bottom also aided the system in this respect.

Larger installations often used a pump to force the water circulation, especially when the tank was located lower than the collectors. Most systems in use today utilize a pump for the same function. Additionally, in installations of this nature, a check valve is used to prevent reverse circulation. Many systems today also utilize photocells for this purpose.

The circulating pump is activated by electric impulses from slow-acting photocells, which are designed so a passing cloud will shut the pump off. Another system currently in use started the pump by sensing the temperature difference between the tank and collector.

Correlation of tank size to collector area is a very important factor in attaining maximum efficiency. If the collector is too small to heat the tank water, the water will never be hot enough to use. If the collector is too large, the water will be too hot to use safely and collector efficiency will also be diminished. Studies conducted in the Miami area indicate that a well-engineered unit will produce 1.5 to 1.7 gallons (5.67 to 6.43 litres) of water, at 130 degrees Fahrenheit (54.4°C.) per square foot of collector area. The following table illustrates some of the guidelines used in the Florida survey.

RESIDENCES

No. of Bedrooms	Occupants	Size of Tank (Gallons)	No. and Sizes of Collectors (Double Coil Type)
1 or 2	3	66*	One: 9 ft. - 10 in. x 4 ft.*
2 or 3	4	82	One: 12 ft. - 3 in. x 4 ft.
3 or 4 (2 baths)	4	100	One: 14 ft. - 8 in. x 4 ft.
Small duplex	6	120	One: 15 ft. - 11 in. x 4 ft.

APARTMENTS

No. of Units	Size of Tank (Gallons)	No. and Sizes of Collectors (Double Coil Type)
3	200	Two: 14 ft. - 8 in. x 4 ft.
6	300	Three: 14 ft. - 8 in. x 4 ft.
10	500	Five: 14 ft. - 8 in. x 4 ft.

Source: Scott, Melicher, and Sciglimpaglia. Solar Heating and Cooling of Buildings, 1974.

*NOTE 1 U.S. Gal = 3.785 litres
       1 U.S. Foot = 130.48 cm
       1 U.S. Inch = 25.4 mm

Many factors determine the efficiency of a flat plate collector system. Heaters using the thermosiphon concept have been found to produce temperatures as high as 165 degrees Fahrenheit when using the double coil system, according to tests conducted in the Miami, Florida, area. Variables include latitude, which also determines the tilt and angle degree of the collector, the number of glass plates, the type of materials used in the absorber plate, and, of course, the size of the collector relative to tank capacity for the temperature of delivered water. The table below illustrates the degree of efficiency in the Miami study.

ABSORBER ARRANGEMENTS AND CAPACITIES
FOR HEATING WATER TO 130°F. IN FLORIDA*

Location	Angle of Tilt from Horizontal Facing South	Number of Cover Glass Layers	Water Heated from Air Temperature to 130° F. (gallons per sq. ft. per day)	
			Minimum Season	Annual Avg.
North Florida ... ...45° (Jacksonville, Gainesville, Pensacola, etc.)		1	1.0	1.5
		2	1.1	1.7
	30°	1	0.8	1.3
		2	1.0	1.7
South Florida ... ...45° (Miami, etc.)		1	1.4	1.6
		2	1.5	1.7
	30°	1	1.4	1.7
		2	1.6	1.8

*Source Scott, Melicher, and Sciglimpaglis, Solar Heating and Cooling of Buildings, 1974.

Maintenance for the early models was more of a problem, but later models were almost trouble-free. It was recommended that the entire system be drained and cleaned at least twice a year. The drain valve was located so both the tank and collector could be drained simultaneously. This periodic draining kept rust and corrosion buildup to a minimum. Additional maintenance included keeping the glass clean, checking the seals and the frame, and keeping the absorber plate and tubing painted.

After the technology was improved, many solar water heater owners in the Miami area added boosters as backup energy sources. Most systems today contain such an innovation, or another version where the heated water is piped into the existing water heater. This reduces the operation time of the conventional system as long as solar-furnished water main-

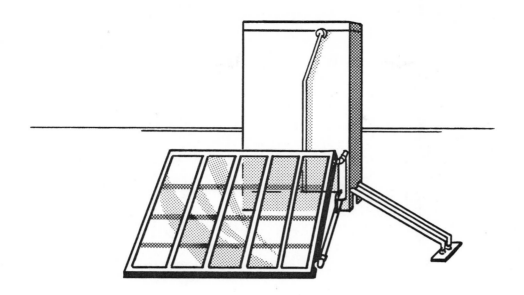

Figure 14: A free-standing solar water heater in Florida

tains the required temperature. The most popular method in the Florida survey was the gas-fired booster which was added to the top of the tank to avoid heating the entire tank. The primary reason for adding boosters in the latter stages of the Florida solar water heater industry was the sudden proliferation of new appliances requiring more hot water, which resulted in the overtaxing of the existing solar unit. The boosters marketed today are thermostatically controlled, generally with a manual on/off switch so the booster can be by-passed when it isn't needed, to cut electrical consumption. This is a good idea during extended periods of long hot sunlit days and at vacation time.

Another example of an efficient, yet inexpensive, solar water heater was built by the Brace Institute at McGill University in Montreal. The original units were built and tested in Barbados so the circumstances relative to the operation are a little extreme. Most places do not have that type of sun exposure. Several models were tested over an extended period of time and have proven to be quite efficient.

As I mentioned at the beginning of this chapter, solar components can be very expensive, moderately expensive, or inexpensive, depending upon the materials used. The Brace Institute model is inexpensive. It is constructed of basic materials and the life expectancy is nearly that of more sophisticated units, provided that regular maintenance is performed.

This unit was specifically designed to be constructed of simple, low-cost materials available almost anywhere, including remote areas of developing countries. The water heater was designed to provide 30 to 40 gallons of hot water a day, ranging in temperature from 130 to 140 degrees Fahrenheit, depending on local conditions.

The original cost per unit in the Barbados experiment was about 45 dollars for all locally-purchased components including: the collector, hot water storage tank, cold water storage tank, and connecting pipe. Labor costs were not included in that figure. The cost for a similar unit in the United States in 1976 would probably run between 200 and 250 dollars. The life expectancy of the system with minimal maintenance, is at least

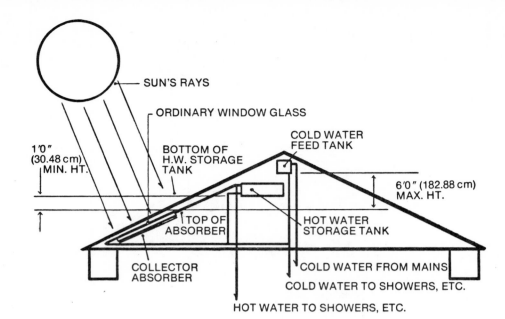

Figure 15: Elevation sketch of the Brace Institute solar water heater

five years and probably longer. The water storage units (oil drums for water tanks) would probably be the first components to expire, so replacement costs would be a minor item. Maintenance consists of draining and cleaning the system twice annually; with rust buildup being the biggest problem, and cleaning the glass occasionally.

The following pages contain all the instructions and drawings necessary to construct a simple, low-cost solar water heater. The components are:

1. the collector/absorber which absorbs the sun's rays and heats the water
2. the collector case which houses the absorber and insulation material
3. the hot water supply tank—suitably insulated—to hold the heated water. An old 55 gal. (208.198 litres) oil drum can be used for this purpose
4. the cold water feed tank, which is also fabricated from an oil drum

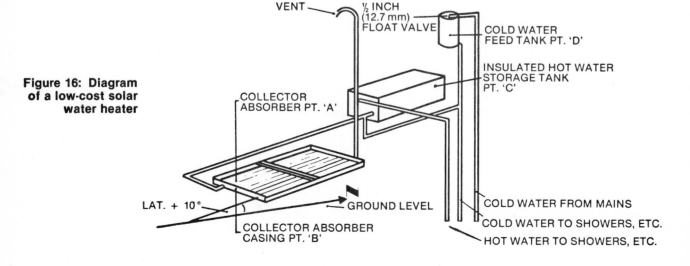

Figure 16: Diagram of a low-cost solar water heater

MATERIALS LIST

No. Of	Material	Size
The Absorber		
1	corrugated galv. steel sheet	*22 gauge, 8 ft. x 26 in.
1	"special" flat galv. steel sheet	22 gauge, 8 ft. x 36 in.
28	galv. steel rivets	¼ in. dia., approx. ⁵⁄₁₆ in. long
2	galv. steel water pipe	½ in. I.D., 9 in. long
2	m.s. machine screw	³⁄₁₆ in. dia., ¼ in. long
2	sticks of solder	
The Absorber Casing		
1	"special" flat galv. steel sheet	24 gauge, 8 ft. x 3 ft.
8	galv. rivets for ends of casing	¼ in. dia., approx. ⁵⁄₁₆ in. long
—	coco-nut fibre or equivalent insulation	20 lbs.
6	22 gauge galv. steel sheet	1 in. x 1 in. x ¾ in., supporting "L" brackets
6	felt strips or suitable insulation	1 in. x 1 in. x ⅛ in. thick
6	galv. rivets for part (10)	¼ in. dia.
4	22 gauge galv. steel sheet	1 in. x ¾ in. x ½ in., hold-down "L" clamps
4	galv. steel self threading screws for part (13)	⅛ in. dia. x ½ in. long
1	22 gauge galv. steel sheet	27⅛ in. x 2½ in., to make glass support rib
4	galv. rivets for part (15)	¼ in. dia., approx. ⁵⁄₁₆ in. long
2	sponge rubber strip, e.g. "Dor-Tite"	¼ in. x ⅛ in. x 17¾ in. long
1	sponge rubber strip, e.g. "Dor-Tite"	¼ in. x ⅛ in. x 22 ft. long
2	window glass	27¾ in. x 44¾ in. x ⅛ in. thick
1	silicone type sealant (or equivalent)	12 oz. cartridge
1	black plastic electrical insulating tape	one roll, 1 in. wide (or nearest)
16	22 gauge galv. steel sheet	1 in. x ¾ in. x ¾ in., hold-down "L" clamps
12	sponge rubber strip, e.g. "Dor-Tite"	¼ in. x ⅛ in. x ¾ in. long
16	galv. steel self-threading screws	⅛ in. dia. x ½ in. long
Hot Water Storage Drum		
1	used steel oil drum	standard size 45 gallons
2	"special" flat galv. steel sheet	24 gauge, 8 ft. x 4 ft.
—	coco-nut fibre or equivalent insulation	30 lbs.
2	deal wood boards	1 in. x 12 in. x 9 ft. long
1	heat resistant paint	1 pint tin
—	diesel oil	1 pint
—	gasoline (petrol)	1 pint
Cold Water Feed Tank & Piping		
1	used steel oil drum	standard size 45 gal., ½ only required
1	plumbing float control valve	½ in.
—	½ in. galv. steel pipe and fittings	to suit particular installation
1	Rust-Oleum or similar paint	1 pint tin

*Note: Gauge is the number of sheets to a vertical inch i.e. 16 Guage = 16 sheets to the vertical inch.

BUILDING THE COLLECTOR

The collector (absorber) is constructed of standard galvanized steel, 22 gauge, 26 inches (66.04cm) wide by 96 inches (243.84cm) long, with corrugations 3 inches (76.2mm) apart and ¾ of an inch (44.45mm) deep. A second sheet of flat galvanized steel, slightly larger all around, is also required. Refer to the preceeding material list, and to the sketches in Figure 17.

1. Cut the corrugated sheet to 26 x 88⅝ inches (69.04cmx 227.65cm) with a pair of metal shears. These can be purchased from your tool supply dealer or, for a one shot job such as this, you can rent them from a tool rental agency.

2. Cut the flat sheet to 26½ x 90⅝ inches (69.85 x 232.73cm). This sheet should also be 22 gauge steel.

3. Place a small sheet of stiff cardboard against the end of the corrugated sheet and trace the shape of the corrugations with a black pencil. Cut along the traced line carefully because the template will be a pattern. Place the cardboard template on each end of the flat sheet steel and mark the corrugations with a black pencil on the flat steel. Cut along the marked lines with the metal shears.

4. Cut 2 holes, 0.84 inches (21.34mm) in diameter (one in each end of the sheet) for later placing of ½ inch (12.70mm) pipe for ingress and egress of system water.

5. Attach a 9 inch (274.32cm) length of ½ inch (12.70mm) pipe to each end of the corrugated sheet. Screw the ³⁄₁₆ x ¼ inch screw into the length of pipe and solder the pipe to the corrugated sheet steel. The 9 inch (274.32cm) length of pipe must also be galvanized.

6. Bend both ends of the sheet steel at right angles. The bent ends should be I inch (25.4mm) long (¼ inch (6.35mm) longer than extreme depth of corrugations to allow some overlap when soldering). Place the corrugated sheet on top of the bottom sheet and slip the ½ inch (12.7mm) pipes into the corresponding holes, after slitting the sheet slightly so pipe will slide into place.

7. Bend the edges of the bottom sheet over the corrugated sheet as shown and solder. The easiest way to bend the flat sheet ¼ inch (6.35mm) from the edge as needed, is to clamp the sheet between two pieces of angle iron and strike with a hammer to get a perfect right angle.

8. Drill ¼ inch (6.35mm) holes for rivet placement on the inverted corrugations. Place ¼ inch (6.35mm) rivets in the drilled holes with heads resting on the flat sheet, as shown, and peen the rivet heads flat. Solder over the rivet heads. This completes the construction of the collector plate.

    a. To test for leaks, place the unit alongside a building in a sloping position and fill with water not under pressure from a water system. Allow it to stand for some time. Note the leaky areas and mark with chalk. If the unit has a few slow leaks and repair procedures doesn't stop them, let the unit stand

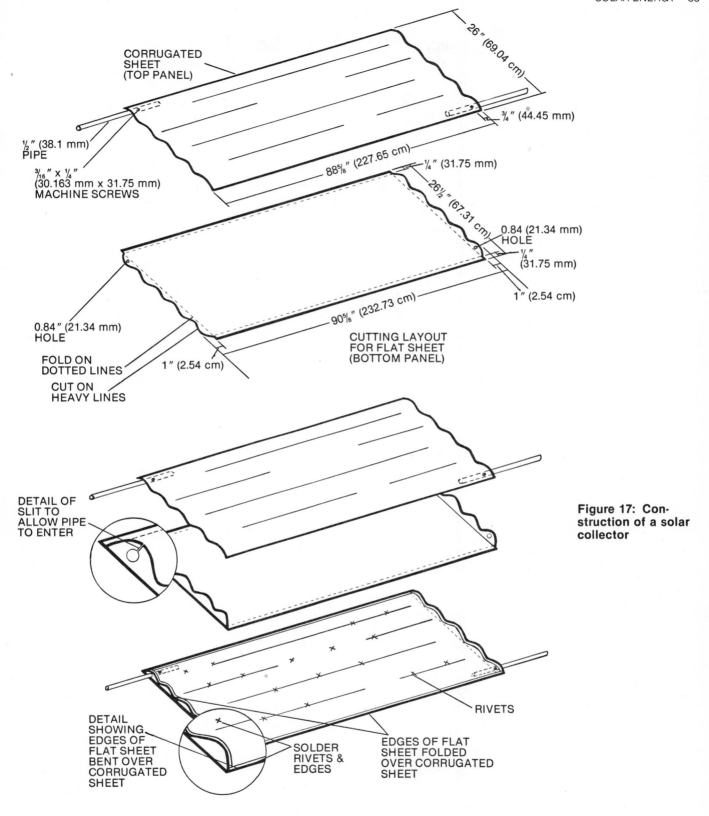

CORRUGATED
SHEET
(TOP PANEL)

26 " (69.04 cm)

¾ " (44.45 mm)

½ " (38.1 mm)
PIPE

³⁄₁₆ " x ¼ "
(30.163 mm x 31.75 mm)
MACHINE SCREWS

88⅝ " (227.65 cm)

¼ " (31.75 mm)

26½ " (67.31 cm)

0.84 (21.34 mm)
HOLE

¼ "
(31.75 mm)

1 " (2.54 cm)

0.84 " (21.34 mm)
HOLE

FOLD ON
DOTTED LINES

1 " (2.54 cm)

90⅝ " (232.73 cm)

CUTTING LAYOUT
FOR FLAT SHEET
(BOTTOM PANEL)

CUT ON
HEAVY LINES

DETAIL OF
SLIT TO
ALLOW PIPE
TO ENTER

Figure 17: Con-
struction of a solar
collector

RIVETS

DETAIL
SHOWING
EDGES OF
FLAT SHEET
BENT OVER
CORRUGATED
SHEET

SOLDER
RIVETS &
EDGES

EDGES OF FLAT
SHEET FOLDED
OVER CORRUGATED
SHEET

for a short time. The leaks should repair themselves. After
the leaks have been stopped, fill the unit with water and
stand it in the sun.

b. Paint the corrugated side with two coats of flat black paint.

BUILDING THE ABSORBER CASE

I. The base of the absorber case is also made from flat galvanized, 22 gauge steel. Start with a sheet 3 x 8 feet (91.44cm x 243.84cm) and cut to 33⅝ x 96 inches (88.74cm x 243.84cm). Flap the corners and bend sheet at right angles along the dotted lines. After the sheet is bent, rivet the four corners with ¼ inch (6.35mm) rivets (2 rivets per corner). Drill 2 each ½ inch (12.7mm) holes in one end of the case for drains. Cut a ½" (12.7mm) circle from the top edge of the case for the inlet pipes on the collector.

2. From scrap, cut 6 L-brackets as shown and drill ¼ inch (6.35mm) holes for the rivets in the brackets.

3. Bond ⅛ inch (3.175mm) thick felt strips cut to I x I inch (25.4mmx 25.4mm) onto L clamps.

4. Drill 6 each ¼ inch (6.35mm) holes, two on each side, equidistant, and one on each end, centered, in the case. Install L-bracket on- to case with flat head rivets with rivet head to the outside.

5. Place insulation into bottom of the case per material list, and use a 2 inch (50.8mm) thick layer of whatever material you choose.

6. Place absorber into the case over insulation, but resting on the L-brackets, and with the black corrugated surface facing up.

7. Form 4 each L-clamps as shown from 22 gauge steel-size ½ x ¾ x I inch (12.7 x 1905 x 25.4mm). Use self-tapping screws and screw the L-clamps in place to hold absorber to the case.

8. Make a T-bar by forming it from a sheet of 22 gauge steel, the same width as the absorber case. Rivet to the case with two rivets at each end.

9. Place ¼ inch (6.35mm) Dor-tite or some type of rubber stripping on the bottom surface of the T-bar.

10. Place ¼ inch (6.35mm) stripping all around the ¼ inch (6.35mm) edge of the case.

11. Install two sections of window glass size 27¾ x 44¾ x ⅛ inch (70.48mm x 1I3.66mm x 3.175) thick in the case, and be sure the glass rests evenly on the stripping all around the case.

12. Apply silicone sealant between the glass and center, and the edge supporting ribs. Allow ⅛ inch (3.175mm) on each side for ex- pansion of the glass. You can use ordinary window putty but silicone sealant lasts longer. Seal glass to case with black elec- trical tape which must be wide enough to cover the seams.

13. Form 16 each L-clamps ¾ x ¾ x I inch (19.05 x 19.05 x 25.4mm) from the 22 gauge steel and drill a ⅛ inch (3.175mm) hole in each clamp. Place ¾ inch sponge rubber strips on the glass over the

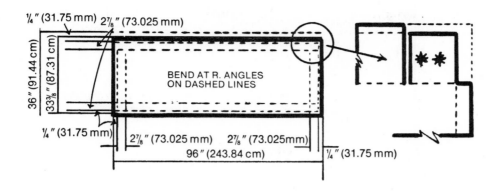

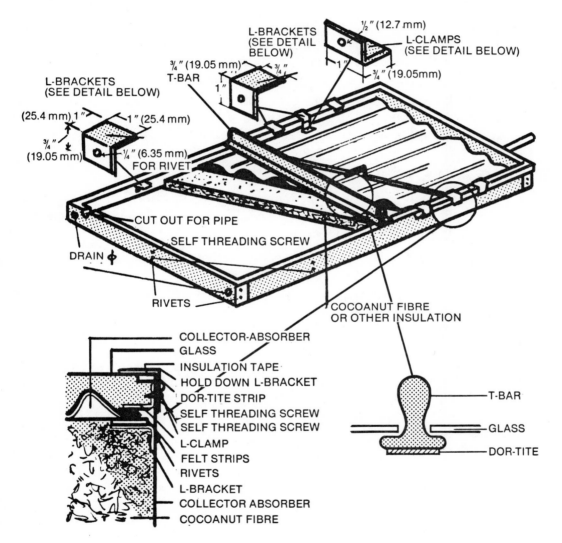

Figure 18: Construction of the absorber case

tape and attach the L- clamps to the sides of the case in equidistant locations. Press clamps over the rubber stripping and drill a hole in the case (⅛ inch hole) (3.175mm) and insert self- threading screws into the clamps until all are in place. This final step completes the collector unit.

HOT WATER STORAGE DRUM

1. Use a standard 45 gallon oil drum for the hot water tank. First, rinse the interior with a half pint of diesel oil to dissolve the oil residue left in the drum. Then rinse again with half a pint of gasoline to dissolve the diesel oil. This should clean the drum of all grease and leave it dry enough to paint.

2. Pour a pint of heat resistant paint into the drum and shake thoroughly until the entire interior of the drum is coated with paint. Allow several hours drying time.

3. Refer to Figure 19 and build a frame for the tank, by following the dimensions.

4. Insert the oil drum into the framework and cover the frame with sheets of 24 gauge sheet steel. Leave the top open so you can fill the empty spaces around the drum with insulation.

5. Place reducers in the two holes of the drum and attach two lengths of galvanized pipe 6 x ½ inches (165.lmm x 12.7mm) one in each opening. After the pipes are in place, fill the remaining space with insulation and nail the top of the frame in place.

COLD WATER FEED TANK

1. Cut a standard oil drum in half and install a ½ inch (12.7mm) float valve*. This part is available from any plumbing supply house. In fact, a toilet float can be used.

2. Paint inside of drum with two coats of Rust-Oleum paint and allow to dry.

3. Obtain lengths of pipe as needed to suit your application (Refer to Figure 16 on page 30). Lengths of pipe are determined by individual applications (i.e. height of roof, location of tank, etc).

ASSEMBLY OF COMPONENTS

1. Use pipe sealant on all connections before tightening them for the final time. Refer again to Figures l6 and 17 for placement of components. Note the one foot difference required between the top of collector and the bottom of the tank.

2. The collector must face south with corrugations running vertically, at an angle equal to the latitude of your area, plus ten degrees.

3. The system will be more functional if lengths of pipe are kept short. Example; if the hot water tank cannot be placed adjacent to the collector, use l inch (25.4mm) pipe instead of ½ inch (12.7mm). If this is not done, the hydraulic resistance of the piping may be so high that the natural convectional circulation of the water between the absorber and the tank will be greatly

---

*See materials list on page 31.

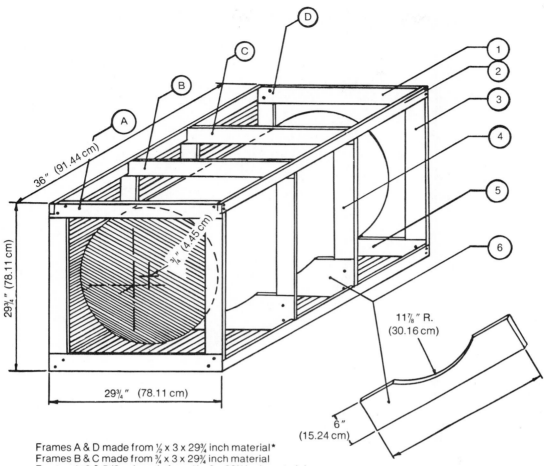

**Figure 19: Con-
structing the frame
for a hot water
storage tank**

Frames A & D made from ½ x 3 x 29¾ inch material*
Frames B & C made from ¾ x 3 x 29¾ inch material
Frames 1, 3 & 5 (8 ea) made from ½ x 3 x 29¾ inch material
Frame 2 made from ¾ x 2 x 36 inch material
Oil Drum size 23½ x 34½ inch. This dimension is for a 45 gallon drum. Make the frame to
correspond with the tank size you will use.
*See Table on page 31.

restricted, and the system's efficiency will be severely
hampered.

4. Finally, allow the unit to function for at least one day before
   drawing hot water. This will give the system sufficient time to
   heat up to the desired temperature. Be sure there is enough
   water in the system at all times, since too little water will create
   abnormal heat in the unit and could cause considerable damage.
   If it becomes necessary to empty the system for cleaning or
   winterizing, cover the collector with a tarp.

THE CONSOLAR HOT WATER HEATER

An efficient solar water heater is manufactured and marketed by Consolar, Inc. of Tucson, Arizona. The unit can be purchased in component form
and includes everything except the connecting piping. A complete set of
plans is also included. Shipping costs are extra. The price range is from
600 to 2000 dollars depending upon the components used. The median
price is about 1000 dollars including installation.

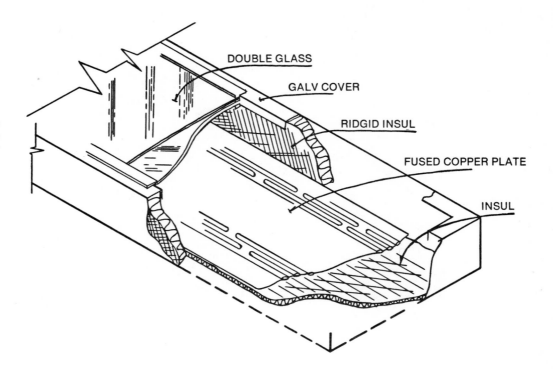

DOUBLE GLASS

GALV COVER

RIDGID INSUL

FUSED COPPER PLATE

INSUL

**Figure 20: The
Consolar flat plate
collector**

This system can be incorporated into an existing conventional water heater system as a retrofit unit, or it can be installed as the primary system with a conventional gas-fired or electric unit as a backup.

An average system consists of two flat plate collectors, 101 x 26 x 4 inches (261.62 x 66.04 x 10.16cm). The collectors (Figure 20) consist of an absorber plate constructed of copper Roll-Bond manufactured by Olin Brass, two layers of plate glass, a thick layer of insulation, ingress and egress manifolds, and two new innovations—a dessicant to reduce condensation in the collector (patent applied for) and an emergency blowout valve on the outlet side of the collector for safety release. Consolar also markets a cover to protect the collectors during periods of non-use. The per panel cost of a Consolar unit is 280 dollars which compares favorably with other contemporary collectors, especially since the absorber plate material is copper.

The centrifugal pump and check valves are integrated into the system as needed. Consolar features a mixer valve which is largely responsible for this system's success. This component mixes cold water with hot water from the tank when the collected hot water is too hot for household use. This adds stability to the system since collecting sunshine can be erratic.

An additional feature of the Consolar system is the erection of the panels with the smaller dimension in a vertical position, similar to the Florida units. Most contemporary panels protrude 7 to 8 feet (213.36 to 243.84cm) in the air. The lower vertical panels should be an improvement in areas with high winds, and could more easily satisfy many zoning laws.

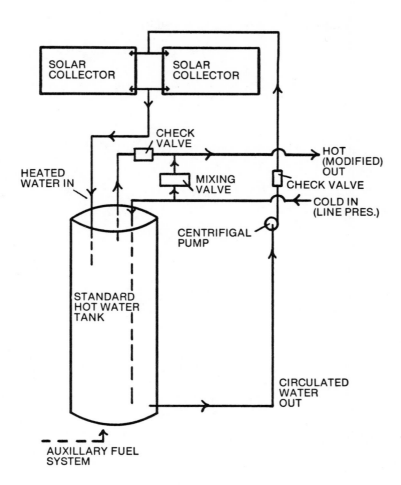

Figure 21: Basic solar hot water heating system

THE SUNSOURCE HOT WATER HEATER

The Sunsource system (see Figure 22) operates somewhat differently from those covered previously. It contains two thermostatic sensors (3, 9) which are located at the collector and at a point near the heater to monitor water temperature. When the difference in water temperature between the two sensors exceeds 15 degrees Fahrenheit, the pump is activated. When the temperature difference is 2 degrees Fahrenheit or less, the pump is automatically shut off.

The Sunsource solar hot water heater system consists of the following components:

> 2 each solar collector panels
> 1 each circulating pump
> 1 differential pump control
> 1 circuit setter
> 2 thermostatic sensors
> 1 tank transfer tube
> 1 manual vent valve

When the system is operative, during sunny daylight hours, the outlet temperature at the collector panel is greater than the bottom temperature of the heater. When that difference is more than 15 degrees Fahrenheit the pump starts automatically, drawing cool water from the water heater

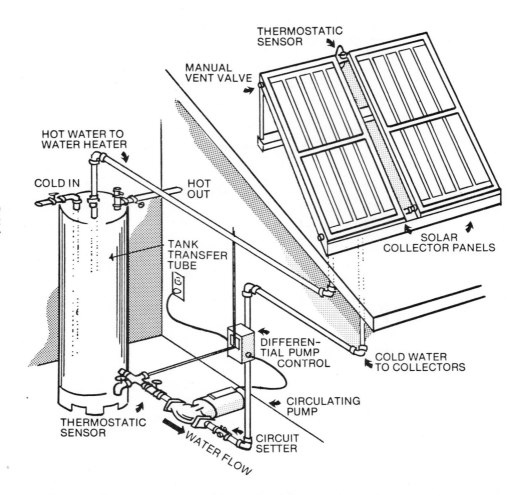

Figure 22: The Sunsource hot water heater

tank, pumping it up the outlet pipe and onto the panels. The panels absorb incoming heat from the sun and transfer it to water passing through the panels, where that heated water is returned to the tank through the return pipe. When the desired temperature is attained and the temperature differential between panel outlet and heater outlet is 2 degrees Fahrenheit, the pump will stop. This stops the flow of water from the collector panels to the tank.

The Sunsource flat plate collector size is 37¾ inches (95.89cm) wide x 73 inches (185.42cm) long, and 3½ inches (88.90mm) in depth. The absorber plate on the standard unit is 1 millimeter galvanized steel, with ½ inch (12.7mm) galvanized steel tubing. Copper or stainless steel tubing is optional and costs more. The standard Model #100 has a single layer, double strength, and glass plate. Double glass layers are optional. The insulation is 1½ inch (38.1mm) thick Rockwool. Urethane and Pearlite are optional at extra cost. The outer housing is galvanized steel and a unit weighs about 100 pounds (45.36kg). The total square feet of the glass area is 17 (1.5794m²). Sunsource estimates the life expectancy of a unit to be more than fifteen years. The unit sells for about 225 dollars with shipping charges extra.

space heating and cooling

The age of space heating with solar energy is here. I have alluded to the misconceptions and mis-stated facts which cloud the solar energy coverage in the mass media where the "somewhere in the future" theme seems to dominate. It is true that there will be a period of time before solar cell arrays will be priced within reach of the average family. But this is not true for the flat plate collector systems, which have been refined to a point of 90% efficiency, depending upon the collector. A well engineered system will do an adequate job of space heating in most parts of the United States. Water heating and swimming pool heating have progressed to a point where the cost factor gaps have been narrowed appreciably. The simple truth is that 90% of the components making up such systems are shelf items now available to the construction industry and the do-it-yourself handyman.

Space cooling is the single exception. Although space cooling systems are currently in operation, the only drawback at this point is the initial installation cost. As technology improves, and it surely will as it has in the aforementioned applications, space cooling will also be within reach of the average family.

When I first started researching this book there were only two or three dozen experimental space heating installations in the United States. Three years later, space heating of dwellings and public buildings has become quite commonplace. In fact, many builders are now incorporating solar systems in new housing starts. This indicates that the use of solar energy for space heating, and later space cooling, is on the increase. The HUD program for proof-of-concept units should give the industry a big boost. As this book is completed, applications are going out to interested parties in different locales, including Albany, Atlanta,

**Figure 23:
The Harold Hay
"water roof" design
is a passive solar
system which
absorbs the sun's
heat for winter
heating (top) and
radiates heat to the
night sky for
summer cooling
(bottom)**

Boston, Columbus, Denver, Des Moines, Honolulu, Los Angeles, Richmond, and Tucson. These are the first 10 of 50 state economic areas selected in the Location Matrix Study by Arthur D. Little Inc.*

Two different systems are presently being utilized for space heating and space heating/cooling applications; the open system and the closed system, both of which utilize liquids primarily. The open system uses an additional medium such as anti-freeze, since the system liquid and the heat are transferred to water by a heat exchanger. The closed system utilizes heated water as the only medium.

An additional difference should also be drawn between active and

*The report, which is the basis for the experimental portion of the demonstration program, was published during the Summer of 1976.

passive systems. The units covered in this section are all active systems. A passive system utilizes no fuels, fans, or pumps, and is completely non-mechanical. An example of a passive system is the experimental dwelling in Phoenix, Arizona which is the brainchild of Harold Hays. The first test of such a system was made at John Yellott's Solar Laboratory in Phoenix. In this system, the entire roof of the structure is covered with approximately 7 inches (177 mm) of water encased in plastic bags, with covering sliding insulating panels above the water. During sunlight hours in winter, the water is uncovered and warmed by the sun. At night, the water is covered so it will retain and radiate the heat down into the house. In summer, the reverse is true. The water is covered during sunlight hours so it will not be warmed by the sun. At night, the water is uncovered so it can radiate to the cool night sky all the heat absorbed in the house during the day. This nocturnal radiation can keep the water as much as 25 degrees Fahrenheit, (14°C.) lower than ambient air temperature. Next day, the cool water keeps the house below very comfortable. The design is, of course, primarily for desert climates.

Figure 24 illustrates an open system for space cooling. It is an absorption system in which solar heat is utilized to cool inside room air. The components of the system include: generator (1), condenser (2), evaporator (3), and absorber (4). The fluid used in the system is a solution of refrigerant and absorbent which have an affinity for each other. Water is the refrigerant and lithium bromide is the absorbent.

When the solution in the generator is heated by solar energy from the collector, the water refrigerant is vaporized to form the liquid solution. The water boils off. It vaporizes at less than 212 degrees Fahrenheit (100°C.) because pressure in the generator is less than normal atmospheric pressure. Heat is removed from the vapor in the condenser where the vapor changes to a cooled liquid which is then revaporized through an expansion valve and passes into the evaporator cooling coils.

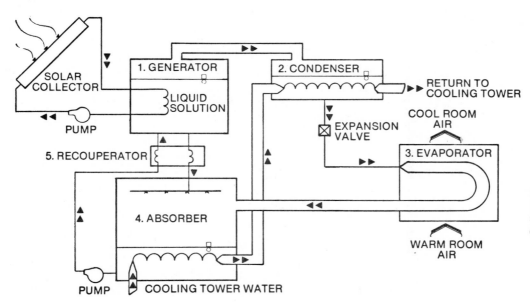

**Figure 24:
Diagram of an open
system for space
cooling**

Vaporization of the refrigerant takes place due to lower pressure beyond the expansion valve relative to pressure in the condenser.

Warm room air blown over the cooling coil of the evaporator is cooled and the cool air is then circulated into the rooms. By vaporizing the refrigerant, the temperature is lowered from 120 degrees Fahrenheit, to 70 degrees (48.9 to 21.1°C.), a difference of 50 degrees (10° C.). The temperature of the vapor refrigerant at the evaporator is about 70 degrees (21.1°C.) lower than the temperature of the liquid refrigerant which makes it more effective in cooling the room air.

Next the vaporized refrigerant is recombined with the absorbent in the absorber. Heat is generated in the recombination, and heat is removed by cooled water from the cooling tower. The temperature in the absorber must be low enough to assure a high-chemical affinity between refrigerant and solution. Finally, the solution from the absorber is returned to the generator and the cycle starts again.

The recouperator (5) is used to cool the high temperature solution in the generator as it passes into the low temperature absorber. It also heats the low temperature absorber solution as it moves to the high temperature generator. This serves to minimize heat loss associated with fluid transfer between the absorber and generator.

The thermodynamic properties of the working fluids in the absorption system are such that absorber temperature and the concentration of the solution in the absorber determine the pressure within the absorber. This pressure, which is the same as evaporator pressure, also determines the temperature at the evaporator and the amount of effective cooling possible. The temperature of the condenser determines its pressure, which is the same as the generator pressure. Generator pressure and the concentration of the solution determines the temperature required to vaporize the refrigerant (water). Therefore, the temperature at the absorber and condenser, and the concentration of the solution determine the minimum temperature in the generator. The temperature of cooling water from the cooling tower—approximately 75 degrees Fahrenheit (23.9°C.) for the experimental home Solar One, which was built and tested by Colorado State University—and the concentration of the refrigerant/absorbent solution, determine the minimum temperature in the generator which must be supplied by the solar collectors before the system will function. This is approximately 180 degrees Fahrenheit (82.2°C.) in the Solar One test house. Another consideration is a temperature reading at the recouperator for a given concentration of solution beyond which the system will encounter problems due to crystallization which occurs about 120 degrees Fahrenheit (48.9°C.)in the Solar One house.

SOLAR ONE TEST HOUSE

The Solar One test house was constructed with NSF Funding. The purpose of the project was to design an effective, yet economical, system of heating, cooling and heating domestic water in a typical residence using mostly the sun's rays. This heating system was designed to handle three fourths of the heating and cooling requirements while maintaining a conventional level of comfort using a fully automatic control system. The remaining one fourth would be supplied by a backup system utilizing conventional methods. Solar One is a modern three bedroom home with 3000 square feet of heated space on two levels. The dwelling specifications are as follows:

Total floor space: 3000 square feet (278.7 m²)

Floor area, main level: 1500 square feet (139.35 m²)

Floor area, Lower level: 1500 square feet (139.35 m²)

Roof pitch: 45 degree from horizontal

Design heating load: 17,600 Btu/degree day

Design cooling load: 26,000 Btu/degree day

Insulation: Ceiling-5 inch (127m) fiberglass batt

Wall: 3½ inch (88.9m) fiberglass batt.

The heating/cooling system is divided into five basic units: the solar collectors (1), solar storage (2), house heating, cooling, and domestic hot water load requirements (3), conventional furnace auxiliary system (4), and automatic controls (5).

Solar collectors make up a total area of 768 (71.35 m²) square feet and are mounted on a south-facing roof at a 45 degree angle from horizontal, which allows for optimum collection on a year-round basis. The best col-

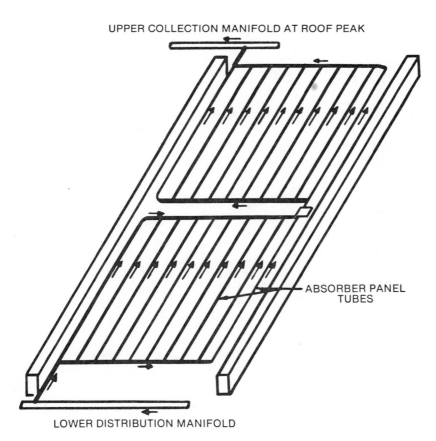

UPPER COLLECTION MANIFOLD AT ROOF PEAK

ABSORBER PANEL TUBES

LOWER DISTRIBUTION MANIFOLD

**Figure 25:
A solar collector
and flow pattern**

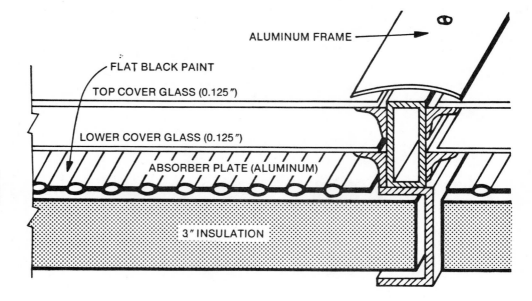

**Figure 26:
Cross section of a
solar panel**

lector arrangement is one in which the collector always faces the sun directly, but this is virtually impossible unless the collector array is programmed to track the sun across the sky. With parabolic collectors this is entirely possible, but is impractical for flat plate collectors. The 45 degree angle in this case is based on the best possible year-round position.

The sun-catching operation is the same. Solar energy passes through the glass plates and is absorbed by the black painted metal plate (Figures

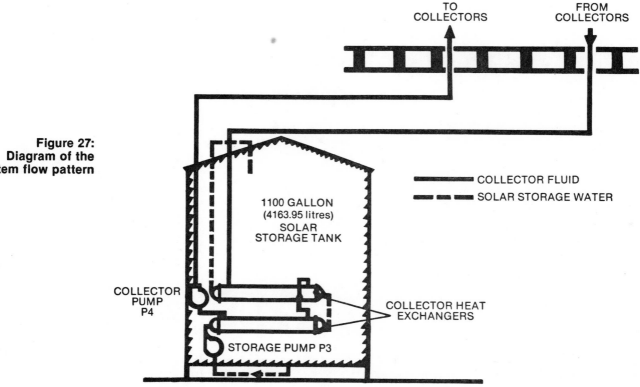

**Figure 27:
Diagram of the
system flow pattern**

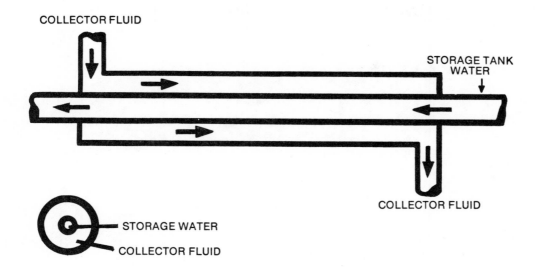

COLLECTOR FLUID

STORAGE TANK WATER

COLLECTOR FLUID

STORAGE WATER

COLLECTOR FLUID

**Figure 28:
Diagram of the heat
exchanger**

25 and 26). This system is somewhat different from those covered previously since the collector fluid (water) contains a 25% solution of ethylene glycol (anti-freeze). It is known as an open system since it contains a heating medium other than water. When water is the only heating medium in the system, it is known as a closed system. In the closed system the water used in heating can also be used in the domestic water heater. In the open system the medium/water combination heat is transferred to the water with a heat exchanger (Figure 27).

The collector fluid (water/anti-freeze combination) is pumped from the basement into a lower distribution manifold, upward through the collectors, and into the upper manifold (Figure 25). Heated fluid then leaves the upper manifold and returns to the basement where heat is transferred to the storage unit (Figure 27).

Since ethylene is quite expensive, the liquid is not piped into the storage tank, but is piped through a heat exchanger (Figure 28). In this manner, the system uses only about five gallons of ethylene glycol instead of the large amount (about $1000 worth) that would otherwise be required.

The absorber plate in this collector unit is made of aluminum plating. The tubing is placed in a vertical position (Figure 25). The cross section drawing (Figure 26) also illustrates the component makeup of the unit. The plate is coated with flat black paint to attain the highest degree of absorptivity. Two plates of double strength glass, ⅛ of an inch (3.175mm) thick, are utilized for increased efficiency and as a safeguard against freezing—a must in cold areas.

The research team on the Solar One project decided to use an 1100 gallon (4163.95 litres) storage tank since a smaller tank would inhibit domestic water usage, and a larger tank would require a larger collector system. Last but not least, the cost would be considerably more.

Forced air is used for heat distribution, a choice which was determined

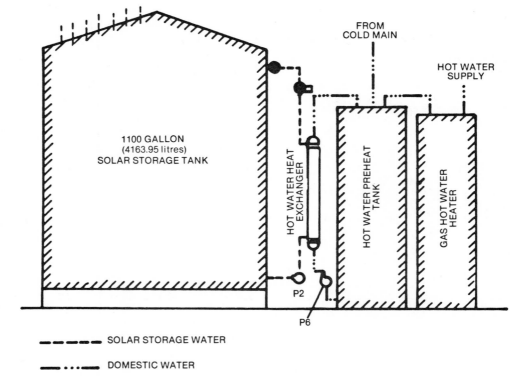

Figure 29: Diagram of a complete heating/cooling system (Solar One House, Colorado State University)

by the heating and cooling requirements. The availability of commercial cooling units was another consideration.

The system functions when hot water from the storage tank is piped to the heating coil or directly to the cooling unit (Figure 29). Air that is blown across the heating coil picks up heat to be carried into the dwelling.

For cooling, hot water from the storage tank is piped to the air conditioner where it provides the necessary energy to operate the cooling unit. The air conditioning unit is a three ton lithium bromide absorption unit converted for use with hot water instead of natural gas.

In addition to heating and cooling, the system also provides most of the required domestic hot water (Figure 29). Water from the cold water main enters the pre-heat tank and is circulated through a heat exchanger. Hot water from the solar storage tank transfers heat to the domestic hot water. As needed, water from the pre-heat tank enters a conventional gas hot water heater which can raise and maintain the water temperature if required. An auxiliary system is included as a backup unit if the solar system doesn't supply the necessary energy.

If the temperature in the storage tank drops below a predetermined point (100 degrees Farenheit for heating and 170 degrees Farenheit for cooling), the auxiliary boiler automatically takes over and provides heat to the coils or the air conditioning system. Under normal operating conditions, the solar unit will provide 75 to 80% of the heating and cooling load. The gas-fired backup system provides from 20 to 25%.

The control system is somewhat more complicated than in a conventionally-heated home since it must also control the collector, storage pumps, and two automatic valves, in addition to those normally required. This fully automatic system has full system control capability. The only requirement for the occupant is to maintain a proper thermostat setting.

It must be pointed out that this experimental dwelling is located in Colorado and not in the Southwest deserts. The common misconception that solar energy systems will only function efficiently in sunlands must be cleared up. The engineering requirements may well vary since the circumstances are not alike, but those adjustments are possible. Variables would include more collector area to capture a maximum of sunlight on fewer sunlit days, and additional components to guard against freezing. But in the case of freezing, those precautions are already taken in conventional homebuilding procedures.

The first solar house was built by the Massachusetts Institute of Technology in the Northeast before World War II. Much of the technology associated with solar energy has centered in that region. Two of the most famous solar homes (Thomason projects) are in the Washington, D.C. area. Don't be mislead by improper thinking. Solar energy can be utilized quite well in all areas of the United States.

The solar energy system in the Colorado State University house is an example of a complete package which includes space heating, space cooling, and domestic hot water. There are several such experimental projects in operation around the country, but as I've noted earlier, the systems involving space cooling are still relatively new and costly. Space heating is here now, and within the price range of many people.

CONSOLAR HOME

A good example of a workable space heating system is the Consolar Home, built by the Carreon Construction Company of Tucson, Arizona. The home, including the solar package for space heating and the domestic hot water system, is priced in the 45,000 dollar range, moderate by today's standards. The solar package is comparable to and somewhat less in cost than contemporary units. The prototype system was around 6000 dollars, about 15% of the total home price.

The house features a separate collector bank for each operation (Figure 30). On the prototype house the builders used two solar collectors for the hot water system and twenty panels for the space heating application. Studies indicate that they could reduce the panel number to sixteen on a home of this size, which is approximately 1200 square feet (111.484 m²). All collectors are Copper plate "Roll-Bond" and are the same size, 101 x 26 x 4 inches (256.54 x 66.04 x 10.16 cm) with the 26 inch (66.04cm) dimension in a vertical position (Fig. 30a).This "low-profile" reduces wind resistance and eliminates some maintenance problems inherent in a higher profile unit. Figure 31 shows what this means in terms of aesthetics since very little of the system is visible from ground level.

**Figure 30:
Consolar home
collector banks**

The system is open, which means no medium other than water is required. The heating is by solar energy with a conventional backup furnace and cooling is by an evaporative method which results in reduced utility bills. Since the building was constructed with an integral solar energy system, the insulation is proportionately greater than in similar dwellings. Figure 32 illustrates the basic makeup of the system.

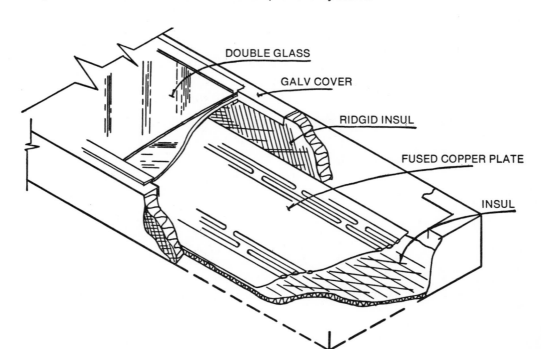

**Figure 30a:
Consolar flat plate
collector**

DOUBLE GLASS

GALV COVER

RIDGID INSUL

FUSED COPPER PLATE

INSUL

**Figure 31:
Consolar Home
(Note the low
profile of the
collectors)**

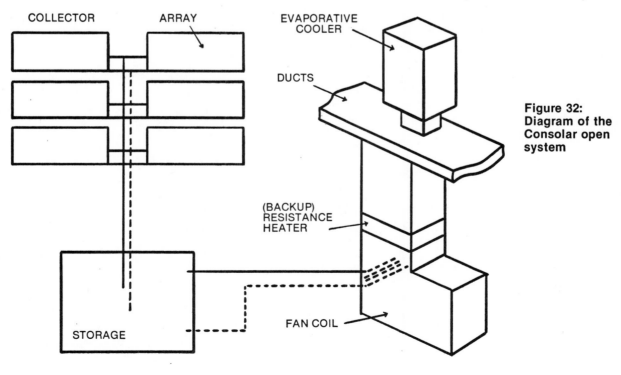

COLLECTOR   ARRAY

EVAPORATIVE
COOLER

DUCTS

(BACKUP)
RESISTANCE
HEATER

STORAGE

FAN COIL

**Figure 32:
Diagram of the
Consolar open
system**

THE MISSISSAUGA HOUSE

There is more to planning an efficient solar heated house than construct-ing a series of collectors, plumbing, and storage tanks. The solar heated house must be built with many considerations in mind: good insulation, a slanted roof with southern exposure, possibly more windows on the south side and less on the other three sides, solid construction that doesn't allow warm air to escape faster than it's blown in, and maximum use of the heat once it's trapped. Rooms requiring more warmth should be nearer the collecting area, especially if the south facing wall has ample windows. The kitchen is pretty much heat producing and may be located at the north end.

The Mississauga House was built in the suburbs of Toronto. It proves that solar heating is a viable alternative in the northern climates of the United States and Canada, as well as much of the Northern Hemisphere.

This house was built by an architect and his associates. It is a somewhat costly project due to several factors such as purchasing all components off the shelf, using commercial sub-contractors, and having to import components such as solar panels from the United States. This meant an import tax of 20% plus 5% federal tax, and freight charges from Guilford, Connecticut, where the manufacturers, Sunworks Inc. is located. Special instrumentation for monitoring the efficiency of the system was also required. The thirty three solar panels in the project cost 204 dollars each. Builders estimate the total cost of the solar energy package in this 140,000 dollar house to be between 20,000 and 25,000 dollars.

The house is a two story dwelling with 1450 square feet (134.71 m²), which includes three bedrooms and two baths but no basement. It was planned to get the optimum energy from the solar system. In fact, the owner states that the main idea was to reduce energy demand rather than to build a solar heated house.

Site selection is always important, but is imperative in the northern climates. The south-facing roof should be designed with solar panels in mind. As is the case of this house, the south wall could be mostly win-dows. Again, insulation is the most important factor with the exception of solar system components. The builder/architect/owner suggests the equivalent of six inches (152.4 mm) of fiberglass in the walls, and eight in-ches (203.2 mm) or more between the ceiling and roof where heat loss is the greatest. To reduce air leakage which is another constant heat loss factor, the builder installed polyethlene or foil sheeting on the inside of the insulation. All windows are sealed with weatherstripping.

Another innovation added to this house to make it air tight was doors which do not open to the outside. One opens into the garage and the other into a vestibule. The house is so airtight that an outside air feed was directed to the conventional furnace so the open flame didn't use all the oxygen from the house.

The solar system is conventional. The rooftop collector array contains

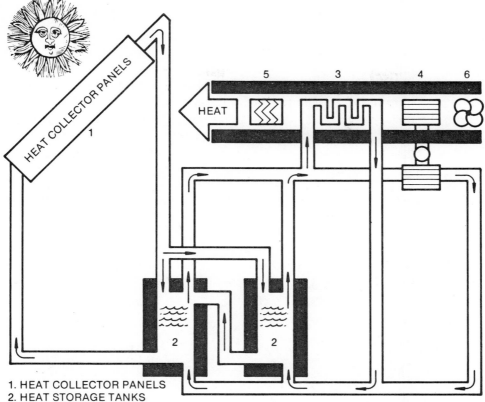

Figure 33:
The Mississauga
heating system

1. HEAT COLLECTOR PANELS
2. HEAT STORAGE TANKS
3. DIRECT HEATING COIL
4. HEAT PUMP
5. STAND-BY ELECTRIC COIL
6. FAN

thirty three flat plate collectors, each 3 x 7 feet (0.91 x 2.13 m), with a total collector area of 690 square feet (64.1 m²). Two storage tanks of 2500 gallons (9463.53 litres) each are installed beneath the house. Water is pumped up onto the collector panels where it is heated by the sun before it returns to the first of the two holding tanks. When the water temperature in the first tank exceeds 115 degrees Fahrenheit (46.1 °C.), it circulates in a direct heating coil which warms the air and is then forced into the house by a conventional blower system. When the temperature drops below 115 degrees Fahrenheit (46.1 °C.), a conventional heat pump takes over and extracts heat from the water and converts it to warm air.

When the solar heating system is unable to keep the house temperature at the desired level, an electric heating unit is activated. However, when the system was first installed it operated between mid-January and the end of February, 1976. With outside temperatures averaging 32 to 36 degrees Fahrenheit, the backup system was never activated.*

THE HOT-LINE SOLAR COLLECTOR

A really different solar collector, which could represent a big step forward in solar energy research, has been invented by an Iowan named Dan Lightfoot.

*Additional information and a Sunday Tour schedule is available from: Meadowvale Information Pavilion/P.O. Box 70, Meadowvale/Mississauga, Ontario, Canada.

The collector module appears similar to the typical flat plate collector, but is actually quite different. The design seems to defy the laws of physics. The module consists of a specially curved reflector which concentrates incoming sunlight onto a wedge-shaped absorption tube. Without moving, the unit tracks the sun through a 50 degree vertical arc and through 150 degrees in the east to west plane. According to pilot test programs, an increased concentration factor enables the collector to operate at greater efficiency than comparable flat plate collectors.

Lightfoot discovered the concept by accident while observing the sun's reflection on a sheet of aluminum which was leaning against an outside wall. Although the sun moved across the sky, the spot reflected from the aluminum to an adjoining wall remained in approximately the same place. Lightfoot experimented with the metal until he found the proper curve to focus incoming light in a line which would move only a short distance, as the reflector was tilted through different angles to the sun.

By bending the reflective metal to that curvature, placing a channel along the focal place of the created reflector, and routing air or water through the channel, he came up with the unique fixed position solar collector. (Figure 34).

The production version of the collector module is 26½ x 96 x 10 inches (67.3 x 243.8 x 25.4 cm) and has a surface area of 16.1 square feet (1.64 m²). Figure 34 shows the construction which consists of an aluminum frame containing pre-formed styrofoam insulation encircling the reflector, a sheet of mirror finish aluminum, in the properly engineered curvature. The triangular section aluminum absorption tube is placed at the deepest part of the curve and is wedge-shaped to accomodate lengthening and shortening of focal lengths as sunlight enters the panel from different angles. The outer covering is Kalwall Sun-Lite fiberglass glazing.

The concept of the Hot-Line collector is relatively simple (Figure 34, bottom). When sunlight enters the collector shortly after sunrise at a nearly perpendicular angle, the reflector focuses incoming rays on either the outermost edge of the absorption tube or on that portion closest to the reflector itself, depending on where the incident light enters the upper or lower part of the reflector. As the sun moves up into the sky, the focal line, or hot-line, hitting the top portion of the absorption tube moves nearer the reflector, while the hot-line on the underside of the aluminum moves away from the reflector sheeting. The incoming light does not fail to focus, nor is it blocked out by the frame until the sun is more than 60 degrees above the horizon or more than 75 degrees displaced on the east-to-west axis.

The Hot-Line starts operating as soon as the morning sun breaks over the horizon and continues concentrating light energy throughout the day until the sun rises more than 60 degrees above the horizon (considerably more than its maximum winter height at the site location in Iowa), and most importantly, does so at a very high efficiency throughout the day.

As in most projects involving solar heating systems, the efficiency of

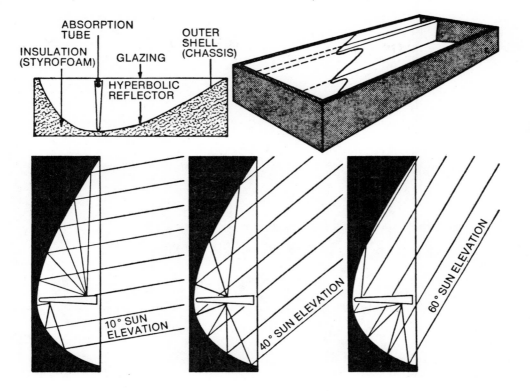

ABSORPTION TUBE

INSULATION (STYROFOAM)

GLAZING

OUTER SHELL (CHASSIS)

HYPERBOLIC REFLECTOR

10° SUN ELEVATION

40° SUN ELEVATION

60° SUN ELEVATION

**Figure 34:
The Hot Line solar
collector**

the unit depends upon factors other than the operation. The unit will per-form much better if the room or house is well insulated. Consideration must also be given to the volume of air to be handled (i.e. the size of area to be heated relative to capacity of the collector).

There are approximately eighteen units in operation in Iowa and all are used for space heating. And there is additional research currently under-way to adapt the system to heating water and perhaps at a later time, in-tegrate a total system involving air cooling into the package.

The current system utilizes a blower to force room air through the ab-sorption tube and straight back into the room without funneling any of the heated air into a heat storage tank, which is different than most space heating systems now in operation.

swimming pool heating

The curtailment of natural gas for swimming pool application is occuring in several states with legislation currently under study in several others including Arizona and California. This could be the best thing that ever happened to the solar energy industry. Although these laws are vigorously opposed by the swimming pool industry, there is every indication that they will be passed and that such a ban will soon be commonplace, which should certainly enhance the use of solar energy for swimming pool heating.

Most pool heating to date has either been with natural gas or fuel oil, and to a lesser degree, with electricity. Solar heaters have been tested in many parts of the country and the response has been mixed. There are indications that this method of heating will function well in Southern California, the southern deserts, Florida, and to a slightly lesser degree in the South. The degree of success becomes more marginal toward the middle and upper United States, and systems in those locales would require more panel exposure to the square feet of the pool to be heated. The result, obviously, is additional costs and could mean the difference between a practical installation and one in which the costs involved could never be realistically amortized, especially since the swimming season in those areas is also shorter.

This brings us to the biggest obstacle in the use of solar energy, the initial cost. In most cases, it is considerably more than for conventional gas, oil, or electrical hookups. However, the amortization time on a solar unit is about five years where pools are not used year round. The exception would be in those areas mostly through reduced utility and fuel bills. After that, the cost of operation is almost nil. An additional plus factor is that, unlike natural gas, fuel oil, or electrical heaters, the maintenance costs are very low. The reason is obvious: no fuel, no additional pumps in most cases, and no additional electrical controls. This is especially true when the solar unit is connected to existing water lines, and pump/filter systems, and also brings that initial cost down. The most comforting part of all this is that the sun's energy is free.

Like conventional pool heaters, the solar heater can extend the swimming season three to four months depending upon where you live. In the Southwest or Zone 1 on the map (see page 92) it means, for the most part, year-round swimming. In the case of flat plate collectors, the system can also be utilized to reduce pool temperatures during the heat of the summer. Activating the system after dark will aid in the dissipation of excess pool heat, without appreciable chlorine loss as is the case with most swimming pool aerators.

Questions always arise when discussing the use of solar energy for swimming pool heating. These include: "How efficient is the system?"; "How much will the temperature rise?"; "Will the system change the aesthetics of our home?"; and "How long will it take to realize a savings?" In most cases, the answers will be on the plus side. For example, regarding efficiency, a pretty safe rule of thumb is that with direct sunlight, and a properly engineered system, the water temperature should rise about 10 to 16 (5.6°C. to 8.9°C.) degrees. An important point to remember is that even on a cloudy or hazy day, the system should still function at 65% to 80% of efficiency. And if the pool is covered between periods of use, it's possible to gain another 5 to 10 degree (2.8 to 5.6°C.) rise; again, under the most desirable conditions.

Refer to the map on page 92 and you will see that certain parts of the country are more conducive to solar energy usage than others, but the fact remains that at least 90% of the United States can benefit in some degree from a solar unit with a large measure of efficiency, and that the entire country can benefit if the unit is properly engineered.

As for aesthetics, many pool collectors are placed flat on the roof and placing collectors on south-facing roofs shouldn't change the appearance too much. It's also possible to screen the collector area to reduce visibility from the street or your neighbor's house and still not shade the units from the sun. Figure 35 indicates how the collector array can blend in with the dwelling. Additional ways of solving this problem include placing the collectors on the ground, or incorporating them as patio covers or as window awnings. It is wise to check with your local plannning and zoning office before erecting a system. The laws in your area may well regulate how the collectors can be erected.

Relative costs have been mentioned frequently because they are important, but it must be emphasized that over a long period of time, a solar unit should be cheaper than a conventional system. It also has the twofold advantage of saving our fossil fuel reserves and allowing the pool owner to use the pool during periods of power cutbacks or fuel shortages. On balance, considering the technology of today, there is no reason why most new pools, and existing pools with a retrofit unit, should not be

**Figure 35:
One method of
mounting solar
collectors to blend
in with a dwelling**

heated by the sun. In view of recent events, it is entirely possible that the solar heater may be the only option.

I have discussed the flat plate collector system in detail but there are other options available to the pool owner including solar discs (Figure 36), air mattresses, and solar blankets. These items are placed directly on the pool's surface and are effective in raising pool temperatures. Removal and replacement are the biggest drawbacks, especially with the solar mattress which is quite cumbersome.

The floating air mattress concept has been used quite successfully in Australia, where tests revealed that reduced evaporation and radiation losses increased pool temperatures by as much as 10 degrees Fahrenheit (5.6°C.).

Solar discs (Figure 36) are easier to handle, but are somewhat less efficient because they don't cover the entire surface.

The solar blanket, such as the Solar Pool Blanket® —manufactured by L. M. Dearing Associates, Inc.—is another relatively inexpensive method used to heat swimming pools. In fact, two Dearing Blankets were installed in the White House pool for President Ford. The concept is quite simple and involves a pool-sized blanket spread over the entire pool area. The pool water is the energy absorber with this transparent cover, as it floats on the surface and traps absorbed heat. The cover contains air filled bubbles which provide a layer of insulation and prevent evaporative heat and chemical and water loss. This system is capable of raising the heat level 10 to 15 degrees Fahrenheit (5.6°C. to 8.9°C.), depending upon where the pool is located, the time of year, and the amount of direct sunlight.

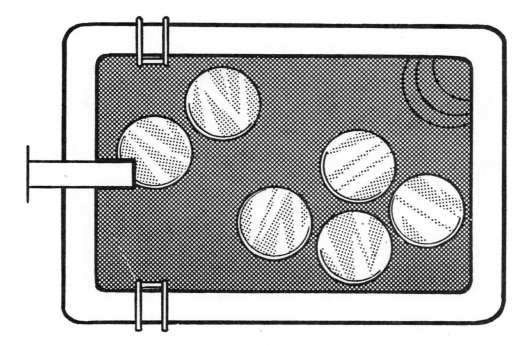

**Figure 36:
Solar discs on the
swimming pool
surface**

A close friend of mine has a severe arthritic condition and recently decided to buy a Solar Pool Blanket.® The results have been astounding and his condition has greatly improved. He credits this change to his ability to spend more time in his pool and at higher than normal temperatures.

The flat plate collector method of heating the swimming pool is becoming more popular as technology improves. This system generally utilizes equipment already installed—the pump/filter combination provides the circulation of clean water to the solar collectors where the water is heated and returned to the pool. The key component is again the collector. Collectors function best when mounted in a south-facing arrangement at an angle which includes the latitude of your area plus 10 degrees. Collectors can also be placed flat, or even slightly west-facing, but the latter two installations would require more collector exposure since the degree of efficiency decreases about 25%.

There are two different types of collectors currently in use for heating swimming pools with solar energy: the flat plate cased collector similar to those used in water heating and the plastic modules such as those featured by FAFCO and Sunergy.

The flow pattern starts as the existing pump (in retrofit systems) pumps the water up to the collectors where it is heated and returned to the pool. An ideal water circulation pattern would be to circulate the entire pool contents at least once daily. Pool size and capacity determines total collector area and the number of collectors required.

If the solar unit is being installed with a new swimming pool, the only components required would be the collector array, connecting piping, and controls to start and stop the pump relative to pool heating. Some systems contain a sensor for this purpose.

The FAFCO system features a collector of extruded plastic with ingress and egress manifolds built in. A cut-away of the component would reveal an interior resembling a corrugated carton. The water flow pattern is through the channels and the entire surface, which is black, functions as the heat transference agent as the water flows evenly through the inner surface. The plastic used by FAFCO is compounded in a manner similar to plastic telephone cable and the estimated life expectancy exceeds ten years. Another positive factor is that plastic is not affected by elements present in all swimming pools to some degree: algae, minerals, corrosives, and pool chemicals.

The panels are constructed so they can be easily joined together. This eliminates plumbing between collector panels. It also simplifies the erection of multiples, whether on the roof or ground-mounted. Figure 37 shows how the panel is constructed and the dimensions which are available.

FAFCO recommends a minimum of ½ to ¾ of the pool's surface in solar

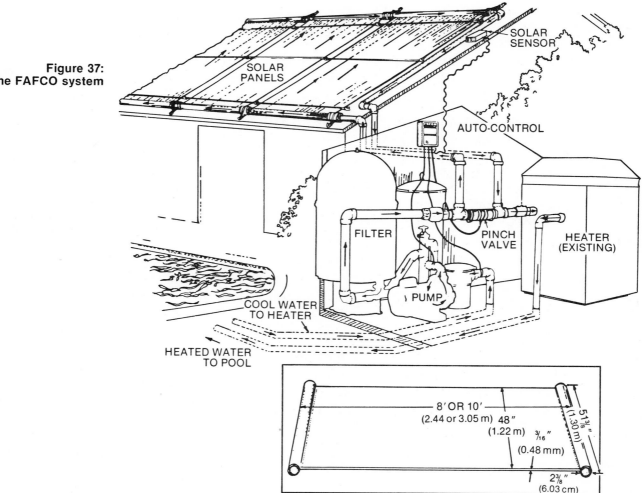

**Figure 37:
The FAFCO system**

panels (i.e. an 800 square foot (74.3224 m²) pool would require 400 to 600 square feet (37.161 to 55.742 m²) of panel area). I mentioned previously that the system's efficiency will increase with additional solar panels. If you have a good south-facing arrangement, the 50% rule would be most applicable. If the roof is flat, or facing west, the ¾ rule would be most applicable. In the middle or upper United States, or in areas such as Florida where year-round swimming is possible, the required solar panel area may jump to 100% of the pool surface area.

Figure 37 illustrates the flow pattern and installation configuration of a FAFCO system.

The system manufactured by Sunergy Pool Heaters also uses modular extruded solar panels. It functions in the same manner as a home radiator heating system, in reverse. Water is circulated through the pool pump/filter system onto the collector panels and back into the pool.

A versatile collector module system allows the pool owner to use as many panels as are required to adequately heat the pool. The Sunergy module consists of two solar panels 4 x 6 feet (1.2192 x 1.8288 m) for a total module size of 4 x 12 feet (1.2192 x 3.6576 m). It should be used for each 100 square feet (9.29 m²) of pool surface area.

This formula can easily be translated. If the pool size is 20 x 30 feet (6.096 m x 9.144 m), the pool surface area is 600 square feet (55.741 m²), and the required number of modules would be 6 each of the 4 foot x 12 foot dimension (1.2192 x 3.6576 m), for a total of 288 square feet (26.756 m²), or roughly ½ of the pool surface square footage. This is based

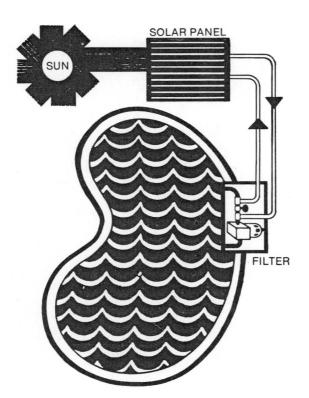

Figure 38:
The Sunergy solar swimming pool heater

on the assumption that a 10 to 15 degree (5.6°C. to 8.9°C.) rise is adequate. If situations similar to those referred to in the previous paragraphs on FAFCO exist, additional panels would be required.

The modules and plumbing components can be purchased as a package and installed by the pool owner, or a pool equipment dealer can do the job for you.

The flat plate collector system consisting of an absorber plate and glass cover is more than sufficient when used for heating a swimming pool. Most of these units are engineered to produce heated water of a much higher temperature than normally required for heating pool water. Components such as thick insulation and double layers of plate glass are a must in domestic water heating, but can be eliminated in a swimming pool application, thus reducing the per panel cost to a parity with the extruded plastic panels. However, if a higher level of efficiency is desired, those components would be required. Additionally, at least one glass plate would reduce maintenance problems.

An inexpensive method of heating swimming pool water can be constructed with the use of corrugated sheet steel (galvanized) as collector panels. In this system, the water flows by gravity down through the channels into a feeder pipe and into the pool. This system requires a feeder pipe across the top, with holes drilled to match channels in the panels, and a feeder trough at the lower end for funneling the water flow back to the pool. In this system, since it is open to the elements, the returning water should be filtered as well. It is also possible to increase efficiency

**Figure 39:
A typical cased flat
plate collector**

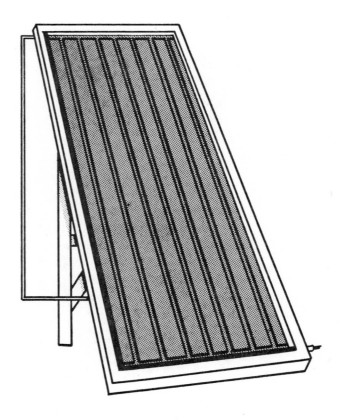

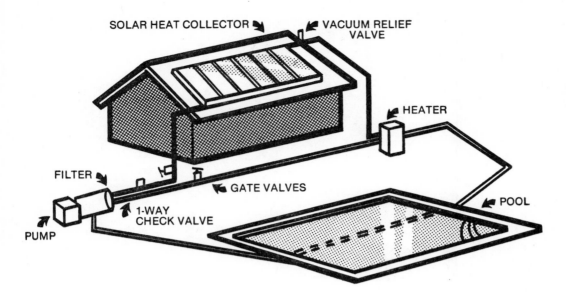

**Figure 40:
A typical solar pool
heating system**

and reduce water evaporation and the need to filter returning water by constructing a case with covering glass for the corrugated steel panels.

The water flow rate should be set between 200 and 300 gallons (757 and 1135 litres) per 100 square feet (9.2903 m²) of collector panel. It should be pumped during the daylight hours only, and although it won't be quite as efficient, the unit can be operated during slightly overcast days. It should be shut down during the night, and when it's snowing or raining, particularly on stormy days.

Cost is the big selling feature of this system. It's very inexpensive, but is somewhat less efficient than other systems.

Another relatively inexpensive system involves the use of black plastic pipe. In this system the black pipe is looped back and forth on the roof or another structure. It is rather inexpensive, but also less efficient, with the degree of efficiency correlated with the amount of pipe used. The pipe is connected to the existing system after the pump/filter arrangement, routed onto the roof and then back into the pool.

other applications

One of the most popular uses of the sun is the making of solar tea (also called sun tea) which requires nothing more than a gallon jar, three or four tea bags, and water. The jar is placed in open sunlight and within a few hours you will have the best tea ever. Sun tea doesn't become cloudy and yet it retains the full tea flavor.

SOLAR COOKERS

There are many different ways to construct a solar cooker, ranging from one constructed of aluminum foil and shaped in a parabolic circle, to sophisticated cookers which contain solar cells. The parabolic shape is important because it directs concentrated heat directly on the cooker.

The construction of a solar cooker is an excellent way to learn about solar energy and how it can be used in other applications.*

A very efficient solar cooker can be constructed with a small flat plate collector and steam cooker combination. The flat plate collector is constructed in a manner similar to those covered in the earlier chapters on water and swimming pool heaters. The dimensions of a unit built by the Brace Institute at McGill University in Montreal are 62 inches long x 21 inches wide and 4 inches (157.48 x 53.34 x 10.16 cm) deep. The components of the collector are basically the same except that a single tube is used to heat the water. The tube is attached to the absorber plate and runs the length of the collector to about 4 inches (101.6 mm) past the

---

*Mother Earth News and Lifestyle (two alternative lifestyle publications) have both featured several different methods of making solar cookers. Copies of the magazines should be available from your local library or bookstores that cater to alternative lifestyle customers.

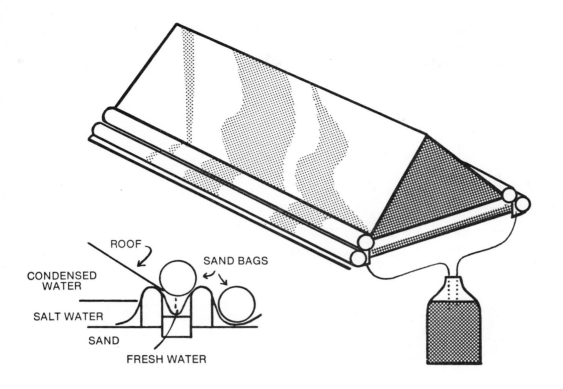

ROOF

SAND BAGS

CONDENSED WATER

SALT WATER

SAND

FRESH WATER

**Figure 41.
Solar still for
distilling water.**

case where it is joined with a similar pipe attached to the steam case, which is built to accomodate an average cooking pot.*

This cooker is quite effective if instructions are followed. The system must always contain water, with additional water added daily to replace that lost through steam. Under normal conditions, steam will be produced within an hour after the sun first shines on the collector, and will continue throughout the day.

SOLAR STILLS

Distilling water with solar energy is nothing new. The concept has been used for years. American flyers in World War II used portable distillers to purify sea water. Many ocean front residents use a similar system for removing salt from sea water. The still in Figure 41 is a typical unit for purifying water.

A basic still can be made by cutting three pieces of glass in a triangular shape and gluing them together with the point up. The glass is then placed over a pan of saline water resting on an insulated pad. When the unit is placed in direct sunlight, the sun will create water condensation which will be carried to the upper portion of the glass by air circulation, where it can be funneled off into a catch-tray. As the process continues, all the water will be condensed, leaving only a salt residue in the pan.

This process is similar to that used to mine salt in many parts of the

*Plans for this cooker are available from the Brace Institute, McGill University, Montreal, Quebec, Canada. The price at the time this book appears is a dollar.

world. In salt mining, saline water is pumped into ponds and allowed to dry. When the water evaporates, only the salt remains to be mined.

Many years ago, the University of Arizona built a desalinization plant on the Gulf of California near Puerto Penasco, Mexico. Although much larger in scope, the principle was the same. And as a result of the pilot plant in Mexico, the University later built a similar plant in the middle eastern emirate of Abu Dhabi. The University of Arizona has been a pioneer in this field and, as a result of various experiments, has built experimental farms for growing vegetables, notably tomatoes, under completely controlled conditions. One such experiment can be seen at a huge farm near Tucson International Airport in Arizona.

Another example of this principle can be found in any desert survival manual. Desert travelers should always carry a piece of clear plastic for producing small quantities of water, even in the driest areas. To produce water, dig a hole in the desert and spread the plastic over it with a slight dishing inward, and place a container on the underside. This simple still can produce up to a quart of water a day, even in the driest of deserts.

future developments

PART A
Heating Public Buildings

In early 1974, NSF let several contracts with RANN (Research Applied to National Needs) funding to add retrofit solar energy systems to four schools in different parts of the country; Minneapolis, Minn., Dorchester, Mass., Warrenton, Va., and Timonium, Md.

Fauquier High School

The Fauquier High School project in Warrenton, Virginia was designed and built by Inter-Technology Corporation, and is one of the two proof-of-concept projects to be covered here.

The Fauquier project consisted of installing a solar system to meet all the heating load needs of five mobile type, detached classrooms. After the project was completed, the cost to the school for heating the five classrooms was about 25 cents a day, and that cost was for electrical energy required to operate the pumps and controls.

After several months of operation, it was determined that solar energy could be incorporated into existing school buildings as a primary source of heat. School Officials further determined that after the demonstration period ended, operation and maintenance of the system could be handled by existing maintenance personnel with a minimum of training. Under terms of the contract, the unit would eventually be turned over to the school.

The amazing thing about all of those projects was that they were to be completed and operational in a very short period of time—about 60 days—and from scratch.

Figure 42: Collector array at Fauquier High School, Warrenton, Va.

At Faquier High School collector plates were constructed of Aluminum Roll-Bond and were selected over such materials as copper tubing on copper plating, and brass tubing on brass plates. The reasons included the quicker availability of the aluminum material which could be fabricated in time to meet the project completion deadline. A special chemical etch selective coating was developed for use with the aluminum at a cost of about 50% of that for alternative coating materials.

The collector array for this project was erected on a hillside adjacent to the school rather than atop the buildings. The separation of the collectors from the buildings was necessary since the buildings to be heated were single room, modular units.

Timonium Elementary School

The Timonium Elementary School was constructed in Timonium, Md., by the AAI Corporation, of Baltimore. (Figure 43). As mentioned earlier, the school projects, in my estimation, prove beyond a doubt that solar energy applications in public buildings can be effective at low cost. The installations were expensive. In fact, the total budget for the four school projects was 1.3 million dollars. But we must remember that they were all retrofit applications which required structural changes and extensive engineering that would ordinarily be included in the original building. There was also the time element, which required crash-program expenditures, and lastly, the installations were constructed while school was in session, which also added to the costs.

The collector array on the Timonium School contained 5100 square feet (473.81 m²) of collector area and a huge 15,000 gallon (56,781 litre) storage tank that provided the water at a rate of three gallons (11.356

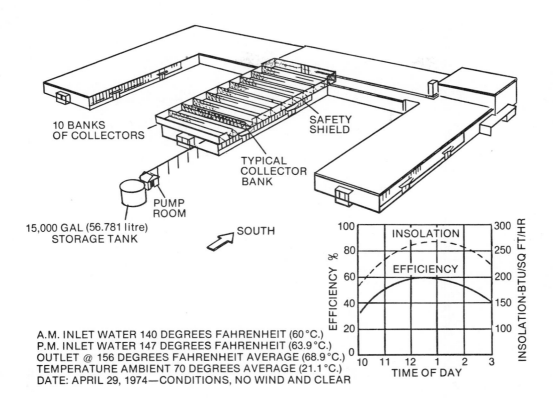

Figure 43:
Drawing of collector array on the Timonium Elementary School, Timonium, Md.

Figure 44:
Efficiency of the Timonium Elementary School solar heating system

10 BANKS
OF COLLECTORS

SAFETY
SHIELD

TYPICAL
COLLECTOR
BANK

PUMP
ROOM

15,000 GAL (56.781 litre)
STORAGE TANK

SOUTH

A.M. INLET WATER 140 DEGREES FAHRENHEIT (60 °C.)
P.M. INLET WATER 147 DEGREES FAHRENHEIT (63.9 °C.)
OUTLET @ 156 DEGREES FAHRENHEIT AVERAGE (68.9 °C.)
TEMPERATURE AMBIENT 70 DEGREES AVERAGE (21.1 °C.)
DATE: APRIL 29, 1974—CONDITIONS, NO WIND AND CLEAR

litres) per collector foot (0.3048 m). It is a large installation, but the variety of data derived from the instruments programmed to record all facets of the operation should aid immeasurably in future projects of this nature. When the proof-of-concept program has ended, the system will be turned over to school officials.

The pilot system was installed in the middle section, of a three section building. By choosing a single section, engineers were able to determine the relative effectiveness compared to the two sections not utilizing solar energy. This experiment has simplified solar system studies and preliminary statistics indicate that the unit is quite effective.

The study indicates a savings of about 1200 gallons (4543 litres) of fuel oil in the period from March 14 to May 15, 1974. During that time, the solar heating system provided 91% of the test section's heating requirements.

Figure 44 indicates the efficiency of the Timonium School solar heating system on a given day. It shows how the efficiency rises and falls with insolation (for a given water temperature).

The collector array was made up of 180 collectors 4 (121.92 cm) x 7 feet (213.36 cm) x 2⅜ inches (60.325 mm), with each unit weighing approximately 90 pounds (40.8233 Kg) (Figure 46). The collector was constructed of two glass covers made from low-iron content double strength glass. The absorber plate was made of aluminum with two thicknesses of aluminum honeycomb which filled the area between the glass and absorber plate. The honeycombing was then notched before being extended into place which allowed for free passage of the water.

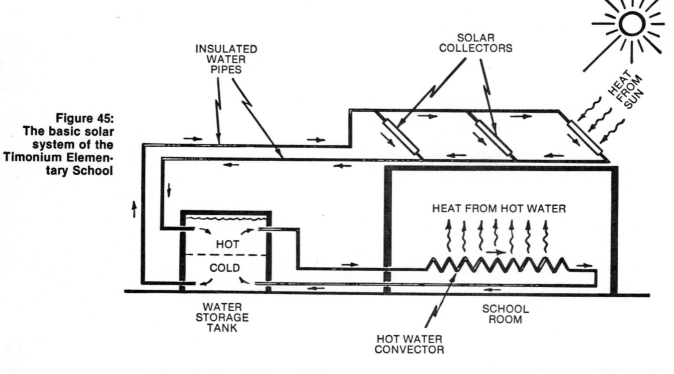

**Figure 45:
The basic solar
system of the
Timonium Elemen-
tary School**

INSULATED WATER PIPES

SOLAR COLLECTORS

HEAT FROM SUN

HEAT FROM HOT WATER

HOT

COLD

WATER STORAGE TANK

HOT WATER CONVECTOR

SCHOOL ROOM

**Figure 46:
Manufacturing the
collector array for
the Timonium
Elementary School**

Figure 47:
The Troy-Miami
County Public
Library

Both glass plates, the honeycomb, and absorber plate were bonded together with two-part epoxy and a 1½ inch (38.1 mm) thick sheet of polyurethane foam; sheet insulation was bonded to the back of the absorber. After the foam edging was applied, a rubber strip was added to seal the unit.

Troy-Miami County Library

One of the latest projects constructed under the Heating & Cooling Demonstration Act of 1974 is the Troy-Miami County, Ohio, Public Library. It is being constructed with funding dispensed through the ERDA program, and is one of 34 non-residential solar energy demonstrations chosen from 308 different non-residential projects reviewed for qualification under the program. It is the only public library in the demonstration program.

The total package is slated for completion under a five year program with the heating system to be completed by early 1977. The projected cost of the project is less than 300,000 dollars. Figure 47 illustrates the general layout including an array of 3617 feet (1102.46 m) of collector area.

The library is a one-story building with a basement and has a total floor area of 23,200 square feet (2155.35 m). The initial portion of the projected total energy system features a heating system which is activated by heated water from the solar collectors. Heated water from the collectors can be diverted directly to the building's air handling units for heating, or if not needed at that time, can be transferred to the storage tank for later use (Figure 48). The system should provide at least 75% of the heating

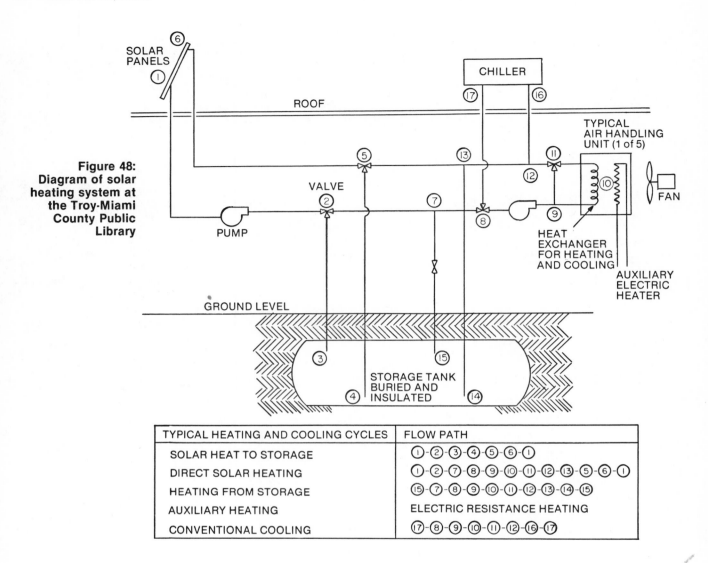

Figure 48: Diagram of solar heating system at the Troy-Miami County Public Library

TYPICAL HEATING AND COOLING CYCLES	FLOW PATH
SOLAR HEAT TO STORAGE	①-②-③-④-⑤-⑥-①
DIRECT SOLAR HEATING	①-②-⑦-⑧-⑨-⑩-⑪-⑫-⑬-⑤-⑥-①
HEATING FROM STORAGE	⑮-⑦-⑧-⑨-⑩-⑪-⑫-⑬-⑭-⑮
AUXILIARY HEATING	ELECTRIC RESISTANCE HEATING
CONVENTIONAL COOLING	⑰-⑧-⑨-⑩-⑪-⑫-⑯-⑰

energy needs of the building. The existing air handling system utilizes electric resistance heating coils for heating and is engineered to provide all the library's heating needs during cloudy days or through times when low storage temperature show that supplemental heat is needed.

The solar collectors are somewhat different from those previously covered. They are an invention of Owens-Illinois and carry the trademark SUNPAK (Figure 49, top).

The collector tubes are a bit unique and resemble flourescent lights. They are constructed of double-walled glass, similar to a vacuum thermos bottle or thermopane window, and are actually a tube within a tube, with an air space between.

The sun's heat is trapped within the inner tube where a special coating permits radiation within but doesn't allow the trapped energy to escape. The dominant feature of this concept is that, because of vacuum insulation, the collector's performance isn't affected by adverse weather conditions such as high winds or low outside temperature. The engineering is such that the total collector area is sufficient to adequately heat the building and is planned to supply at least 75% of the total heating requirements. Additionally, the energy collected will be sufficient to drive two 25 ton solar powered water chillers when the cooling system is added later.

The existing system utilizes chilled water cooling coils to cool the building. Part of that system will be used during the winter to carry solar-heated water from the collectors to the cooling coils in the air handling units, which will warm those coils while the air handling unit fans circulate air across the coils to deliver heat as required. During the summer, the cooling coils will be supplied with chilled water from the conventional water chiller until adequate solar cooling systems are available. However, through far-sighted planning, the system will be ready for adaption when cooling components make such a system feasible.

They have also engineered the existing room temperature control system so it can be modified to permit automatic control of solar and auxiliary electrical heating cycles, thereby assuring desired room temperatures at all times.

The project team estimates that up to 76.9% of the Troy Library heating load can be supplied by the solar system, with a conservative annual savings of about 3500 dollars, not including maintenance and operating costs of the system, which are estimated at 600 dollars annual-

**Figure 49:
Prototype of tubular solar collectors and collector panels similar to those used on the Troy-Miami County Public Library**

ly, for a net savings of around 2900 dollars annually. Those savings will increase when the cooling cycle is added.

Another big plus in this program is that the Troy Library is using the system as an educational vehicle to obtain and pass out information to the public. They have planned a varied program for disseminating information on solar-related technology, including a solar system display in the library lobby, separately maintained library holdings on solar energy, information and technology, library tours and solar energy short courses.

PART B:

Generating Electricity With Large Scale Systems

Much of the emphasis to this point has been on individual units and on the topic of space heating/cooling and heating water. It is obvious that an industry geared to individual systems can make an impact on total energy needs when spread out over a long period of time, but to make a real impact on our total energy needs, systems must be devised to generate electricity on a large scale.

One of the first, if not the first, houses integrating both space heating and generating electricity in the same unit was built at the University of Delaware with support funding from the Delmarva Power & Light Company. The experiment was under the direction of a leader of solar energy development in the United States, Dr. Karl W. Boer, Director of the Institute of Energy Conversion at the University of Delaware.

The house contains a combination of solar heat collectors and solar cells made of cadmium sulfide which convert sunlight into both heat and electricity. Additional advantages include a system of converting the DC electricity from the cells to AC current needed to operate standard household appliances. The house also contains a system for drawing on conventional power systems when the solar unit is not functioning. This system has a two-fold purpose since it supplies about 80% of heat and electricity from the sunlight and the balance from the conventional source, mostly at night when the sun isn't shining, which takes the load off of the conventional system during peak hours. The project is known as The University of Delaware's Solar One home.

Figure 50 illustrates the estimated United States energy demand by the year 2020, as compared with today. The chart shows that the expected difference in requirements will be made up from nuclear energy, but the fact remains that much of that required energy could be solar.

As mentioned in Chapter One, the yearly incidence of solar energy in near-earth space is approximately 130 thermal watts/ft. (.0929 m²) and on the ground in the continental United States the figure drops to approximately 17 thermal watts/ft. (.0929 m²) average. The large loss in energy from near space to the ground is caused by atmospheric absorption, cloud cover, periods of darkness and geographic location. And the key word is average. Reduced to simple terms, enough energy hits every

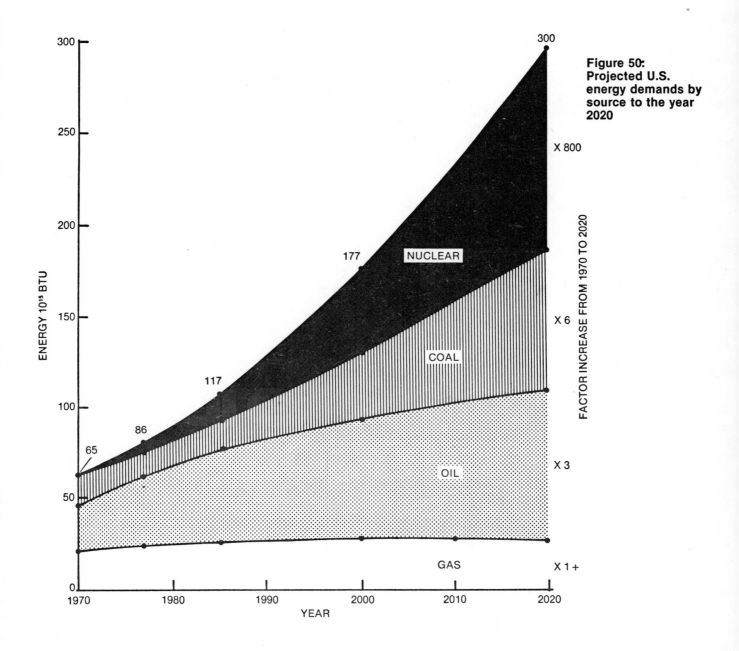

**Figure 50:
Projected U.S.
energy demands by
source to the year
2020**

square foot of ground, on a nationwide average, to supply twice the energy required to heat and cool the average house, if you could harness that energy at the right time and the right place.

One example, on a larger scale, is found with the Potomac Electric Power Company (PEPCO), which in 1969 sold a daily average of 30,000,000 kilowatt hours to 425,000 customers in an area of about 643 square miles (1,665.362 km²). In principle, PEPCO could provide the same electric power on a solar collector area of 27 square miles (69.930 km²), or 4% of the area serviced. This is figured by converting the 17 thermal watts/ft. into electricity at the 10% conversion efficiency factor which most solar energy scientists feel is realistic at this time. This would result

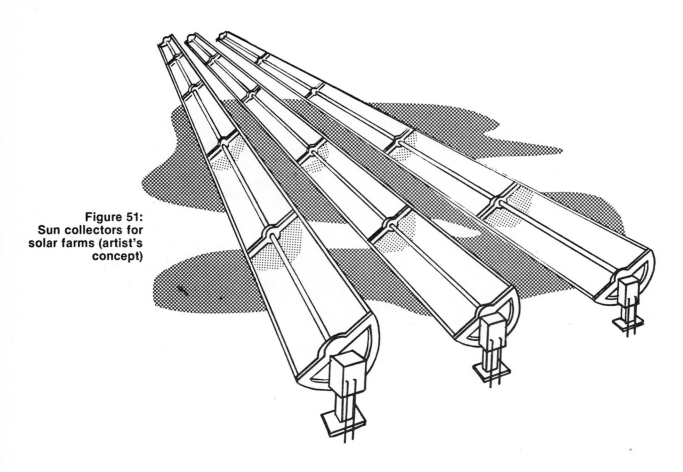

**Figure 51:
Sun collectors for
solar farms (artist's
concept)**

in an average daily output of approximately 1,140,000 kilowatt hours per square mile.

To sum it up, using the 10% conversion efficiency factor and United States average solar incidence, the total electric energy consumed in this country in 1969 could have been supplied by the solar energy incident on 0.14% of the Unites States land area.

The huge energy loss from near space to ground is one reason the space station concept for collecting the sun's rays has been given more than a passing glance, even taking into account the huge capital expense involved.

There have been several ideas presented for the large scale generation of electricity from solar energy. The huge solar farm concept has had different authors with various notions of how this form of generating electricity might be created.

I witnessed a presentation by Helio Associates, a firm in Tucson, Arizona, founded by Drs. Aden and Marjorie Meinel from the University of Arizona. The Meinels have been pioneers in the field of solar energy, both academically and later in private industry. They have long espoused the use of solar farms situated in remote desert areas of the Southwest. Their concept features sunshine collecting tubes which concentrate collected heat (very hot) and transport it to a liquid metal coolant (such as liquid sodium) which could also be stored during cloudy periods and at night.

They estimate that one square mile of collectors could generate enough electricity to supply a city of 75,000 people.

The one big difference between collecting sunshine for space heating/cooling and water heating, and storing sunshine for generating electricity is the temperature. In the case of the former, the necessary temperature range is in the range of 150 to 200 plus degrees Fahrenheit (65.6 to 93.3°C.), while temperatures required to operate steam turbines or other mechanisms needed to generate electricity are considerably higher; somewhere in the 500 degree Fahrenheit (260°C.) range. The term generally associated with those higher temperatures is Solar Thermal Conversion, although, technically, this term also applies to lower temperature requirements as well.

In addition to the Meinel theory, another concept currently under study is the use of individual concentrating collectors which convert the highly concentrated energy to steam right at the collector and then pipe it to a central location where turbine-generators produce the electricity (Figure 52).

An additional version of a massive collector field features rows of mirrors which reflect solar heat to a boiler mounted atop a tower which acts as an absorber/heat exchanger. Large amounts of steam are generated at the tower then piped to a turbine/generator plant to produce electricity (Figure 53).

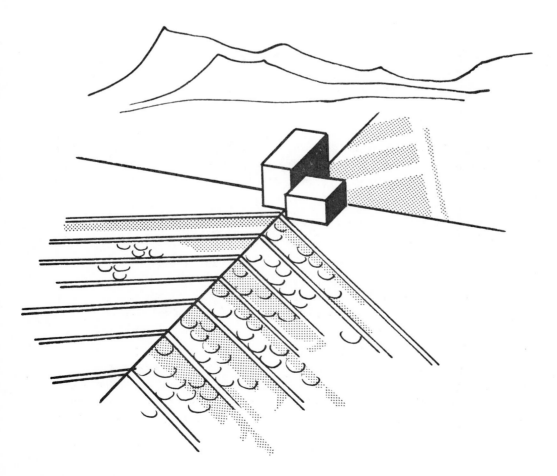

**Figure 52:
Individual concentrating collectors which convert energy to steam (artist's concept)**

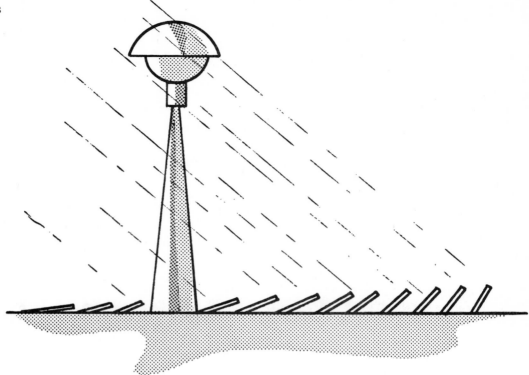

**Figure 53:
The tower heliostat
system featuring
rows of mirrors
(artist's concept). A
contract to build
such a system at
the Sandia
experimental range
near Albuquerque,
N.M. has already
been let by ERDA.**

The difference between the distributed collector and tower heliostat systems is that the first accomplishes a concentration of solar energy by optics and thermal concentration (accumulation of heat in the piping system) and the second does this with optical concentration alone.

There are strong indications that both the distributed collector and the tower heliostat systems can produce electricity on a cost basis comparable to existing conventional power plants, for a limited time of production (i.e. during a sunlit day). The study of the tower heliostat system is being conducted at Colorado State University, Fort Collins, Colorado.

These are just a few of perhaps a dozen different concepts of how to harness all those fleas Ms. Ray alluded to in her Tucson, Arizona speech. The fact is that, although there are variations on the basic concept, the capability for performance isn't that far away. It will require cooperation from both the government and the utility companies. And the awarding of the contract to construct the 10,000 watt plant should establish the fact that it is feasible and that the government and private sectors can work together to bring it about.

The availability of low cost energy in the not too distant past has transformed the United States and the utility companies have had no small part in this process. The simple life of my youth has become almost totally unacceptable to most Americans. Many of us have become slaves to automatic appliances and labor saving devices, most of which are operated by electricity or fuel. Day by day the precious surplus is being eroded.

You might say the American public has been subjected to the most intensive brainwashing known to man. In many ways I've come to an understanding with the dissenters and dropouts of the 1960's and early 1970's. The growth of the alternative lifestyle movement is too great to be without merit. The back-to-the-land migration is so great that most large cities are showing a drop in population. They are right, in many respects. We have become a very materialistic nation and the selling job was, and is, second to none. It just doesn't make sense for utility companies, both publicly and privately owned—virtual monopolies—to constantly exhort us to buy more air conditioners and appliances. The money spent on advertising alone, by utilities since World War II, could bring us a viable solar energy program.

Where were the utility companies when the energy crunch hit the country? They suddenly switched to the role of public savior by urging consumers to conserve energy so we wouldn't run out of fossil fuel reserves. Was this posturing a new direction for the utilities? Did they follow their own advice? Rarely, and the result has been skyrocketing utility rates. They seem to be saying, "time is short, we're running out of fossil fuels, so let's get it while we can." The situation is so critical in some areas utility bills are higher than mortgage payments. And finally, we have the ultimate irony. When the message did get through and Americans used less energy, it meant, of course, less revenue, which resulted in a mad dash to regulatory agencies for rate increases. The big sales pitch for rate increases was that profits were down (in the case of investor owned companies at least) and they needed more profits to keep a good investor image so they could sell more stocks, and of course, make more profits for investors. It was also necessary to keep up a good bond rating so they could borrow more money, which is needed to build more generating plants. And since most new plants on the drawing boards are designed for

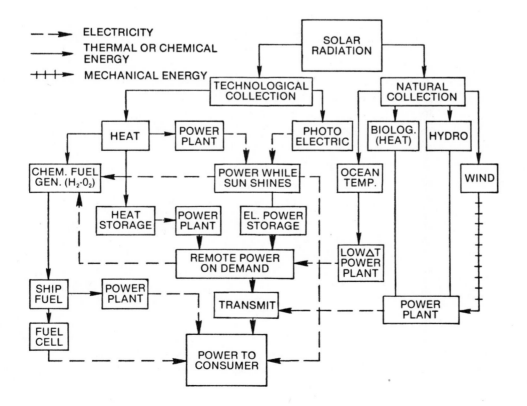

Figure 54:
Diagram of
conversion of solar
energy to electricity

nuclear energy, we can now see why the direction taken by the Atomic Energy Commission was so important, and why solar energy has been like a poor relative in the total energy scheme of things.

It could be a tremendous plus to the solar energy program if utilities used some of their profits to aid the cause. There are indications this may come to pass, especially if the pilot generating plant is successful.

In any event, the use of solar energy on any level will have the dual effect of diluting the strength of some of those giant utilities and saving fossil fuel reserves.

There must be a happy medium and I'm convinced that position can be filled through the widespread use of solar energy. We have alluded to the need for large sums of money to get any kind of full-scale program off the ground, and that fact cannot be emphasized enough. As has been the case with gas and oil exploration, some kind of government subsidy is a must, at least to get the ball rolling. We all know that once government money is involved, private industry won't be far behind. It's a fact that has been proven many times over, not just in the gas and oil industry, but in health care, aerospace, and other sectors too numerous to mention.

Another concept under consideration for mass generation of electricity is a satellite circling the earth at the equator. A satellite in synchronous orbit around the equator receives solar energy 24 hours a day, except for brief periods around the equinoxes. In this orbit, a satellilte receives six to ten times the amount of solar energy available in suitable terrestrial locations in the United States. As illustrated in Figure 55, the DC power generated in space by such a satellite would be beamed via microwaves to the ground and there reconverted to high voltage DC or AC power to meet base or demand load needs. In addition, such satellites could serve as communications or observation bases.

The use of microwaves at a frequency near 3GHz for power transmission from the satellite to earth provides minimum loss in the ionosphere and troposphere. This loss has been estimated to average 6% and to remain moderate even during severe rainstorms. To obtain adequate beam definition at this frequency, a transmitting antenna approximately 1 km in diameter is needed. The transmission efficiency is expected to be in the 55 to 75% range from DC in space to DC on earth.

The transmitting antenna diameter determines the economical system size which ranges from 4000 to 15,000 MW power output on earth. This concept is being pursued by the Raytheon Corporation.

The plan as initally conceived features the use of two solar panels equipped with silicon solar cells 2 mil in thickness. Microwave generators with more than 5kw output and 76% efficiency have already been demonstrated. Highly directional, self-steering (retro-directive) antenna arrays have been developed by the Air Force for radar and communication purposes. For the receiving antenna system, rectifier diodes with 75% efficiency are now available. Preliminary concept studies have been carried out for the space power station system which will be 100,000

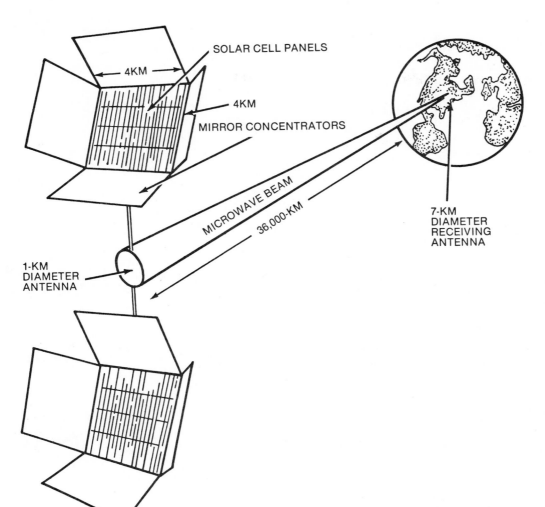

SOLAR CELL PANELS

4KM

4KM

MIRROR CONCENTRATORS

MICROWAVE BEAM

36,000-KM

7-KM DIAMETER RECEIVING ANTENNA

1-KM DIAMETER ANTENNA

**Figure 55:
Space station plan
for generating
electricity (artist's
concept)**

times larger than the Manned Space Station. The solar arrays are projected to be several miles square. There are also other factors involved and the demonstration of commercial readiness assumes the availability of planned space shuttle programs for moving people back and forth from earth.

The cost of several billion dollars for each phase of such a venture absolutely boggles the mind, but so did the cost of space ventures a few years ago. There still remain many special engineering problems to be solved, including weight reduction for the solar arrays and their deployment in extremely large structures of low weight, combined with the requirement for orientation and attitude control. The interaction of large flexible systems with attitude control operation requires special investigation. Additionally, methods for assembling the systems composed of many components, by automation or man-assisted methods in space, would have to be developed, as well as low-cost transportation to synchronous orbit.

The microwave transmission system requires additional engineering development based on existing technology. This is expected to be eased through repetitive use of a few component types in benign operating modes.

All in all it's an ambitious undertaking, but so were the moon flights.

PART C:

Future Trends

Fortunately, several Senators and members of Congress are working within the system to bring about change and appropriate much needed funds for research and proof-of-concept projects. The House bill, and the Senate version by Senator Cranston and Senator Gravel, were so close in concept that a joint conference quickly solved the differences, and in a rare showing of solidarity, passed the Solar Heating & Cooling Demonstration Act of 1974. In brief, the Act earmarked 10 million dollars as a start, and then 50 million dollars spread over a five year period to fund the addition of 2000 solar energy heating systems for public buildings, and another 2000 heating and cooling systems in family dwellings to be tested in various sections of the United States.

The two Federal agencies charged with handling the Solar Heating and Cooling Demonstration Act of 1974 are NASA and HUD. One of the programs is funded by a several million dollar grant, administered by HUD, which will dispense funds for new housing units utilizing solar units. It will also include as full payment grants to builders or individuals who add solar energy packages to homes. The grants are for the solar package only and do not cover the conventional backup system. The following is an in-depth explanation of the plan from an official HUD bulletin.*

Scope of HUD's Responsibility

HUD, through its Office of Policy Development and Research, Division of Energy, Building Technology and Standards, will carry out four activities to implement the residential demonstration portion of the solar heating and cooling program:

1. Residential demonstrations in which solar equipment will be installed in both new and existing dwellings.
2. Development of performance criteria and certification procedures for solar heating and cooling equipment.
3. Market development efforts to encourage the rapid and widespread acceptance of solar technologies by the housing industry.
4. Dissemination of demonstration and market development results. As outlined in the Heating & Cooling Demonstration Act of 1974, HUD will conduct several cycles of residential demonstrations using solar heating technology by the end of Fiscal Year 1977, and

*Residential Energy From the Sun. Department of Housing and Urban Development, March 1976.

using combined solar heating and cooling technology by the end of Fiscal Year 1979.

To accomplish these objectives as rapidly as possible, HUD's key strategies include:

1. A series of time phased demonstrations in various climatic and geographic locations.
2. The active involvement of the housing industry.
3. The rigorous study of various potential barriers—economic, social, legal—to widespread utilization of residential solar energy systems.
4. Determination of methods to stimulate market demand for such systems.
5. Investigation of needs and types of possible incentives to promote the marketplace supply of standard systems, sub-systems, and components.
6. Encouragement of energy conservation in dwelling design and construction in conjunction with solar energy.

How The HUD Residential Demonstrations Are Structured

Two parallel series of demonstrations are planned. Each series will consist of five cycles, repeated at intervals of nine months to a year. Potential participants who may not be ready for earlier cycles will have a chance to participate in later cycles, thereby encouraging a continued dynamic technological growth.

In both series, the first two cycles will focus primarily on systems for space and domestic hot water heating. The third, fourth and fifth cycles will concentrate on combined solar heating and cooling systems.

All projects will utilize systems ready or "available" for demonstration. In general, a "project" will consist of from one to twenty dwelling units.

Integrated Project Approach

One series of demonstrations will involve "integrated" projects. These are residential projects which have been designed to incorporate a particular solar energy system, or which have been designed so that the building structure utilizes passive measures within the structure to collect, store and distribute solar energy. Normally, an "integrated" project will have been developed to the point that engineering design is complete, financing has been identified, approvals have been received, and construction is imminent.

The "integrated" project solicitation for the first demonstration cycle was issued in September 1975.

Matched Site/System Approach

The second series of demonstrations will match available solar energy systems with appropriate locations around the country. The demonstration locations will be selected through a matrix which correlates data on climate, types of housing units, types of solar energy systems, local building codes and land use regulations, financing practices, construction procedures, market conditions, architectural preferences, and demography. Using the location matrix, this series of demonstrations will be carefully structured to provide technical information on the performance of the solar energy systems as well as data to support HUD's market development efforts.

Solar Energy Systems Solicitations

This second series of demonstrations begins with an ERDA solicitation of solar energy systems and sub-systems through a Program Opportunity Announcement. An interagency evaluation panel will select those systems which are considered ready for demonstration use. These systems considered ready will be provided an opportunity for demonstration in various parts of the program—in the HUD residential demonstration program, in the ERDA commercial demonstration program, or in federally-owned projects of other agencies.

System manufacturers will be asked to indicate those geographic areas in which they wish to market their products. Systems requiring additional development may request support funding from ERDA.

The Program Opportunity Announcement for solar energy systems for this first demonstration cycle was issued in September, 1965.

Residential Project Solicitations

Following the match of demonstration locations with selected solar energy systems, HUD will request specific residential project proposals within the demonstration location from builder/developers, State and local agencies, and other qualified parties. In general, proposals will be accepted from developers who are constructing residential projects and are willing to use one or more buildings for solar energy systems, while maintaining other, similar buildings within the project as experimental controls with conventional energy systems. The assignment of solar energy systems to specific locations will take into account the system manufacturers' marketing programs and objectives.

HUD will select the projects to be used based upon the qualifications of the developer, the quality of design of the proposed project, and the degree to which the project will support the program objectives. The proposers will be required to demonstrate their ability to provide the land and financing, to integrate the solar energy system into the building design, to obtain necessary approvals, to construct and market the buildings, and to provide suitable warranties to the purchasers.

The successful proposer will receive a limited design contract to integrate the solar hardware into the house, and will be required to involve the solar system manufacturer in the design effort. This procedure is

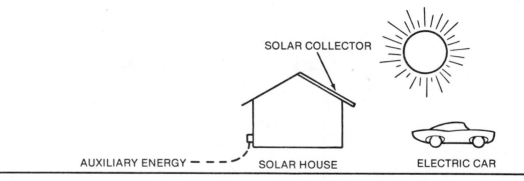

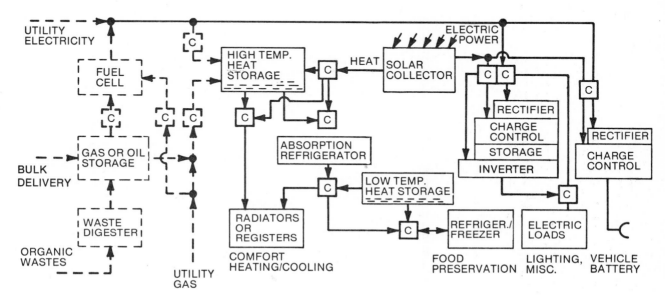

**Figure 56:
Diagram of a solar
energy system for a
residence**

analogous to the normal relationship between a builder and his mechanical contractor. The result of the design integration process will be a complete set of construction plans, specifications, and cost estimates.

If the design and cost estimates are acceptable, the developer will be awarded a contract to purchase and install a solar energy system.

In addition to the preceding program, HUD intends to assist in developing a widespread marketing program which should help get solar energy development off the ground.

HUD further advises that for the present time at least, it will be unable to accept unsolicited proposals. And this seems fair, since the agency is trying to establish certain programs and criteria that will fit into the overall plan. The HUD officials also state that this might change at some future date and if so, a widespread announcement will be issued to that effect.

As mentioned previously, the Federal agency most directly responsible for coordinating all alternative resource programs is the Energy Research and Development Administration. ERDA was originally directed to handle the Solar Energy Information Service (which I found to be most helpful and cooperative) with an original 2 million dollar grant to fund a NSF study and to establish a new Solar Energy Research Center in the United

States. Many states are seeking this center but at this time the site has not been chosen. There have been some late developments in this plan and frankly, they don't sound good. There are indications that the site selection may become a political "plum" for the right state or locality as witnessed in a recent speech in Florida by Gerald R. Ford, while still President, when he stated that Cape Kennedy (Canaveral) would be a good location for the Institute. Florida probably picked up some more points when the International Solar Energy group announced plans to locate the international headquarters in that state. Press releases from Washington later indicated the site selection committee might consider looking at facilities that once served another purpose (i.e. a closed defense plant, abandoned military installation, etc.) and that a vastly reduced sum of money was now the plan. So it appears that original plan for a large central program, with the express purpose of finding a viable program for generating electricity on a grand scale, is now reduced to smaller pilot projects.

One plan under active consideration is the building of a 10,000 kilowatt generating plant, for which several states are vying. This project is under the sponsorship of ERDA and calls for completion of a pilot plant by 1980. In Arizona, a consortium of three utility companies, Arizona Public Service, Salt River Project, and Tucson Gas & Electric is bidding on the project. The Arizona plan calls for a 10,000 kilowatt plant with a total funding of approximately 75 million dollars, of which 15 million would come from the private sector, and 55 million from the Federal Government.

The private money would cover site purchase and installation of backup or auxiliary equipment, while the federal money would finance the solar generator equipment, including a huge collector array. Arizona is competing with Florida, Southern California and New Mexico, as well as other states for this project. It is a great idea and should give researchers an opportunity to see firsthand if large scale systems are economically feasible. The 10,000 kilowatt plant is small by most standards, and present plans call for just one such project, but it is a beginning, and a reason to be optimistic.

It does appear that we have made a start and that full-scale solar energy research and development is underway; perhaps we can now go a step farther and direct some of those resources into an area of genuine need, the low income family, not only in the United States, but in the rest of the world as well.

One of the tragedies of increased energy costs is the effect it has on low income families and the elderly struggling to survive on fixed incomes. These groups are having increased difficulties when it comes to paying ever-climbing utility bills, and since it is almost impossible to bring about equity through utility companies (although some areas do subsidize utility bills for the very poor) and cheap energy is gone forever, there is a definite role for solar energy.

As we know, solar energy is nothing new and has been indirectly aiding all people in one manner or another since the beginning of time. But the fact remains; we haven't used this energy source to directly improve the lives of poor people around the world. There is now existing technology to build basic systems on new houses and housing projects. This was done in Florida in the late 1930's and financed with Federal money for new, as well as retrofit units on existing houses, once they are upgraded with proper insulation and structural strengthening. The prototype units wouldn't have to be too sophisticated, and for a start, only water heaters and space heating systems would be installed, with perhaps cooling systems at a later time when that technology is more advanced.

The Brace Institute in Montreal has conducted on-site experiments by constructing several low-cost solar water heaters in Barbados. These units proved to be most effective. Plans for building such a unit are covered in Chapter Three.

Think of the millions of people who could go to bed each night with a hot bath and heat throughout the house. This is altruism that would have a far-reaching impact on many parts of the world.

A basic system, with minimal collector area, and connecting pipes to a storage tank and simple blower with a distribution system could improve the lot of many people. And when used in concert with existing systems such as a backup to conventional water heating capabilities, a basic system could reduce utility bills substantially. It seems to me that if our leaders in Washington really want to assist the less fortunate, this would be a great place to start.

The bureaucracy for handling such a venture is already in place. Existing programs within HEW and HUD could coordinate the plan.

In fact, a project similar to Model Cities could be implemented; a plan in which the people themselves would help defray a portion of the cost at some level.

Under my plan, a simple solar energy system would be constructed from materials and technology supplied by the government, while the labor would be supplied by the homeowner or renter. By using less costly materials, such as corrugated sheet steel and steel pipe, instead of the more costly but more durable copper plate and tubing—along with rocks which are most everywhere in abundance, and metal tanks which could be obtained from several sources including United States Government surplus depots, a relatively inexpensive system could be constructed.

There is an abundant energy source, the sun, and a huge potential market—the low income people of the world. And we could accomplish two very important goals: firstly, reduce reliance on conventional energy sources, and secondly, upgrade the standard of living for millions of people. It is the utlimate of situations; beginning an industry by starting with a huge market and basic systems and building from the ground up. It will prove that solar energy is a viable alternative to fossil fuels, and that by starting with a basic system, any home or office building can benefit. Since installation of the demonstration units is where the money must go it's simply a matter of aiming for that point and taking off.

One final word about low income dwellings. An additional study should be made to determine how well most of those homes are insulated and since many are sadly lacking in insulation, an amended plan for insulating all homes of need might be integrated into the total package.

A significant side effect would be a dramatic reduction in illness due to improper heating of homes and lack of cleanliness due to lack of hot water. This reduction in health-related problems would result in fewer doctor and hospital bills, with a subsequent drop in the cost of public health services and government sponsored health programs. By placing federal money in an area of great need, we could reduce federal spending in another.

Food preservation is another topic for consideration. Many poor families lack proper nutrition because they can't preserve those foods that could improve their diet. A solar drier is one item that wouldn't be too costly and yet could become an asset to the low income family anywhere in the world.

There are so many applications for solar energy that could be utilized to aid mankind. It is tragic that more of them are not being implemented. Perhaps there is good reason. We might ask ourselves a few questions. Is there a reason why certain segments of the government are not more involved? Is there a place in our society for solar energy, or is it merely a fad, a glamour subject meant to conjur up dreams of energy independence, or on the darker side, a get-rich-quick plaything destined to enrich a select few and sucker in millions of unwary investors or users? Indications are that solar energy may be both of these, and more, since in anything new or faddish (not that solar energy is new) there are elements of controversy.

Opposition almost always centers on comparative costs, with most of the emphasis on start-up costs, whether on an individual system level or relative to array collector construction for generating electricity on a large scale. And the advocates point to the free source and amortization of initial costs over an extended period. In either case, the discussion finally arrives at X cents per kilowatt hour compared to conventional system costs (this generally includes hydroelectric, coal fired, or nuclear plants).

Critics who cite high initial costs conveniently forget the massive funds associated with existing power plants including power lines strung all over the country. As mentioned previously, money spent in nuclear research alone absolutely boggles the mind. The total outlay for hydroelectric and coal-fired plants is certainly not a small figure. And while it's true that much of that funding was, and is, private money, there is a goodly amount of federal money in our energy projects around the country. All things are relative and if we continue to use the finite resources we now take for granted, a crash program in solar energy may be costly indeed. If the same money spent on fossil fuel and nuclear energy research since World War II had been spent on solar energy research and projects, we would now be enjoying lower utility bills instead of ever increasing costs. And we would be well on our way to energy independence with a greater reserve of fossil fuels for future generations.

One of my favorite people, President Harry S. Truman, stated to the Materials Policy Commission in 1952, "Efforts made to date to harness solar energy economically are infinitesimal. It is time for aggressive research in the whole field of solar energy, an effort in which the United States could make an immense contribution to the welfare of the free world." That was almost twenty five-years ago. If we had started then, much of the current debate would be academic.

Another facet of solar energy dialogue involving government concerns the use of tax credits for builders of solar systems. Included in the many tax bills under consideration in several states are income tax credits, sales tax exemptions and property tax credits. Indiana was the first state to pass such a law and at this writing nine others have followed. They include Colorado, Montana, Maryland, North and South Dakota, Florida, Texas, and New Hampshire. Arizona is one of several states currently considering similiar legislation as of spring 1976. The Indiana plan calls for property tax deductions up to 2000 dollars annually. It would be a good idea to check on the tax situation in your particular area since a sizeable credit could cut your installation cost over a given period of time.

There are other variables that involve local governmental entities and some of these bear consideration. The one very real problem is with existing zoning laws. Zoning laws should not be a factor in commercial or industrial areas since there is generally a wider allowable variance in those locales, but residential zoning can be quite another matter. Most everyone agrees that a solar system with flat plate collectors standing on a rooftop is not the most attractive sight in the world though residents of the Southwest have learned to live with a similar projection, the swamp cooler. Part of the failure of solar energy programs is psychological, and aesthetics plays no small part in this. There has already been a case in Tucson, involving a variance request in the upper middle class neighborhood of the Catalina Foothills. In this case, which went to court, the zoning variance was denied.

My advice is, check local zoning laws thoroughly, and this applies to retrofit units as well as original equipment installation. If such restrictions are present, work with your local officials to have them changed.

In fact, we the public are much to blame for the lack of action by our government. If enough public pressure is applied in the right places, we'll get solar energy programs, and we'll get them fast.

The question of "free sunlight" is another consideration. It will apparantly face an early court test in California where state legislators are currently wrestling with the problem. This is more than a simple issue because the entire question involves financing of solar energy packages, both individual and on a larger scale. Financial institutions aren't about to loan money for any venture that isn't legally sound. This includes a clear definition of user's rights.

Some of the questions involved are: (1) Who owns the sunlight that strikes your property? and (2) How much are the sun's rays intrinsically worth? If landowners had the rights to sunlight striking their property, and could sell and transfer those rights, there would be an immediate increase in solar energy implementation.

Another question, moral as well as legal, is whether a neighbor has the right to plant trees or erect a structure which might blot out a portion of the sunlight, rendering your solar system inoperable, or at the very least, diminishing it's capability to serve you. This question is even more applicable in the building of a skyscraper which could alter the sunlight to several buildings, including family dwellings. The right of sunlight is a question that must be answered before any viable program can get off the ground.

It's sad but true that any new industry seems to attract shady operators with fast buck schemes. If the solar energy industry is to be successful, industry leaders and governmental agencies charged with solar energy research and development must establish standards and guidelines to insure product effectiveness and safety. There must be some basis for comparison enabling the consumer to judge a system on its merit and at the same time be aware of what he is purchasing. And this must be accomplished soon. One of the most important considerations must be a compatibility between system components and the buildings where they are attached or installed.

If the industry establishes a good reputation from the beginning, the

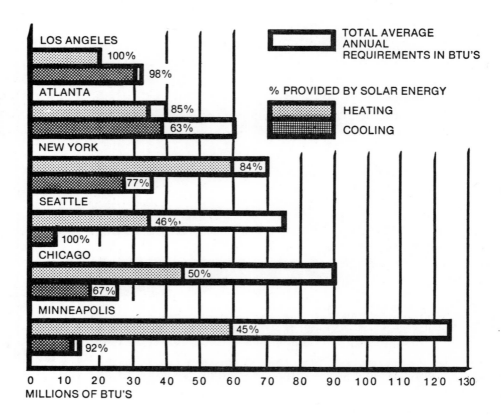

Figure 57: Energy requirements of major American cities

chances for success are great. But if shoddy practices are allowed, without some type of industry self-policing, there could be rough times ahead. The American consumer is much more aware of bad business practices than in years past and if the word ever gets around that the solar energy industry is a rip-off, it may never get off the ground.

Mass production of solar components, especially solar cells and instrumentation, will bring more large manufacturers into the industry which should have a stabilizing effect. This is not to imply that small companies in the industry are dishonest, but the reputation of the new major manufacturers, together with those already in the business should enhance public acceptance of the program.

The industry must also make it quite clear that solar energy is not a panacea for all energy problems. For example, there are certain limitations such as insufficient insulation of existing buildings that would preclude a retrofit solar system since it would be a waste of money. Another consideration would be sub-standard buildings that would not adapt to a retrofit unit. This is especially true in space heating/cooling combinations.

Items such as this must be pointed out in the beginning to avoid later problems. The worst possible approach at this time would be that of overselling the program.

Figure 57 illustrates the requirements of different cities in various sections of the country and the percentage of energy that could be provided from solar sources.

It all boils down to whether there will be a large scale solar program developed by government or big business, and if so, at what level. There are dangers on both sides. If the government becomes involved in an overt program (i.e. Tennessee Valley Authority), big business might not get involved, especially if there is no profit motivation. But if the government involvement continues on its present course of primarily research and development and demonstration programs, will solar energy grow? Probably not. Private enterprise with the profit factor would appear to be the answer.

There are two separate segments involved in the private sector. First, is the manufacture of components primarily for the individual or small scale market. This is where current growth patterns in the industry are emerging. Second are the large utility companies and their suppliers of large scale generating equipment, much of which is already in place waiting for delivery system of solar-related energy. This is the area where solar energy will make it or not. If the utility companies of the country determine they can harness the sun and make a profit doing so, the program will get off the ground. It has been determined that initial costs of new solar energy plants will be greater than conventional generating plants so that places us back at square one.

We must push harder for cooperation between the government and utility companies. If we can convince them our energy salvation is with solar energy and only a joint effort will bring success, the battle will be won. We must bring pressure to bear in every legal way possible. This will require a concerted effort by energy-conscious people everywhere, not only in the United States and Canada but all around the world.

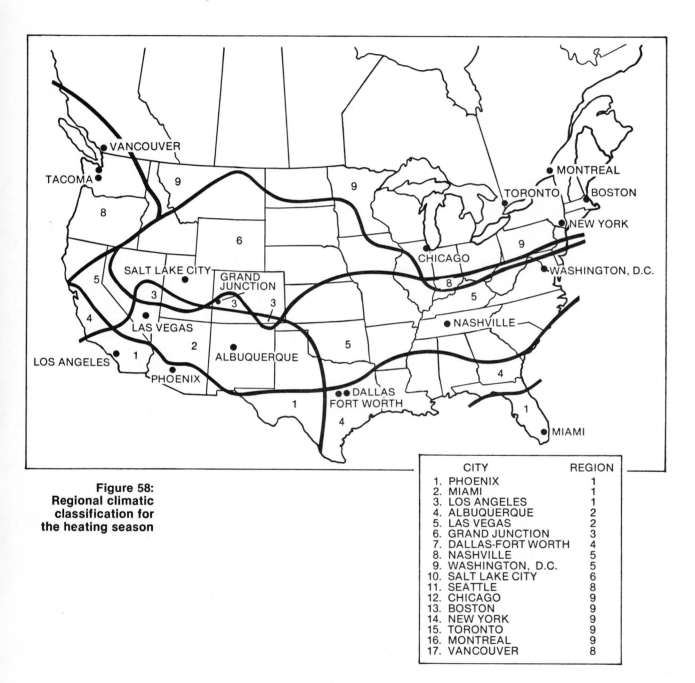

**Figure 58:
Regional climatic
classification for
the heating season**

CITY	REGION
1. PHOENIX	1
2. MIAMI	1
3. LOS ANGELES	1
4. ALBUQUERQUE	2
5. LAS VEGAS	2
6. GRAND JUNCTION	3
7. DALLAS-FORT WORTH	4
8. NASHVILLE	5
9. WASHINGTON, D.C.	5
10. SALT LAKE CITY	6
11. SEATTLE	8
12. CHICAGO	9
13. BOSTON	9
14. NEW YORK	9
15. TORONTO	9
16. MONTREAL	9
17. VANCOUVER	8

BIBLIOGRAPHY

Books, Articles, and Reports

An Assessment of Solar Energy as a National Energy Resource. NSF/NASA Solar Energy Panel, 1972.

Clark, Wilson. Energy for Survival. New York, Doubleday, 1974. Energy sources of yesterday, today, and tomorrow. Extensive information source and guide to sources.

Daniels, Farrington. Direct Use of the Sun's Energy. Westminister, Md., Ballantine Books, 1974.

Engineering Information and Publications Office, Solar Energy Laboratory, 331 Joseph Weil Hall, University of Florida, Gainesville, Fla. 32611. Misc. publications on topics including solar water heating in Florida and solar refrigeration and air conditioning.

Gibson, Edward G. The Quiet Sun. Houston, Tex., Manned Space Flight Center, 1973.

Halacy, D.S., Jr. The Coming Age of Solar Energy. New York, Harper & Row, 1973. An overall view.

Handbook of Applications. ASHRAE Sales Dept., 345 E. 47th St., New York, N.Y. 10017, 1974.

Handbook of Fundamentals. ASHRAE Sales Dept., 345 E. 47th St., New York, N.Y. 10017, 1972.

Hottel, H.C. and J.B. Howard. New Energy Technology. Cambridge, Mass., MIT Press, 1972.

Keyes, John. The Solar Conspiracy. Dobbs Ferry, N.Y., Morgan & Morgan.

Low Temperature Engineering Application of Solar Energy. ASHRAE Sales Dept., 345 E. 47th St., New York, N.Y. 10017.

Mathew, Henry. Solar House Plans. Box 768, Coos Bay, Oregon 97420. Plans of the Coos Bay solar heated home, one of the examples that contradicts the assumption of impracticability of solar heating of northern homes.

Putting the Sun to Work. Arizona Solar Energy Research Commission, 1976.

Reprints, American Section, International Solar Energy Society. c/o Dr. Jay Shelton, Physics Dept., Williams College, Williamstown, Mass. 01267. Reprints of articles of general interest from journals; mainly articles dealing with flat plate collectors.

Residential Energy from the Sun. Washington D.C., Dept. of Housing and Urban Development, 1976.

Scott, Jerome E. with Ronald W. Melicher and Donald M. Sciglimpaglia. Solar Heating and Cooling of Buildings; Solar Water Heating in South Florida, 1923-1974. AAI Corporation, 1974. Prepared for the National Science Foundation, RANN Program.

Solar Energy School Heating Augmentation Experiment. InterTechnology Corporation, 1974. Prepared for the National Science Foundation, RANN Program.

Solar Heating: Proof-of-Concept Experiment for a Public School. AAI Corporation, 1974. Prepared for the National Science Foundation, RANN Program.

Solar Energy. Energy Research and Development Administration, 1975.

Steadman, Philip. Energy, Environment, and Building. New York, Cambridge University Press, 1975. Compendium of information on solar energy, wind power and small scale water power. Over 100 pages of bibliographies and appendices. Lists solar hardware manufacturers.

Surcliff, William. Solar Heated Buildings: A Brief Survey. 19 Appleton St., Cambridge, Mass. 02138, 1975. Describes 138 buildings, including houses, schools, and commercial buildings, that are partially or fully solar heated.

Swartz, Marie Sokol, ed. Harvesting the Sun's Energy: A Solar Collection. Fullerton, Calif. Designs III Printing Co.

Thomason, Harry E. Solar Houses and Solar House Models. Edmund Scientific Co., 150 Edscorp Building, Barrington, N.J. 08007

_____. Solar House Plans. Edmund Scientific Co., 150 Edscorp Building, Barrington, N.J., 08007

_____. Solar Energy Plans II-A. Edmund Scientific Co., 150 Edscorp Building, Barrington, N.Y. 08007.

Newsletters

Advanced Solar Energy Technology Newsletter. 1609 W. Windrose, Phoenix, Ariz. 85029. $60/year.

Bibliographies and Directories

Solar Energy, Other Sources of Energy. International Solar Energy Society, American Section, 12441 Parklawn Drive, Rockville, Md. 20852. An annotated list of books, reprints, pamphlets, and newsletters.

Total Environmental Action, Church Hill, Harrisville, N.H. 03450. Bibliographies and information lists include: Solar Energy Books; Wind Energy; Energy Conservation; Brace Research Institute Publications; Designing for Solar Radiation on Building Surfaces; Solar Heating (Domestic Hot Water and Swimming Pools); Solar Energy Hardware (Over 70 manufacturers and distributors of solar energy equipment); and Wind Energy Hardware (Sources of wind energy equipment).

WHERE TO PURCHASE SOLAR SYSTEMS OR COMPONENTS

AERCO (Alternate Energy Resources Co.) Airport Terminal Building Ottumwa, Iowa 52501
"Hotline" solar systems for space heating, as well as other solar-related products

ARKLA-Solaire Arkla Industries Inc. Evansville, Ind. 47704
Air conditioning equipment compatible with solar systems

CSI Solar Systems 12400 49th St. North St. Petersburg, Fla. 33732
Solar collectors which can be integrated into existing hot water heaters

Consolar Inc. 800 W. Panorama Rd. Tucson, Ariz.
Full space heating or water heating solar systems. Solar collectors.

E & K Service Co. 16824 74th Ave. N.E. Bothell, Wash. 98011
Liquid type solar collectors for space heating

Edmund Scientific Co. 300 Edscorp Bldg. Barrington, N.J. 08007
Thomason Solar Home Plans and the most complete line of solar-oriented components in the United States.

Energex Corp. 481 Tropicana Rd. Las Vegas, Nev. 89109
Solar components, primarily collectors

FAFCO Inc. Bohannon Industrial Park 138 Jefferson Drive Menlo Park, Calif 94025
Swimming pool heating systems which use plastic extrusion collectors

Helio Associates Inc. Mountain State Mineral Enterprises I-10 and Vail Rd. Tucson, Ariz.
Plans for air style collectors—space heating

Hitachi America Ltd. 437 Madison Ave. New York, N.Y. 10022
Solar system components

International Solar-thermics Corp. Box 397 Nederland, Colo. 80466
The Sungazer, a free-standing auxiliary home heating system using air

Kalwell Corp. 1111 Candia Rd. Manchester, N.H. 03105
Solar collectors

Olin Corp. Stamford, Conn. 06904
Roll-bond solar collectors

Revere Copper and Brass Inc. Rome, N.Y. 13440
Copper solar collectors

Reynolds Metal Co. Torrance, Calif. 90508
Aluminum solar collectors

Fred Rice Productions 6313 Peach Ave. Van Nuys, Calif. 91401
SAV hot water cylindrical collector for hot water or space heater; imported from New Zealand

Skytherm Processes and Engineering 2424 Wilshire Blvd. Los Angeles, Calif. 90057
The Harold Hays system

Solar Energy, Co. Marlboro, Mass. 01752
Do-it-yourself plans and materials for space heating systems

Solar Energy Research Center P.O. Box 17776 San Diego, Calif. 92117
Solar components, including Solapak collectors, imported from Beasley Industries Ltd. in Australia

Solar Power Corp. Village Square New Port Richey, Fla. 33552
Solar collectors

Solar Systems Inc. Tyler, Tex. 75701
Aluminum solar collectors

Solaron Corp. 4850 Olive St. Denver, Colo. 80022
The Dr. Lof system which uses air as the medium

Sol-Therm Corp. 7 W. 14th St. New York, N.Y. 10011
AMCOR flat plate collector which can be used for space heating or water heating; imported form Israel

Sunsource Division Daylin Inc. 9696 Santa Monica Blvd. Beverly Hills, Calif. 90212
The licensed manufacturer in the United States of the Miramit solar collector from Israel

Sunwater Co. El Cajon, Calif. 92020
Solar collectors

Sunworks Inc. 669 Boston Post Rd. Guilford, Conn. 06437
Solar collectors

Tranter Inc. Lansing, Mich. 48909
Econocoil flat plate collector

index

TOGETHER –

Memoirs of a Pastor's Wife

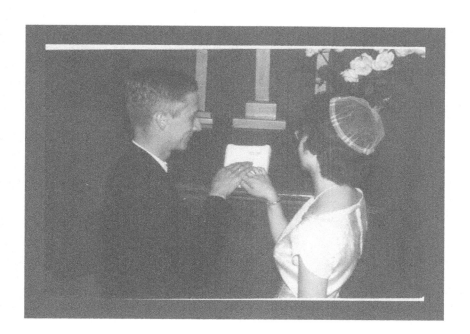

Phyllis E. Leininger

Dedication

This book is written in memory of my husband of over 56 years, Verne Henry Leininger, who left this world on October 14, 2019. He believed in me, encouraged me in every school and church program and musical that I directed, and cared for me in selfless ways especially when I was fighting my unwelcomed visitor, cancer.

It is also dedicated to my children, Verne Edward, John Henry and Barbara Jean and to my grandchildren and great grandchildren. Thank you for the joy that each of you bring to my life.

You are each God's special workmanship. I love you all.

Mom/Grandma Phyllis

Acknowledgements

From our dating days, my husband, Verne Henry Leininger, and I looked forward to being together in the Lord's work. Thus, I was planning to call this book, "TOGETHER."

 I owe immeasurable gratitude to my son, Verne Edward, who looked at the list of chapter titles I sent him and suggested additional words to the title, "TOGETHER: Memoirs of a Pastor's Wife." His suggestion tied the chapters together in a continuing story.

To Debbie and Terry Tench, I cannot offer enough thanks for your encouragement, prayers and sharing of how I could go about getting my book published. Without your help, my book would still be sitting helplessly in my computer.

My sister, Carol Shirey, spent hours helping with proofreading. I hope you still have good eyes, Carol. Many times you pointed out missing commas. I didn't know I put two periods at the end of so many sentences. Thanks for finding them. Probably your most important contribution was reminding me of the birth of a family member that I had inadvertently omitted from the story. Thanks for saving me in that regard!

My granddaughter, Morgan Greer Dickason, deserves more thanks that I can express for her work on the cover and for her expertise in formatting my book for publishing. Thank you so much, Morgan.

God's hand has provided for all my needs – even the needs for this book. To God be the glory!

Chapters

Preface

When I began to write, I didn't remember all the details I share in this book, but I knew where to look to connect the dots of my life. My dear husband, Verne Henry Leininger, saved all his yearly Brethren Reminders from his seminary days through the end of his ministry. He wrote very small in these little books but left me an accurate history of our ministry. I saved many annual Christmas letters I wrote with summaries of important events for given years. I recorded many details in journals, although there were gaps when I didn't write. Calendar notations were also a source of information. And most fun to read were the saved letters that Verne Henry and I wrote to each other that contained long forgotten memories.

"I can't wait for the weekend when I can see you and we will be together. I look forward to being together. . . I wish we were together." These or similar statements were included in most of the 300 letters that Verne Henry and I wrote, especially when he was in Bethany Theological Seminary and I was studying at Defiance College. This longing to be together in God's work provides the title for my book, Together.

After graduations we served churches together. I was not a pastor, but I was always involved, with music, with Sunday School, with meetings, with youth work and on and on.

We raised our family together. Verne Henry always scheduled time for his children's activities. We both worked with 4-H.

We gardened together as a couple and as a family. When we had to travel to a meeting, often the children and I were shelling peas or snapping beans in the car on the way while Verne drove.

When I presented cantatas and musicals at school or at church, Verne Henry was usually running sound, after lugging our huge Peavey speakers to the needed location.

Finally we retired and went most places together.

This autobiography is about life from my perspective. I love all my children and grandchildren and I write about them as they are a part of my story. I cannot write from my children's perspectives. That may be their privilege some day.

I hope that my family and friends, even those I have yet to meet, will find enjoyment and blessing through the reading of Together.

Then the Lord God said, "It is not good that the man should be alone; I will make him a helper as his partner." Genesis 2:18 NRSV

Birth

I was born in the hospital at Warren, Ohio on September 20, 1943. I entered the world weighing 9 pounds 6 ounces. I was the firstborn of my parents, Edward Chester and Ida Mae (Williams) Mahan. My paternal grandparents were Charles and Ruth (Fuller) Mahan. It is through Ruth Fuller that my ancestry goes back to Edward Fuller who came over on the Mayflower. My maternal grandparents were John B and Edna Williams.

Enough about being born. If I hadn't been born, I wouldn't have lived the stories that I am about to share with you. I hope you find them enjoyable.

Event Prior to My Memory

When I was a toddler – probably two years old or maybe a bit younger – my Grandpa and Grandma Williams were adding on to their house at Cortland, Ohio. There was a small step going down from the original house to the addition. I don't know if family members were helping with the build or just visiting. The story goes that my mother's sister(s) were playing with me and chasing me around when I fell on the new step and cut through my right eyebrow. My father got me to the hospital before he passed out. At least since my teen years or before, I have always covered the scar with eyebrow pencil.

Aging has lightened both my hair and my scars, including the one on my right eyebrow. It no longer stands out as an "eye sore" on my face.

My Siblings Arrive. . .

December, 1947. My earliest memories are of the days right around Christmas. The night before Christmas I was sleeping on the front edge of what I guess was a studio couch or some kind of sofa that made into a bed. I was in Grandma and Grandpa Williams' (my mother's parents') living room at Cortland, Ohio. My sister, Carol, three years younger than I, had to sleep at the back of the studio couch next to the wall. I was four years old. Carol has just turned a year old on December 8 and was probably in diapers, but I don't remember that part.

The Christmas tree was right beside me near the head of my bed. I don't know what day we opened the gifts, but I remember one gift that I got that year and that was always special to me. It was a wooden number and letter board with moveable numbers and letters in the groves so that they could be moved around to spell words or do math problems.

The next thing I remember is my parents, Edward and Ida Mae Mahan, coming through the front door into the living room. It was likely at least a couple days past Christmas, the way they did things back then. Mom was carrying a bundle in her arms – my baby brother, Frederick Lee Mahan, born December 23rd.

Before the birth of the twins, Sharon and Karen, Mom had a painfully sad time although I was too young to know much about what was happening. I have heard that when mom suffered a miscarriage, she lost a baby boy. Dad badly wanted another boy, so this was very difficult.

And then mom was pregnant again with her tummy so large that she could set her plate on it at mealtime. She had undulant fever during this time (from unpasteurized milk, I think).The fever was the doctor's concern – not how many babies might be inside her. One day I said to mom, "I think you are having twins." Mom replied, "If I have twins, you will be lucky to get one new dress a year." It happened that when I was nine years old, our pastor, Rev. Holly Garner, I believe, retired and went to our district's Camp Zion as caretaker for the summer. I went to camp for the first time that summer and loved it. But, when on July 9, Rev. Garner came to tell me that he'd got the call that my mother had delivered twins, I went to my cabin, threw myself on my bunk and cried – because now I would be lucky to get one new dress a year. Dresses were what we wore back then – dresses all the time, dresses – even at camp! This was 1953.

Twins were a shock to dad. Instead of his boy, he had to prepare for two baby girls before bringing mom home. Meanwhile, Saturday arrived and camp was over. Church people brought me home, but dad was not there. I went across the road and talked about camp with my neighbors, the Everetts. Dad had gone fishing on Lake Erie. I don't remember how long I was at the neighbors before he returned.

One more try for another boy. This time it was December 28, 1954. The twins were about 18 months old and we needed a live in nanny or caregiver. I don't know the lady's name, but even at eleven years old, I remember being praised by this live-in worker for all my help and feeling like that was her way of getting me to do more and more. Anyway, Baby Elizabeth Ann (often called Betty) was not a boy. The sad story has circulated in our family that Dad tried to trade her at the hospital for someone's baby boy. Good thing they wouldn't trade. Betty is smart, gifted and a wonderful addition to our family.

Childhood days

The old gray-shingled house on Thompson Clark Road at Bristolville, Ohio is the place of lots of memories. I could run right through the middle of the large kitchen, in the back door and out the front door to the porch across the front of the house. But if my brother was chasing me with a chicken in his arms, I usually ran from the back door to the big living room where mom often sat sewing. Then I tried to get under the sewing machine, safely between mom's feet. As long as I can remember I have wondered why I was and am afraid of chickens.

I think my parents raised a lot of chickens in my infant and toddler years. Why else would there be a starter house, a brooder house and a two-story cement block chicken house for laying hens or fryer or roaster birds out back? I have a very faint recollection of squawking birds and of my parents killing and dressing birds at one end of our unfinished basement. I have a vague memory of cones there to put the birds in upside down. Anyway, I believe as a toddler, I was left upstairs, probably at night in bed and heard this raucous and troubling noise.

My brother, Fred, did keep things interesting for my four sisters and me. There was a maple tree on each side of the path behind the house. Fred loved to rig tin cans of water in one of these trees and make sure it got dumped on an unexpecting sister. On down the path was the "out house." I had to be sure when entering there that there was no can of water set to dump on me when I opened the door.

Back in the house, the large kitchen was the center of much activity. The big oak table seated our entire family and occasional childhood friends or relatives. The laundry equipment – ringer washing machine and rinse tub and eventually a washer with a separate spinner attached and a dryer were at one end of the kitchen along with the studio couch where we usually folded the clothes. In front of the wide window at that end of the kitchen was an automatic dish washer that I think Dad got because he worked at Youngstown Kitchens. I think the company went out of business. I don't know. I just know that the dishwasher sat below that window and was never hooked up.

Coming in the back door to the right was the counter where the bucket of drinking water sat. It was pumped with the hand pump behind the house and carried. The sink was next with a window above it with a taped over hole where Fred had shot a bee-bee through it. If there was water at the faucet, it came from the cistern, which was just to the left as you went outside the back door. I remember heating water on the stove for doing dishes. That end of the kitchen also had the stove, refrigerator and a white metal table. Also on that side of the kitchen, just inside the front door to the left as you entered was a large chest freezer – often covered with piles of homework, papers, etc.

Our first TV was a small screen in a huge case. Dad put it in the kitchen. Later it was moved into the living room – maybe when the dishwasher arrived. Anyway, a TV in the living room was a problem for me. I came home from school and wanted to practice the piano. Carol got off the bus and raced for the TV and American Bandstand. With both the piano and TV in the same room, that was a big point of contention between us. However, I learned that if I didn't get to practice the piano before supper, I could beg off doing dishes to practice the piano. That usually worked.

When one of us children had a birthday, Great Aunt Jennie who lived at Warren, Ohio always arrived for the birthday meal bringing a tall angel food cake with way more thick butter cream frosting than one cake needed. . After we ate, Aunt Jennie would get down on the living room floor with us children and take her turn shooting crows off a wire with a cork gun.

There was a small bedroom off the living room. Grandma Mahan slept there before she put a trailer on our property. She took a lot of care and there were no depends back then.

Opening the door and going upstairs from the living room one first came to a large hall – with a dark or black colored chest where I remember putting some of Dad's clothes away. There was also a large, tall wardrobe in the hall, but it was moved into my sisters' and my room to make room for Fred to have a bed in the hall. Fred moved out of the small upstairs bedroom and my parents used that little bedroom when Grandma came to live with us. Grandma had the bedroom downstairs.

Sleeping arrangements worked fine – at least until I went 200 miles off to Defiance College and didn't sleep at home much. Carol and I shared a double bed. The twins and Betty shared a double bed on the other side of the room. The "top" of their bed was the long side.

In the summers I played outside often imagining creating something worthwhile when I peeled reeds and found fragile white cylindrical sticks inside. I also pretended to make doll food with the bass wood seeds from the tree in our front yard. That was the tree that we couldn't go past as we waited for the bus on the driveway, and that distance was a good ways back from the road.

One winter there was ice outside and so I used my mother's white ice skates to try ice skating myself. I went out in the pasture where there was some standing water that had turned to ice. So far so good. Then I came to a large hole that seemed well covered with ice. I skated onto it and immediately fell through. It was the hole where the pigs had rooted and it was not a clean place to fall into. So that ended the day's ice skating as I was cold, wet, and dirty.

I always wore dresses or skirts and blouses to school. That was what girls wore. There was no kindergarten at Bristol Township School at Bristolville, Ohio where I attended for all twelve grades. I remember going up lots of steps in first grade, There were steps into the building. Then, because there were so many of us first graders, some of us were placed in a combination first and second grade room at the top of the stairs in the high school area with Mrs. Miller. I would be in seventh grade before I had a classroom on that upper floor again.

I remember fun times with Mrs. Noffsinger in second grade. My friend Loretta got to go home and spend the night with Mrs. Noffsinger once. Mrs. Welch, who had taught my mom in sixth grade, was my third grade teacher. That year I worked and worked to add up how many were going to St Ives. Of course I was wrong. "As I was going to St Ives, I met . . ." Only one person was going. During the year I was in Mrs. Bates' fourth grade, I went to the solo and ensemble contest with a piano solo for the first time, I played the Spinning Song and got a I rating. In Mrs. Hall's fifth grade class I sometimes played for the class to sing..

In sixth grade I was downstairs in a new section with Mr. Davis. .We wrote with pens dipped in bottles of ink. One day when I wore my royal blue dress I spilled my bottle of ink all down my dress. Thankfully the dress was blue. I don't remember if the ink was blue or black. Mr. Davis sent me to the home economics room where I had to take off the dress and wait – where I don't remember – for it to be washed and dried.

I was afraid of chickens, but I liked ducks. Ducks have rounded bills, not scary pointed beaks like chickens. I wanted some ducks. One early summer day when I was twelve years old, Rev. Walter Coldren, our Pastor at the Bristolville Church of the Brethren, drove into our driveway. He did not come in his pastor role, but rather as a Post Office employee, either part-time or substitute. I ran out to his car and received my box of 50 fluffy, yellow baby ducklings. I took them in the house to give them food and water. Soon I set up a circle of chicken wire fence that I could move each day. I thought watching ducks eat was interesting as they washed their food down with water as they tipped their heads back to swallow.

As fall came and days grew cooler, my dad took the ducks to be sold for me. With the $60.00 that I earned from the sale of my ducks, I purchased a dress coat which took me to important events through my coming high school years.

Teen Years

In my memory lots of events happened when I was about 14 or 15 years old. I am sure I played for my first wedding at age fourteen as I have written about elsewhere. I was nearly fourteen years old when Pastor Walter Coldren baptized me on August 18, 1957.

My mother had her four-hour varicose vein surgery during this time period. I remember how worried I was about mother and there was no way for me to find out how things were going. Dad came home late that night and I was embarrassed because the spaghetti that I fixed for our evening meal had long since turned to "mush." But he was appreciative anyway.

4-H projects helped keep me busy during the summers. I took outdoor cooking with Roberta Coldren, our pastor's wife, as our leader. I took sewing projects for a number of years at Mrs. Shaffer, our leader's house. She lived just south of Grandma and Grandpa Mahan on SR 45. I would ride my bike to my grandparents' house, turn off the side road onto their side entrance pedal past the barn and milk house, leave my bike at their house, go out their main drive and walk to Mrs.

Shaffer's for 4-H. It seems like Aunt Clara was also my 4-H sewing leader for a short time. I remember sometimes frosting boxes instead of real cakes in cake decorating 4-H, I made a lot of roses out of frosting. I created a scrapbook of beautiful cake pictures for every month of the year. I don't remember who led cake decorating.

I remember a fun 4-H field trip to Higbee's Department Store at Cleveland, Ohio to purchase fabric. I bought some pretty blue and white checked fabric with black bows on it. It made a pretty dress – pretty until a dog grabbed the skirt when I was biking to 4-H and put a three corner tear in it.

Decorating our 4-H booth at the Trumbull County Fair was another fun time. Each club's assigned booth was big enough to walk into- maybe 6 x 6 feet or even 8 x8 feet. We hung our sewing projects and dresses along the walls of the booth. We designed our booths with our club name and theme and competed for a booth ribbon for our club. A tape or ribbon of some kind was stretched across the completed booth. For some unremembered reason one year I was displaying my postcard collection. When it was time to bring things home, my very old wooden postcard was not there. I was very disappointed that it had been taken.

Sunday evening Youth Fellowship meetings at the Bristolville Church of the Brethren were very formative times in my life. I also was blessed whenever I was able to go to an overnight Northeastern Ohio Youth retreat. It seems miraculous that I had a way to go as my mom didn't yet drive and dad never took me. Once our Bristolville youth group invited the Northeastern Ohio COB Youth Cabinet to our church for a Sunday morning. Our Sunday school class met in the basement and had two benches set in an L shape against the wall in our "corner." Our guests sat on one of the benches and immediately one end of the bench let go and down it went. It was an unforgettable welcome. I don't remember anyone being seriously injured.

One cold snowy winter Sunday evening, my neighbor, Roger Christlieb, was driving some of us home from youth meeting. The road was icy and we slid into a tree on Route 88 somewhere near Bristolville. I needed stitches in my knee. Dad was not very happy to have to come and get me. I don't remember where I was taken for the stitches. When we got home, Dad wanted me to go upstairs to bed, but I think mom convinced him to let me stay downstairs on the couch that night.

Camp Zion was one of my favorite, most loved places. I first went the year the twins were born and returned every year until a summer job prevented me from going. Year after year I looked forward to seeing my camp friends, especially Bonnie Throne and Joy Powell and being at this inspirational place. I was so excited when I was asked to be a Junior Counselor from June 29 to July 5, 1958. I would turn fifteen in September. This is younger than Counselors in Training would be accepted when I worked at Camp Mack years later. Moreover, some of our activities posed possible liabilities that modern ACA accredited camps would never allow in 2020. But it was the most fun-filled week of my life thus far and I wrote a long paper for school detailing the week. The following are some excerpts from my very detailed paper.

Shortly before seven, the portable organ which had been borrowed from the Kent Church of the Brethren was taken by car to vesper hill, and I prepared to play.

Vespers was a time to come close to God through worship as the sun was setting behind the hills. Each evening one or two leaders were in charge of the service.

One thing which the campers loved and looked forward to was receiving treats. They received treats such as popsickles, candy bars, potato chips, pretzels or ice cream bars, twice a day – usually after assembly and vespers. Now, after vespers, they raced to the camp store to receive their first treat. Treats are included in the cost of the camp - $16.00.

Campfire was one of my favorite times of the day. We sat around the campfire and had fun singing. Then one of the leaders would tell a story and we would sing "Taps."

Besides being a cabin counselor and helping with music, one of my tasks was working with crafts. Campers wishing to make clown boards, of which I was in charge, had three choices: Clown boards, Do-Do boards, or Beano. Mostly boys made these.

The tin cans were my problem. The beano games were the most popular of the game boards, and each beano required four tin cans which could not be nailed to the board in their original shape. Cuts, one to one and a half inches apart and about half the length of the tin can, had to be made in the cans so that the tin strips could be bent back to provide something that could be nailed to the wood. It was hard to cut cans fast enough to keep the campers satisfied, although Rev. Overly, who had the afternoons free, did help me.

One day about 5:00 p.m. I was putting shellac, paints, and etcetera away in the crafts when several little boys began throwing love-notes in to me from the door of the crafts room as fast as they could write them. The things they wrote were really comical. I even received one marriage proposal. When I showed the notes to Roberta, she wouldn't give them back to me. She said she thought she would have them printed in the camp paper, and I was really frustrated for that was the last thing I wanted to happen.

Mail was passed out by the dean immediately after supper while everyone was still seated at the tables. This evening when Walter gave me my mail, it was a slightly different kind than usual. It consisted of the love notes the campers had written me and another letter which had something in it. The last letter was from Roberta and Walter containing a candy bar.

We leaders of the girls' cabins got together and planned for the girls to go to serenade the boys on this night. The girls got ready for bed, and we turned out the lights as usual so the fellows would suspect nothing. Then we told the girl's about our surprise for them and they were very excited. We waited until the boys' cabins were quiet, and then the girls put on wraps or dusters. So that the boys

29

would not hear us coming – they would hear us for sure if we went over the swinging bridge – we went by a round-about way. Upon nearing the boys' cabins, we begin to sing softly "Campfire's Burning." As we reached the cabins, the girls shouted "Fire! Fire! Fire! Fire! And instantly flashlights snapped on inside the cabins, and boys' heads appeared at the windows. After singing several other songs, we began singing "Good Night, Gentlemen" and returned to our cabins via the swinging bridge.

When I tried to get into bed that night, I found it a little hard to do. I had been short-sheeted. Saying nothing to the girls, I did the best I could to get into bed without making it over.

Another night. Vicky had told me earlier in the evening that the girls had short-sheeted my bed again. To get even with Vicky, the girls short-sheeted Vicky's bed, and when Vicky tried to get into bed, she couldn't. This being Vicky's first year at camp, she didn't seem to understand that the girls only short-sheeted her bed for fun. She cried and cried and cried, and Miriam and I had quite a hard time trying to quiet her.

On Thursday, the camp manager, Dave Horn, led us on our big hike. It can only be described as being similar to an obstacle race for we climbed over barbed-wire fences and crossed a small stream. We stopped for a while and rested under some pine trees and then went on to reach our destination, a level, grassy spot. Walter had gone ahead in his car and had taken frozen candy bars and ice-cold Kool-aid.

Walter said that Joy and I could go back to camp via the road, and so we started to do so. Then Joy (I'm not sure how it all came about) got on the trunk of the dean's car and was riding back to camp. Although Walter was driving very slowly, I could not keep up with the car by walking, so, partly because Joy had, and partly because I was not sure of the way back, I, too, asked Walter to stop and climbed onto the trunk. Over in the field the campers saw us, and their boos could clearly be heard. The next time I know I'll walk back!

That evening, after cabin devotions, Joy and I went to the kitchen and, with Barbara and Charlotte, made kool-aid. Into Paul's and Ray's kool-aid we poured cod liver oil to which Joy, being camp nurse, had access.
The guys came, and we all went down to the swimming pool to sit on the diving board, talk, and drink our Kool-aid. I think we put too much cod liver oil in Ray's and Paul's Kool-aid for as Ray

lifted his to drink, an odd smell told him there was something in it and he and Paul threw the fine beverage we had fixed for them in the pool.

Our Friday night campfire was our Consecration Service. The portable organ was used for this service – the only time it was used at campfire. While I played the organ softly, each leader and camper placed a small stick in the fire watching how much brighter the fire grew as each of our sticks became part of the fire. This represented the fact that each one of us should shine for Jesus, for even the smallest flame is important.

Because Miriam had to work on the camp paper, I had to stay in the cabin until all the campers were asleep. After everyone was asleep, I went to the crafts room to help Roberta finish the crafts which the campers had not finished, so that the campers could all take home finished products.

About an hour later, someone came running to the crafts room to get Roberta for a girl was gasping for breath in cabin four. Paul carried the girl to Walter's car: Walter, Roberta, Joy and the girl were on their way to the hospital. Walter, not knowing where the hospital was, stopped at a police station and soon they were being led by police escort with sirens blowing, to the hospital.

Now the strangest thing happened. The girl walked into the hospital breathing excellently. Doctors could find nothing wrong with her. She was there quite a while, while doctors made examinations and tests. She was told to go immediately to a hospital if this ever happened again, and then she was released.

Meanwhile, the camp paper had to be run off so that it could be passed out to the campers Saturday morning, and no one knew how to run the mimeograph machine except Walter who had gone to the hospital. Roger studied the machine and was finally able to run it.

At about two o'clock in the morning we finished assembling the paper and were reading it and drinking Kool-aid and eating crackers. Shortly the group returned from the hospital, and leaders gathered by the benches in the grove and talked over the events of the night. I went to bed between 2:30 and 3:00 a.m., but some of the leaders stayed up even longer.

I had been disappointed because the boys had not serenaded the girls this week. They usually do so the night after the girls serenade them or vise versa.

.

My disappointment disappeared at 6:30 a.m.
Saturday morning, one whole hour before time to
get up, when I woke up to the words, "Fire! Fire!
Fire! Fire! Oh well, four hours is plenty of sleep,
isn't it?

After breakfast we sang and sang and sang while
still seated at the tables. The campers asked for one
song after another continuously. Then we formed a
friendship circle on the lawn and had a song and
prayer. The camp papers were passed out and the
campers received their last treats. Parents were
waiting to whisk campers away.

For me this week at Camp Zion was a week of
indescribable fun and also a week where I learned and
tested new leadership skills.

Later that summer, the last summer before I had a
summer job, I was blessed with the opportunity to
return to Camp Zion for Youth Camp. I write in
another chapter about my calling to serve as a
deaconess to help prepare the Youth Camp Love Feast.
Another memorable event.

My cousin Marilyn Mahan, my friend, Loretta Lew,
and I were very involved in Youth for Christ which
met in Warren, Ohio on Saturday evenings. We were

on a quiz team. We memorized whatever book we were currently quizzing on and practiced together at our local meetings. Teams competed. The first person up on either team could try to answer the question or complete the verse if it was a complete the verse challenge. Our team won in the Warren competition one year and went to state competition at West Liberty, Ohio. Our matching outfits were gold colored pleated skirts and gold and white tops. We stayed all night in people's homes. At state the chairs were wired so there was no question as to who was up first. Moving fast was important. We did well, but I don't think we got first place there.

The spring of my Junior year of High School I decided I wanted a summer job, so I started watching ads in the Warren Tribune Chronicle and came across an ad for a "child supervisor." Mrs. Mildred Force was a working grandmother who needed child supervision for her three grandchildren, Millie, Allie and a boy, Junior, who was not there all the time. I applied and got the job. Then I had to find a way to get to work. Elizabeth Everett took me into Warren early in the morning when she went to work. Then I walked in the early morning hour to Homewood Avenue where my family lived, arriving before 7:30 in the morning. Then I had to meet Elizabeth or maybe another neighbor to get a ride home.

It was a good summer job and the title was appropriate. Mildred wanted me to be sure the children did their chores. The children and I also canned peaches – without directions. I hope they were edible. I took them to the city pool, going by bus. I even had time to sew on my boss's sewing machine which she sat on the dining room table for me to use. We got along well and I worked there after my high school senior year as well. The last full summer I worked for Mrs. Force was after my freshman year of college.

Sometime probably during my teen years, my parents had purchased new windows for the large kitchen. The windows were installed but there was no framing around them inside and no windowsills. With money I earned during a summer I hired my Uncle Cecil to trim the windows on the inside. I remember a window behind the long chest freezer, a window behind the sink – the one that Fred shot a beebee through – and the large wide window at the far end of the kitchen with the never-hooked-up dishwasher in front of it. Those are the windows that Uncle Cecil finished. The windows in the living room were not replaced at that time.

When I was about a junior or senior my parents painted the living room a chartreuse color and put some linoleum on the living room floor. They arranged furniture so that the door from the porch to the living room was accessible and I began to teach piano pupils foreshadowing one way that I earned money throughout my life. As a college student, I taught Defiance College professors' children. I had piano pupils wherever we lived. I often accompanied students at solo and ensemble music contests.

Dad always insisted that I could and should be the class valedictorian. I used to think that insistence was a bad thing. It was like I had to do it. But I was capable. So maybe it was a good thing. At least good grades helped get me scholarships for college.

I graduated from Bristol (Ohio) High School in May, 1961. Then our class left for a senior trip to Washington D.C. and New York City by bus. In Washington DC I enjoyed the beautiful ceiling in the Library of Congress. At the Smithsonian, I marveled at the ornately carved harpsichords and other instruments. When we went to New York City, there was a man sitting cross-legged in a low entry way one night in Greenwich Village who claimed to be Jesus and looked like Solomon's painting of the head of Christ. It was eerie.

Soon the wonderful trip ended – that was the furthest from home I had ever been. Then it was time to focus on summer work and preparations for the next chapter in my life.

One night in August of 1961, I was both playing the piano and directing the choir at Bristolville Church of the Brethren. At the end of the evening's practice, someone in the choir informed me that the choir wanted to march around the sanctuary singing "To God Be the Glory." That seemed like a strange request, but how could I refuse these wonderful people? They got me to march, too, and we marched right around the sanctuary and down to the basement where they had prepared a going-away-to-college party for me. What a special surprise! I appreciated their support as I was soon to go two hundred miles across the state to The Defiance College at Defiance, Ohio.

Music Is Part of my Life

I started taking piano lessons the summer after first grade from my cousin, Jim Mahan, Aunt Gladys's and Uncle Harry's son. He was about a senior in high school and known for his piano playing ability. He and his family lived a couple of houses down on the same side of the road as the Bristol School where I attended first through twelfth grades. (Aunt Gladys taught fourth grade at Bristol for years. I think her husband, Harry, was my Grandpa Mahan's brother. That's what I think, anyway.)

Back to the piano lessons. When I sat on the bench my legs didn't reach the floor. So my mother put a cardboard box in front of the piano bench for me to rest my feet on. That was fine until my teacher, Cousin Jim, insisted that I should learn to use the pedals. Well, I couldn't reach and I wasn't going to play pedals I couldn't reach. So ended my lessons with Cousin Jim.

I remember that as a child I visited overnight at my Aunt Ruth and Uncle Buck's home at Warren, Ohio. One afternoon I played my small repertoire of piano songs repeatedly for two hours. Their son, my cousin

Doug, let me know that he did not enjoy my long and repetitious playing, but I think that his mother did.

Mrs. Klingler was my elementary school music teacher. She lived across the road from the school. So I could walk to piano lessons after school. And then wait and wait and wait for my father to get around to picking me up. In a few years Mrs. Klingler had me play for my 5th grade class to sing sometimes when she taught it music.

Somewhere along the way I started going to a really advanced teacher in Warren. She had a studio and a waiting room. As usual, I had to wait for Dad to pick me up. I wish I could remember that teacher's name. She charged by the month and usually graciously waited for her money. We were poor. For me to have lessons was probably a sacrifice by my parents that they couldn't give to each of their children.

As a sixth grader I became the Bristolville Church of the Brethren Sunday School pianist. From seventh grade through high school I was the Church Worship service pianist. When I was fourteen years old, Donna Jean Hluchen got married and moved a pump organ into the church for the occasion. That was the first wedding where I was the musician. I also accompanied a vocalist on the piano..

My school band experience never got off the ground. Here's what happened. My parents recognized my musical ability and dad rented a marimba for me. It had a beautiful tone. I was in Junior High at the time

41

and was supposed to get out of class to take a lesson in the band director's office on a xylophone as the school had no marimba. Well, repeatedly the band director didn't show up and teachers who let me out of class were displeased. Away went the marimba and my school band possibility.

Sometime around the time I entered high school I began taking lessons from another really good piano teacher. This one lived near the center of Bristol. She worked with me with the Sherwood Music School Course out of Chicago. I sent theory lessons to Chicago to be scored and received free music and other awards like the Sherwood Music School pin, when I completed so many lessons. In good weather I never had to wait for Dad to pick me up. I rode my bicycle to and from lessons. One free piece of music that I received was called "Golliwog's Cake Walk." I distinctly remember immediately putting it in the wastebasket! Why? Because I was very involved with church and I believed that dancing (except for folk dancing) was wrong. I knew that sometimes as a High School Class fund raiser I had to furnish a cake for a cake walk at a dance. In my young mind, if dancing was bad, so were cake walks!

I played for the Bristol High School Choir all my high school years and also accompanied band students in solo contests.

Soon I was off to Defiance College which was fine with my parents because I got a large scholarship. That's another story. Anyway, after starting to major in

English and minor in music, I switched them around and majored in music. I had a great advantage in music theory classes having had the excellent resource of the Sherwood Music School. Again, I played for the choir and was on stage at Defiance College as pianist when former President Dwight D. Eisenhower was there on stage to speak at a graduation.

I remember getting a basic education in college classes on playing all the woodwind, brass, string and percussion instruments. Finally, at Defiance College, besides playing for choir, I got to be in concert band. The band director complemented me on the "musical" way I played the bass drum! I kept the beat, but I didn't just pound it!

From my high school and college days, to every congregation we served, to my time at Greencroft Retirement Center prior to the COVID-19 pandemic, I have loved teaching persons from children through adults to play the piano. It is a joy to know that some of my students are pianists in their own congregations; one student became a music professor.

I have owned and played many different "percussion" instruments with children at church. My collection included an autoharp, guitars, dulcimers, tone education bells, various hand drums, tambourines, triangles, shakers, maracas, a rain stick, wood block, and other instruments. Children in all churches we served loved playing my instruments. I still love sharing the joy of making music.

A number of my small musical instruments were given away when I moved to Greencroft Retirement Community, but I have two pianos in my small apartment.

College Days

Dad and mom took me to Defiance, Ohio on a Saturday in early September, 1961. Dad drove; neither mom nor I could drive at that time in our lives. I was 17 years old and would turn 18 on September 20, a few days after I signed all the papers and I was an official student. I walked up the wide wooden stairs of Trowbridge Hall to the floor where my room awaited me with two girls already moved in. My roommates, Shirley and Jean, were already best friends from the same high school and I was just a third person to fill the beds in the room. We lived peacefully with each other, but rarely did things together.

Someone from my home church, the Bristolville Church of the Brethren, must have let Pastor Floyd Emrick know that I was coming to his area. He met Mom, Dad and me the day I moved in and invited my parents to stay that night with him and his wife. Pastor Emrick explained that he served two Brethren churches: the Defiance City Church and the Poplar Ridge Church, a country church. He also shared that Helen Hornish, a member of the Poplar Ridge Church of the Brethren lived in the white house directly across the street from my dorm. He challenged me to try out both churches. I attended the city church that first Sunday with my parents.

This country girl didn't take long to become active at Poplar Ridge. Again, maybe someone from my home church had shared that I played piano and organ. I don't know. But in late September or early October, a handsome young man came to church when I was playing the organ. After church his parents introduced us. Verne and Esther had seen me pictured in The Bryan Times as a scholarship student standing on a rope laid out in the shape of an "S." They showed their son, Verne Henry, the picture of the "new girl" attending Poplar Ridge. Now we are introduced. And Verne Henry says something about this smart student who can't even stand on the rope. I hit him and said, "I am standing on the rope." That was the beginning of our lifetime relationship.

Week night curfew was 10 p.m. I usually studied in the library until almost curfew and then walked back to the dorm singing or humming "How Great Thou Art." I was there with a scholarship and I was determined to keep it. On weekends we could be out until 11 p.m. Twice in a semester I could get permission to be out until 1 a.m. on a weekend. But I didn't usually need to do that.

I began my freshman year as an English major. I remember that one of the first papers I wrote was copied – I'm not sure how back then – and passed out in class as an example of good writing. Wow! I studied a lot and kept up on my assignments. I remember having Dr. Frey for biology. I hope I didn't upset him too much. He said I was the only student until that time to ever score 100% on one of his exams. He thought that just wasn't done.

Dr. Sayre was my piano instructor. He could not teach all of the professor's children who wanted lessons. So he recommended me as their teacher. Among my students were the registrar Gerald Mallott's children and Dean Alton Kurtz's children. When the Kurtz family purchased a new piano, they gave me their huge old upright. That was the piano we moved into the County Line parsonage, laid on its back with much manpower, and restored in the inside. I put pin tight around the pins to hydrate the wood so the piano would stay in tune, replaced all the leathers and also some of the dampers. But that is getting way ahead of my story.

A Northwestern Ohio Young Adult meeting happened during the winter of my Freshman year. Verne was already coming home from seminary each weekend. During Sunday School class Verne invited persons to go with him to the meeting. Actually looking back, I thought he was just inviting me. At any rate, Verne drove to Trowbridge, came in and turned heads when I left with him. I had special permission to go. When we arrived, there was Lorraine Stutzman, a girl whom Verne had dated. I guess she thought Verne belonged to her and was not happy to see me there. I later heard that they broke up at that event.

Following that retreat, Verne came home on Friday evenings, and then came to Defiance and we studied together in the library most Saturdays. Meanwhile, we wrote letters every week. I remember the first time we went out. We went to a restaurant in downtown Defiance. I remember having hash brown potatoes which I had never had before. I have no idea what else I ate. It was an enjoyable evening and I was back in Trowbridge by curfew.

I went home for the summer after my freshman year at Defiance. I continued to work at "child supervision" for Mildred Force in Warren on weekdays. Verne would often come from Alliance, Ohio where he was serving as summer pastor for seminary credit, to visit me. On the 4th of July, 1962, we were lying on a blanket in the front yard at my Bristolville home when Verne asked me to marry him. I really wanted to say, "yes," but I told him that I would think about it. I thought that was the proper response. (No one had ever asked this girl, who had not yet turned nineteen, to marry her before!) I guess Verne was devastated and didn't know whether he should ask me again. But I don't think it was too many days before I told him "yes." Instead of an engagement ring, Verne got me a beautiful service for 12 of Melmac dishes with a red rose on a white background. There were large and small plates, cups and saucers, cereal or soup bowls, sugar bowl and cream pitcher, and other serving items. I thought they were very pretty. I think I helped pick them out. This seemed to us to be a good use of limited funds with both of us going to school.

Even though I was with Verne nearly every weekend that summer, we wrote often during the week. Letters, not phone calls, were our means of distance communication. In a letter dated July 11, 1962, Verne asks diplomatically, "Phyllis, I don't know what you think, but I think we should tell your folks about our plans before we get the dishes from Warren Saturday. I think it would be better to tell them right out than to make them guess and be uncertain about our plans. You can think it over and have your answer ready Saturday morning. If you want to not tell, I suppose this would be possible also."

Verne mentioned that he planned to wear the shirt I made him when we went to pick up the dishes. I had made each of us matching shirts from a colorful blue plaid. As I shared earlier, Mildred Force had set her sewing machine on her dining room table for me to use when I had time. So I did some sewing at work.

A wife-to-be needed to know how to drive. Verne and I agreed that I should get my driver's permit that summer and that he would teach me to drive. It was not an easy endeavor for either of us. We did learn some patience and forgiveness skills in the process. I was still learning at the end of the summer.

Even before we were engaged, members at Alliance invited me to stay all night at their homes. The date of Verne's first sermon at Alliance was June 3, 1962. Here is an excerpt from a letter dated ten days later, June 13. "One of the main reasons for writing today is that they want you to play the prelude for the Sunday morning worship service. They hope you will play more than just a hymn. They hope for a number written for a prelude. I hope you won't mind. I told them to count on your playing the prelude. . . I have a place for you to stay. You can trade the room to stay in for the prelude."

Leaders from the Alliance congregation were in charge of the Sunday morning service at Westview Manor, the Church of the Brethren Home in Northeastern Ohio on July 29. The church's instrumentalists would be at Westview Manor that day. Here is a small portion of Verne's letter of July 21. "Frank and Peggy will be singing a special number. If you agree (and you had better as we are counting on you) you will be playing the

piano for church and possibly Sunday School. . . ."
Verne then lists the hymn numbers as well as the
responses for the Call to Prayer, The Prayer
Response, and the Offertory Response. He doesn't
state a name for the special number. By that time I
was well accepted at Alliance and had at least two
choices of places to stay overnight.

Early in June, Gordon Bucher, the District
Executive for Northeastern Ohio Church of the
Brethren visited Verne. Among other things
Gordon shared was the need for Camp Counselors
at Camp Zion that summer. And so it happened
that when my job concluded mid August, Verne
and I spent the last week of Camp Zion's Junior
High Camp together as counselors.

It had been a busy summer. Verne had 12 students
in his Vacation Bible School Class. I helped with
Bible School at Bristolville in the evenings. We
tried playing tennis, something I had never done
before. We took my sisters to an outdoor concert
at Warren. We hosted my parents at Alliance.
After our week at camp, we attended District
Conference and then headed to Defiance to begin
another school year at Defiance College and

51

Bethany Theological Seminary – and another
season of letter writing,

Whitney Hall, a much newer dorm than
Trowbridge, was my home during my sophomore
year. I roomed with Carol Maddox, a black girl
from Cleveland, Ohio. She liked to borrow my red
pleated skirt, so we must have been about the same
size. During my sophomore year I got a
permission letter from my mother allowing me to
go to Verne's home for Sunday dinner and later for
weekends. Sometimes Carol or my Church of the
Brethren friend, Barbara Cocanaur, would go to
the Leiningers for Sunday dinner as well.

Between semesters of my sophomore year, I
planned to go to Bethany Seminary, which was
still on Van Buren Street in downtown Chicago, to
visit Verne. Verne's father took me to the train
station at Archbold, Ohio in a blizzard. Trains
were dealing with lots of snow and my scheduled
train to Chicago did not arrive. Another train
stopped and said I could go on it. Verne kept
calling the train station to check on my train. It
seems the train station didn't know when or if my
train would arrive or that I was on a different train
than originally scheduled. Verne went to bed.

Very late that night or early morning, I arrived at the Chicago train station which was completely foreign to me. This was my first train experience. Somehow I found a phone and had a number to call the Brethren hospital which was right across from the seminary and someone from the hospital went over to the seminary to tell Verne that I was at the Chicago train station.

We were very glad to see each other. Verne, who shouldn't have been on the ladies' floor where my assigned room was, nevertheless tucked me into bed that night. I didn't go back to college on the train. I went back with Verne when his classes were over for the week. He was as frugal as possible going to school. His sister, Ruth Ann, was my age and was a student at Manchester College. That must have put a strain on his family's budget. I will share that Verne often only ate one cooked meal a day at the hospital where seminary students ate. Much of the time, he lived on cereal cookies that his mother sent back with him each Monday. He was saving money so that we could eat when I was at seminary.

The 1962-63 school year was the last year that I lived on the Defiance College Campus. The summer after my sophomore year held wedding plans.

Communication at College

I remember taking stamps – first class stamps were 4 cents each - and envelopes when I went to The Defiance College in the fall of 1961. A dollar would buy twenty-five stamps. I arrived at Trowbridge Hall to find I had two roommates – both friends from the same town. The three of us shared the room and of course the bathroom was down the hall. There were no computers, no TV in the room, no boom boxes. Still I liked quiet for studying and during week days/nights could usually be found by myself at a study corral back in the stacks at the library.

There was no phone in our room – and we certainly didn't have cell phones. There was some kind of a buzzer system that let me know if I had an incoming call down at the front desk (a very rare occasion) or if someone (like Verne) was in the lobby to see me. Guys certainly couldn't come up to our room. Trowbridge was a women's dorm. I rarely had any phone calls. But letters were pretty special.

We did not have keys to the dorm's outside doors, and since the doors were locked at curfew, we made sure we were in the dorm. If we wanted to go off campus, we signed out and signed back in when we returned. I do remember when Verne took me to town at Defiance on a date, we had to be careful to get back in time. When I was engaged to Verne and wanted to go to his family's home for a weekend, I had to have my mother's written permission –by letter - on file in order to sign out.

Verne was in Bethany Seminary and we wrote each other every week. So I knew what he was doing and when he would be coming home. Letters were our weekly communication. I always looked forward to mail – from Verne, from my mother and from others. I remember when my mother sent me an envelope containing a sizeable Elk's scholarship that had arrived for me at home. I didn't know I had won it. Nowadays, I likely would have been notified by phone. Instead of talking on the phone, I was writing, receiving, and answering letters.

My education has given me opportunities in life, and the family's and Verne's letters of love and encouragement to do my best were a true blessing. I wonder how I would have survived if there had been a constant bombardment of cell phones, computers, and television in my room. I don't know.

Love Letters

As I look at the 300 plus letters that we saved from each other, I notice two things immediately. First of all, a first class stamp was four cents when we began writing; first-class stamps on our later letters cost five cents each. Second, addresses were simpler. There were no zip codes.

As noted earlier in my story, I had played the organ at Verne Henry's home church, Poplar Ridge in Northern Ohio on the Sunday in early October, 1961 when Verne's parents introduced us after worship. Verne began coming home from seminary each weekend to lead a new Sunday School class for young single adults. I went home for Thanksgiving and again for the longer Christmas break. When I returned, I checked my mailbox.

January 2, 1962
Dear Phyllis,

     I suppose you are surprised that you are getting a letter from me. It looks like this will be one of those days when my pen can't spell and write correctly. I hope you will be able to make this out.

I have completed all of my classes today. I did not go to work today. Right now I am lying on my bed. My doctor ordered me to stay off my feet as much as possible. In case you are wondering, I cut my leg with an ax on Christmas day. I have been having a hard time getting around. That Christmas present I would rather not have received.

Well, the (Sunday School) class has gotten under way. The first Sunday there were 9 present. I have a book ordered for you . . . I will see that you get a book as soon as they arrive. . .

I was also wondering if the college library at Defiance has any books and material on St. Augustine. . . .I am writing a term paper for Church History about his life and contributions to religion. . .About the only time I will have to work on the paper is weekends. . . If the library does have material, is it possible for me to use it? If I could use the material, when is the library open?

You probably will not have time to write and answer. I hope to see you Sunday, if not on Saturday. I may have to come to Defiance for something.

Study hard and be ready to help with the class at Sunday School.

Yours in Christ,
Verne Henry Leininger

P.S. If you do write, send it to R.R. 1, Stryker, Ohio

January 4, 1962
Dear Verne,

Just for St. Augustine's sake I'll answer your letter before I go to bed. I was really surprised to receive mail so soon after I got back.

I am really sorry to hear about your leg and hope it doesn't hinder you very long.

My Christmas vacation could hardly have been more wonderful! I saw so many people that I hadn't seen when I was home for Thanksgiving.

If the Augustine you are writing about was the bishop of Hippo in northern Africa, there are quite a few books about him listed in the card catalog.

You can use the library. In fact, by signing your name and address on a card, you can check out books. The library is open from . . .

Yours in our Savior,
Phyllis

January 16, 1962
Dear Phyllis,

Maybe I can surprise you again by writing. I suppose you always look for mail. I know I do. I don't like to be completely forgotten. I especially liked letters the first year I was in college. . .

Bob Martin, that's the minister at Adrian, Michigan and I got back to seminary all right last night. It took us longer than usual. Some of the roads were slippery with packed snow. I left home about 1:45 and we got to seminary about 6:15. However, that would be 7:15 your time.

. . . Today after class ended at 12:25, I put on a suit right away and left for work at the Department of Radio and Television of the Church Federation of Greater Chicago. I worked until 5:20 tonight. I just made it back in time for supper. . .

Then I worked on my sermon some more. The text that was assigned to me is Exodus 3:5. "Then He said, 'Do not come near; put off your shoes from your feet, for the place on which you are standing is holy ground.'"

What would you say in 10 minutes if you had that text? You can tell me this weekend. I'll tell you my idea. It is still in the rough stage

1. God calls leaders . . .
2. We are to respect God and be reverent as we work for Him . . .

I found in the Manual of Worship and Polity the duties of the different offices of the church. I will quote the duties of the deacons since you were wondering what they do in the church.

"It is the special responsibility of the deacons to help care for the needy within the congregation, and to help maintain the church fellowship. They can help the pastor in counseling and in ministering to the sick, the unfortunate, and the needy. They may assist with the anointing services. In addition to these, they should assume general oversight of the physical arrangements for observing the ordinances of the church, such as baptism and love feasts."

I sure do enjoy being with someone who is really interested in church work and in the history of the church. I hope we can spend many hours together studying and growing in the Christian faith.

I suppose you are wondering if I am going to write a book. This is not my intention. I just felt like I needed to share with someone tonight some of my thoughts and things I had done, so I am writing to you. I hope you don't mind.

It kind of worries me when I write to you. I feel that I need to use perfect English since I am writing to an English major. I hope you can forgive the mistakes I make. There are probably some I don't even know I made. . .

I am looking forward to seeing you Saturday morning in the library and eating dinner together. Until then, good-bye and God bless you.

Your friend,
Verne Henry Leininger

January 22, 1962
Dear Verne,

Hi! Did you expect I'd write, or are you surprised? . . . I have 20 more minutes on desk duty. This is the night I was scheduled to do it from 7-10 p.m. . . .

I have my typewriter down here now. I finished typing my theme about 9:00 p.m. I surely wish I could hear you give your sermon.

Now I have a question! Did you say that your mother's sister's last name was (is) Garner? I remember your saying once that you were looking through some books on Brethren history that your grandfather who was a minister had. Last night an

60

idea "hit" me. Is your grandfather Rev. Holly Garner? (I think that was the first name of the Rev. Garner who was the minister of our Bristolville church.)

While I'm down here I'll see what our phone number is. It's 7-2991.

Since they've postponed putting Glenn into orbit, you'll probably have the radio program to work on this week, won't you?

A couple professors are giving part of their finals this week. . .

January 23, 1962 – Chapter 2

According to the calendar in my college catalog, Easter vacation begins at midnight on Saturday, April 14. . . . The vacation ends at 8:00 a.m. on Tuesday, April 24.

We're allowed two unexcused absences in Phys. Ed., so I'm going to take one today and go to the library until supper. Our head English professor just gave us such a long list of things that we should review that I don't know when I'll get them all covered.

Tonight I'm going to play records for my piano professor while he gives a talk on music to faculty wives.

Bye for now,

Phyllis   1st Thessalonians 5:28

January 23, 1962

Dear Phyllis,

I hope your Biology test went all right and you get an A on it. I also hope you got your theme typed on time. I was thinking of the things you had to do yesterday as we were sliding back to Chicago. I finished my sermon and read the book of I Kings Monday before we started back. . .When we got to Indiana, there were just tracks. When we were about 50 miles into Indiana, the roads were just covered with ice. No tracks, salt, or sand on the road. It was that way for about 30 miles and then there were bare spots occasionally. We arrived here all right about one hour later than usual.

Tonight I went over my sermon for the last time. It's going to be quite different from when you saw the script. I'll let you see the final script.

Now I have to start thinking about my next sermon. This time I was assigned a complete chapter which is James 5. . . .

I wish I could take off a week from classes and work . . . and just study. Maybe I could catch up. Since that won't happen I'll just have to keep long hours.

I will see you Saturday morning between 10:00 and 10:30 a.m. at the library. Until then, study hard for your exams, but don't stay up too late and I will try to do the same.

Yours through Christ
Verne Henry Leininger

January 31, 1962
Dear Phyllis,

I guess I had better get a letter written because I won't have the chance to write any more in January 1962. This month has sure gone fast. I guess especially so since I am teaching Sunday School Class on Sunday. I am anxious for school to be over actually. Seventeen years is a long time to be in school. I am anxious to be in a church. But I guess that will have to wait until I get my schooling.

I suppose your exams are all over by now and I suppose you will get all A's on your exams. Well at least you can hope. . .

Tomorrow you will be home. I'll bet you enjoy these vacations. I know I always do. They usually go too fast, however.

Oh, yes, before I forget. If you need a note from your folks to go to the Young Adult retreat March 3rd and 4th, you could get that while you are home. . .

I hope you haven't gotten my cold. . . I managed to record my program for WIND before my voice gave out completely. I'm thankful for that.

Have a good vacation and come back to school ready to study. . . Until then, good bye and may God be with you.

Your friend,
Verne Henry

February 2, 1962
Dear Verne,

The mail has already gone today, but since the twins (8) and Betty (7) have Bible Club at school tonight after school, and the Post Office is right across from the school, I should be able to mail this when Mom goes after the "little kids." (We speak of the "3 little kids" and the "3 big kids.")

Well, the roads were slippery yesterday morning and it took us two hours to reach the Fremont entrance to the turnpike. After one stop, we reached Cortland (about 10 miles from Bristolville) at 1:00 p.m. Oh yes, we left at 8:00 a.m. Dad met me at Cortland, and I got home at 1:30.

It sure seems wonderful to be home! This morning I baked some oatmeal cookies with nuts, raisins, and oranges in them. I'm afraid I'll forget how to cook by the end of four years without practice. . .

Did I ever tell you that Dad's mother lives with us? Now she is pretty sick with uncontrollable diarrhea. She has been in bed since January 16. I just hope I can relieve Mom some while I'm home. . .

We are going to have a Mennonite transfer student from Bob Jones University in our dorm this coming semester. Maybe she would go to Poplar Ridge with me. (If she doesn't mind being late – ha!)

I'm really happy. Dad has promised to go to church Sunday. He seldom does, although Mom is a member and she takes the children. Dad isn't against the church; if fact, I think he's "in favor of it." Of course the last statement can't explain what I mean. I'll try to explain when I see you. I started to play a sonata by Beethoven today, and Dad asked me to play some Gospel hymns with lots of runs in. Really, I'd rather play the piano and add "extras" than play almost any organ.

As for going March 3rd and 4th, Mom has suggested that she give me a note allowing me to go on any church-related trip.

Thank you for your letter. I feel privileged to get mail at home!

Take care of your cold and God Bless You.

Yours in Christ,

Phyllis

February 6, 1962

Dear Phyllis,

. . . I knew that your folks raised cattle, but I didn't know they raised **goats** "Three little kids" and "three big kids." Also when I read that part of the letter I told mom I had heard the story of the 3 bears by never about 3 kids.

Keep up the good work of trying to get students interested in our class at church. I suppose Hornishs have almost a car load. However, I can come to college on Sunday mornings and take a car load to church (on time).

I will be coming home early this week. We have a district ministers' retreat at our church and Bob and I are going to that. I will be skipping my classes on Friday. I guess that will be all right since you felt justified in skipping a Phys. Ed. class. Really though, I think the meeting will be good and worth skipping classes for. We will leave Chicago about 4:00 p.m. and I will get home about 9:00 to 9:30 p.m.

You were wondering about changing draft classification from 1-A to 1-O, which is from the army to a C.O. It is possible to change. It usually is a long process, but if a person is truly convicted that he cannot participate in the military forces, it can be changed. . . I would like to talk with the fellow who shows an interest in changing. Maybe I could possibly help him. Maybe we could arrange to meet him this weekend. I was wondering about meeting you Friday night. . . Also, I thought maybe we could talk to the fellow interested in C.O. I could probably get to Defiance by 7:00 p.m. unless you let me know differently.

I also have to work in the library on Saturday.
Good bye and may God be with you.
Yours in Christ,
Verne Henry

February 7, 1962
Dear Verne,

. . . I have a question to ask you about altars in Churches of the Brethren. I can not remember ever seeing an altar rail in any of our churches that I've been to. . . Rev. Higelmire wants our church to have an altar rail for people to kneel at when they accept Jesus as their Savior.

I really enjoy being able to write to you what I'm thinking. I hope you don't mind.
Sincerely,
Phyllis   Ephesians 3:20-21
P.S. No, Verne, I don't want to be a licensed minister, but my cousin and I always end our

letters with one or two verses, and I look forward to seeing what verse is at the bottom of her letter.

February 13, 1962
Dear Phyllis,

. . . Phyllis, I am glad and willing to read anything you want to write. Feel free to write as you desire. I like to get your thoughts and feelings. This is a way we can get to know each other better.

If you have other topics for sermons, please write or tell me about them. I am glad someone is interested enough in what I am doing to offer suggestions.

I have my sermon written and typed. I made some revisions. I suppose I will revise it some more. I will be practicing it Thursday afternoon. I will preach it Friday about 11:40 Chicago time or about 12:40 your time. Please remember and pray for me as I preach. . .

I will be at the library sometime Saturday morning and will see you then. May God be with you in all you do.

Your friend,
Verne Henry

February 13, 1962

My Valentine's Day card to Verne says "You're Someone Who Means a Lot to Me" and is simply signed "Phyllis."

Verne Henry gave me a small heart-shaped box of candy with a small stuffed dog. I think his mother had purchased two of each of these – one for Verne's sister, Ruth Ann, and one for Verne Henry to give to me. The small, blue, black and white stuffed dog and the little empty heart box have stayed with me through all of our moves.

February 20, 1962
Dear Verne,

Well, Glenn's back in the atmosphere. I think I can write to you while I listen to the radio with my roommates, both who are fighting the flu. I'm fine, and I hope you are, too – you've got three more finals left. (That's not really the only reason I hope you're fine.)

Verne, I had such a wonderful time Sunday. Now, after seeing some people I know, I remember others that I haven't thought about for a long time.
. .

It will be a little different studying on Saturday, but I imagine you'll be glad you don't have to study. My work is starting to pile up, so I'll have enough to do. . .

Sincerely,
Phyllis   John 14:12-14

February 21, 1962
Dear Phyllis,

I'm sure glad you had a good time Sunday. I know I did, even if it was bad driving home. I sure enjoy being with you. I'm looking forward to this weekend.

I am certain you won't have a hard time keeping busy Saturday. I want to get some things done around home Friday afternoon and Saturday. . .

I hope you get all your studies done before Sunday so you don't have to go back to college as early as the other time you were at our place for dinner. So study hard this week while I begin to take it easy for a few days. . .

Until Sunday, keep well and may God be with you.

Love, (1st time Verne uses the word, "Love" to end a letter)

Verne Henry Leininger   II Timothy 2:15

February 27, 1962

Dear Verne,

Last Saturday morning I looked up the many definitions of recipe and receipt and was going to write my definition paper on similarities and differences of those words. In fact, Monday afternoon (yesterday) I wrote my first draft.

I asked my professor about it this morning and he said I should choose a more abstract topic. Well, I was a little disturbed because I don't want to spend my weekend trying to define an abstraction. (I have a speech due this Thursday.) But then I got an idea. I've decided to define Christian faith. . . Now I'm glad I'm not writing on receipts and recipes!

. . . I'll never get over having peanut butter and bananas at your house! I had such a good time Sunday. And, you know, now that I learned how to play male quartet music, I'd like to try it again sometime.

Oh yes, I talked to the fellow from Nigeria again. He's heard of Garkida, but never been there. He will go to church with us March 11. . .

With Love, (My first use of the word love in a letter to Verne)

Phyllis   Hebrews 11:1

February 27, 1962

Dear Phyllis,

I received my Interpreter's Bibles today. They are really nice. They will be a big help in my work. I am going to leave the New Testament volumes here at Seminary as I will use them. The Old Testament volumes I will take home as I hardly have room for them all here at seminary.

I checked some books in the library today on Jonathan Edwards. I will list them and if Defiance College library doesn't have them and you want to use them, I can check them out of this library. . .

I sure enjoyed myself last Sunday. Especially Sunday night. I am looking forward to being with you this weekend. Until Friday night, be good and study hard.

With love,

Verne Henry   Numbers 6: 24-26

The weekly letter writing habit is now established. As our relationship intensifies, the letters increase in frequency, until two a week from each of us is common before we are married. Here are just a few excerpts from some of the many letters.

March 5, 1962
Dear Phyllis

    I felt like I should write to you tonight. Our good night seemed so short last night. I hope you didn't mind. I thought you were probably tired and I know I was. Also Galen had told me he didn't want to stay very long. We had been together a lot over the weekend and I sure enjoyed your company.

    Study hard and get your rest while I'm not around to bother you. May God be with you in all that you do.

    With love,

    Verne Henry   Romans 15:13   1st Corinthians 2:5

March 6, 1962
Dear Verne,

    Well, Barbara (my roommate) is really glad she went to the retreat. In fact, I think she enjoyed the whole weekend. I hope that Galen (Verne's roommate) did, too.

    I think the quality of planned recreation was really good. Usually it seems difficult to find recreation for our age group.

    I enjoyed the entire weekend. I especially like retreats and camping. Only this retreat sort of made me miss the people of my district that I would see if I went to something similar in Eastern

Ohio. I thought too much of how things would be at home, but this didn't occupy me completely by any means. This was the kind of an activity (retreat) I really enjoy.

I'm looking forward to Saturday. Take care of yourself – don't forget to eat and sleep.

With love,
Phyllis   1st Timothy 4:10

April 3, 1962
Dear Verne,

Last night I went to see Mr. Ryan about my English research paper. . . Mr. Ryan was a lot of help. Of yes, the paper is going to be about formula versus form in the short story.

Yesterday I looked over the Digest of Motor Vehicle Laws. However, would you mind too much if I didn't take my test on Saturday? Even if I could pass it then , I wouldn't have time to practice driving before vacation. Perhaps I could get my permit when I go home – or at the latest right after I come back.

Does it seem possible to you that this is the last weekend before vacation?

I really enjoyed our walk last weekend. I hope we can take some more – maybe even longer ones – sometime.

Take care of yourself, Honey. I think it's easier to study and more profitable if a person gets a reasonable amount of sleep. God guide you and help you do His will.

With love,

Phyllis   Philippians 4:13

March 20, 1962
Dear Phyllis
    Phyllis, those verses you typed out really mean
a lot to me. They sure helped. Also just being with
you helped me get over my depressed feeling. It is
carrying over into this week. I suppose things
seem to be going better because I have a good
attitude toward everything after this last weekend.
Thank you dear for listening to my problems and
troubles and helping me to get over them. This is
something I sure like about you. If a person is just
around you he can't help but feel better because
you always seem to have a smile and you just beam
forth with a true Christian faith. You are like the
moon. You always show your bright side to the
world and keep your dark side or moments to
yourself. I shouldn't compare you to the moon,
but I still think the illustration fits. Maybe you
could think of a better way to express the same
idea.
    I will see you sometime Saturday morning at
the library. Until then study hard and get your
rest so I don't have to see a sleeping beauty, but
can look at and be with one that's awake.
    With love,
    Verne Henry   St. John 14:12-14

March 27, 1962
Dear Verne,

I'm still thinking about our Sunday School class. I don't want to make excuses, but perhaps different subjects are easier topics for discussion than others. For example, most of us probably didn't know anything (much) about early Brethren newspapers except what we read in our text. So we had to agree with the book because we didn't know enough about the subject to have our own opinions.

I was especially interested to note the reasons that Kurtz gave for starting the <u>Gospel Visitor.</u> If one ran into a difficulty in seeking knowledge, he could send his problem to the <u>Gospel</u> <u>Visitor</u> and Kurtz would print it; then if another member had an answer, he could send it to be published.

Maybe we could try to get more meaning besides just facts from what we study. In other words, why did we, the Brethren, do something? What is our scriptural basis?

Study hard, but try to get your sleep, and God guide you.

Love,
Phyllis   John 20:21

April 11, 1962 – Wednesday
Dear Verne,

Tomorrow morning the Y is holding a sunrise service at Fort Defiance at 6:30 a.m. The service is open to the whole campus. After the service we are going to have breakfast at a professor's house.

Tomorrow I'll start getting ready to go home. When I'm home I'll see if I can find some recent pictures of the family.

Mrs. Blanchard, a world traveler and speaker, spoke at chapel yesterday on the topic Faith, Freedom, Fertilizer and Refrigerators. She was really interesting. Last night several of us Y members ate supper with her. She told about someplace in the Orient, I believe, where sheep were roasted whole, and the guest of honor was given one of its eyes, a delicacy. Well, she was the guest of honor, and she said she was prepared to swallow it whole if need be, but they didn't give it to her, because they didn't think an American woman would eat it.

Verne, I really like the New English translation of the New Testament. Last night, even though I was tired, I could hardly lay it down.

Something strange just happened – it seems good to be able to tell someone. Before Sociology class at 1:00 (I just came from it) Mr. Kavolis came up to me and asked me to stay after class. He also asked Niyi and some other fellow. After class he asked us to come to dinner at his house at 12:00 o'clock tomorrow, and he gave us his address; he lives near here. Thursday is the only day I don't have a one o'clock class, so I accepted.

I hope you get your Easter program all finished this afternoon.

Take care of yourself and may our God guide and be with you.

Love,

Phyllis   James 1:3   Colossians 3:17

April 12, 1962
Dear Verne,

Sunrise service was impressive. It was pretty cold so early in the morning, but I shouldn't wish to be so comfortable after what Jesus suffered for me.

Oh honey, what a dinner I had. I wouldn't care to eat so elaborately every day. I think that the meal lacked only the candles. It included three salads and two rich desserts. The first dessert was beaten frozen strawberries and whipped cream. The second was a very beautifully decorated cake with three fillings in it. The cake was such as I've never tasted anything like. It was so moist I think I could have squeezed water out, and the fillings were very light and foamy. . .

I would like to know what was in that cake. I kept tasting it during Phys. Ed. after I got back at 2:00 p.m.

Surprisingly I got inspired from being there. Mrs. Kavolis, in saying we should really try to convince our friends to take advantage of some of the concerts, said we really have to believe in something to convince people. There were five students there, three girls and two fellows.

Friday morning – 8:30 Well, I'd better start packing I have classes from 9 – 2 p.m. So I'll see you in a couple weeks – and I'll write while I'm home.

Love,

Phyllis   Psalms 28:8

April 15, 1962 - Palm Sunday
Dear Phyllis

It seems so different not seeing you this weekend. It seems like I have forgotten to do something. I have been thinking about you a lot. I know that you were anxious to see your family. I hope you are having a good time.

I will tell you about today's activities after I go out and do chores.

Well, the chores are all done. The little calf really ate tonight when I fed him. He is really growing. In fact all the calves are getting big. They also seem to be able to drink a lot of water. I have been watering them.

There were seven in our class today. We had a pretty good session on the dress question. We also planned the order we were going to discuss the rest of the book. Remember you are in charge of Chapter 26, Brethren Service on May 6. So plan accordingly.

There were six babies dedicated and thirteen were baptized today-two from the Defiance Church and eleven from our church. The church services were not over until about 12:00 noon. Lois Hornish was wishing for you this morning. During baptizing they always play the organ very softly. She really had a lot of playing and she said she really was tired. I'll say you will probably have a lot of organ playing when you get back.

I want to remind you to get your folks' permission to go to Manchester College and stay overnight for May Day, the 4th and 5th of May. We will stay overnight there just Friday night. If you want to stay overnight here Saturday night you can. I will leave this up to you to decide.

Ruth Ann got good tickets for the play – center section and the third row next to an aisle.

I will be glad when I get to see you again, but until that time may God be with you in all you do. Good night dear, and write.

With lots of love,

Verne Henry   Philemon 1:3-6

On the back of the envelope Verne wrote: For best results, open before reading.

April 23, 1962

Dear Phyllis,

Well, vacation is just about over. I hope yours has been a good one. Mine has, even though I didn't get my papers written. I have most of the reading done for all of my papers. Now I just have to write them. That shouldn't take too long, once I get started.

In less than six days I hope to see you again. It seems like it has been a long time since we were together.

Honey, study hard and may God be with you in all you do.

With lots of love,

Verne Henry   Psalms 133:1

April 22, 1962
Dear Verne,

Wednesday night at 6:45 Mom and I went to choir practice. Mrs. Holko, the woman who's been taking lessons and playing the organ for church wasn't there because her mother was sick, so I played. It was just like old times, and I felt more at home in church here than during past vacations when I was only one of the congregation – not that I don't enjoy sitting back and listening – I do. But to do so in my church here where I played since sixth grade seems strange. Oh Verne, I hope I'm not bragging. I just enjoyed choir practice and seeing all the ladies. Our choir has no men; in fact, most everything in our church is done by women.

My project for Thursday night was decorating candy crosses for the children for Easter. I used 10 cent Milky Ways – 2 ½ bars for each cross. The crosses were 1 ½ bars high with half a bar at each side. In the center of each cross I put two pink roses and then leaves (of frosting, of course). The roses were placed on the diagonal. Then I outlined the crosses in light green with my decorator.

I decided I wanted to sleep in some morning, so Friday morning I had just woken up (10:40) for the final time that morning when Freddie came up and asked me if I'd play basketball with him. I got right up intending to go right outside without breakfast so we could play longer, because Dad, home for Good Friday, had gone to the hardware for some belt lacing for the belt to the tractor, and we thought he would want Freddie when he got home.

But when I got downstairs I saw that Freddie had fixed me half a grapefruit and a dish of what he thought was my favorite cereal. He looked like he'd had fun fixing my breakfast, so I had to eat something. However, Freddie didn't mind when I didn't eat the cereal, because it meant we could go outside sooner.

. . . I'll say that Mom and I went to Sunrise service but didn't stay for breakfast. Most of us went to Sunday School, but I felt especially good when Dad and Grandma came to church. Moreover, Dad asked Grandma if she wanted to go next Sunday. (She's Methodist and would rather go there. She is quite lame, though, and it's difficult for her to go anywhere very much.)

This afternoon I read <u>Looking Forward to Christian Marriage.</u> But, Dear, I will write when I get to school. I wish tomorrow were Saturday, but it's Monday. Good night, Honey.

4:12 p.m. Monday

I met Mr. Sayre and Mary Morse in Cortland at 10:00 a.m. this morning. We had a good trip and arrived here at 2:40 p.m.

I'm really looking forward to seeing you. Well, I'll say what I'm thinking – I'm anxious for Saturday.

Now may God be with you and guide you in everything you do.

With love,
Phyllis   Romans 8:37-39

80

April 25, 1962
Dear Phyllis,

. . . Oh yes, about the Saturday coming up, remember that you have to sign out on Friday to come to the Young Adult party at our house on Saturday night. You can go home with me when we finish studying in the library.

Maybe we can decide Saturday what we want to do Sunday. I'm assuming that you will want to be with me especially from your letter. I know I want to be with you. It seems so long since we last saw each other.

I'm wondering what it will be like this summer. If you get a job, you will have weekends off and my weekends will be busy. Well, maybe we will be able to work something out when the time comes. .
.

May God be with you and keep you and God willing I will see you Saturday morning in the library.

With love,
Verne Henry   1st Corinthians 13, especially 13:13

April 30, 1962
Dear Verne,

I was really wondering about you this afternoon. Just before supper the sky here got really black . . . I wondered how the weather was driving back.

I really enjoyed our walk Sunday. Your woods has so many different kinds of flowers.

I was a little upset today. Mr. Sayre wants me to play for the recital the piece I am least sure of. It takes a lot of endurance and I'm afraid I might not be able to do it on a new piano, which will probably have stiff action. And grands are usually harder to play. So Mr. Sayre is taking me to the high school after chapel tomorrow to play the 9 foot Grand there. The grand pianos in his office are 7 foot pianos, I think.

. . . I just want to add that I'm not worried about the recital anymore. I decided I surely should have more faith than that.

Verne, I really enjoy being with you. I enjoy being able to talk to you.

Love,

Phyllis   1st Corinthians 15:55-58 and 16:23-24

May 2, 1962
Dear Phyllis

First of all I will tell you about the trip back. We left home a little earlier than usual, but got here later. About Kendallville we ran into the storm. The clouds came clear to the ground. Limbs, dirt, and anything lose was flying about. We had to turn on the car lights and the street lights also came on. It was just about as dark as night. We were glad we had Bob's 1956 Chevy and not his English Ford. He had a hard time keeping the car on the road.

There were several trees part way across Route 6. In two places there was one-way traffic. The storm slacked just before we got to Nappanee. In Nappanee a lot of big windows were broken out of stores. Several trees were blown out by the roots. There was one garage completely flat and one house partly gone. Lots of branches were in the streets.

The damage was not so heavy again until we got to Walkerton. There the electricity was off and stop lights were not working. A tree was blown into one house and caused a lot of damage. Also the top part of one factory was gone. Several house trailers were blown over and one house trailer was completely smashed. Several barns were heavily damaged with one about totally destroyed, although part was still standing. Lots of hog coops and small buildings were blown over.

There wasn't much damage in this part of Chicago, although the southern part received considerable damage.

I guess the Lord was with us as we made it back to Chicago all right.

Honey, that worship we had together was sure inspiring. It's been a while since I had a worship experience that has meant so much to me personally. It was very simple, but yet it was something that really spoke to my needs at the moment. I sure want to continue to worship together. I am so happy that you are also interested in doing this and I feel that it is not just because I want to do it, but because you also really

want to worship when we are together. I think
that it is really important that our relationship
with each other should be under girded by God
and the Christian fellowship.

Honey, I love you and hope that our
relationship will grow in Christian love and
understanding. . .

With Love,
Verne Henry   Jude 17-25

May 14, 1962
Dear Verne,

Honey, I'm going to miss you so much this
summer. But, right now, it's more important that
you get a church than it is where the church is
located.

With lots of love,
Phyllis

May 15, 1962
Dear Phyllis,

. . . I haven't heard about a summer pastorate
as yet. The meeting at Elgin was today and I think
tomorrow.

Love,
Verne Henry   1st John 4: 1-3

1805 South Freedom
Alliance, Ohio
May 31, 1962
Dear Phyllis,

Oh, honey, I don't know where to begin. I have a nice room. Most of my things are put away. The above is my address. My phone number is . . . It is a direct dialing phone. It is also a private line.

We are on fast time here. It is 11:10 here, but would be 10:10 p.m. at home.

My room is larger than the one at college. A curtain separates the room in about the middle - one part for office and the other for living area. About everything I need for cooking is furnished.

Tomorrow night the Youth Fellowship is having a wiener roast. Saturday afternoon from 1:00 – 4:00 is a conference for teachers and leaders of the city-wide Vacation Bible School. Sunday I plan to visit the pilot critically injured in a plane accident. They say he does not recognize anyone.

Honey, I will be thinking about you as you play in the recital and also as you are taking your exams.

I am looking forward to seeing you. It was lonely last night after everyone left.

With lots of love,
Verne Henry   Philippians 1:3-11

June 1, 1962
Dear Verne,

This morning I got a letter from Mom saying that Mrs. Force, whose children I stayed with the last two summers would like me to work for her again this summer. So I just wrote to her to tell her I'd like to.

Her older two children will go to school in Cleveland this summer so I'll only have Allie, ten years old. Of course, she'll probably want me to play with her with her brother and sister gone. It seems sometimes like there are not so many things for children to do in the city.

I'll earn $20 a week. And I'll only be needed this summer until about August 13. Mom doesn't say why – usually I work until school starts.

I imagine you're finding a lot of people to meet all at once.

May our God and Savior keep you close to him and help you know and do his will.

With lots of love,

Phyllis   John 21: 15-17   1st

Thessalonians 5: 16-26

P.S. I promise longer letters after finals are over.

June 3, 1962

Dear Phyllis,

Oh honey, I wish you were here. I have sure missed you this weekend. . . Last night I went visiting and stayed until about 11:00. I was lonely here by myself. The lady where I was visiting, Mrs. Leo (Esther) Stuckey, said she had an extra bed if you wanted to stay here some weekends. I told her about dating you and she offered without my asking.

I have had some wonderful experiences already. I only wish you could share them with me. Esther Stuckey seems almost like another mother already. Oh yes, I go to Esther and Leo's to take my baths.

I will enclose a bulletin so you can see the order of service and the announcements. . . It seems strange to see my name listed as pastor of the First Church of the Brethren. (Editor's note: His full name was listed: Rev. Verne Henry Leininger.) Oh, Phyllis, I love the work so far. I am really looking forward to working with these people . . . They make me feel right at home.

(Editor's Note: This, as well as most letters, read like a diary of visiting, Bible School planning, choir practice, committee meetings, and sermon plans.)

I miss you dearly, Phyllis, but I hope to see you soon. I will probably not send any more letters to college . . .a letter will probably be waiting for you when you get home. May God give you strength and wisdom to face the tests ahead.

With lots of love,
Verne Henry   I Timothy 4: 11-16

June 6, 1962 9:45 p.m.
Dear Verne,

It's only been a week
But, oh, it seems a year
Since you last told me good night
And since you held me near!

Hi, Honey, forgive my above attempt, but Stormie and I were just reading poetry and I guess I'm still in that mood (whatever mood it was).

It seems so funny that I didn't study tonight. It didn't seem right to do nothing but have fun this afternoon and evening. Maybe I take studying too seriously, but I don't think I'd feel right doing any less than my best. As long as I don't get too involved to witness or keep Jesus first.

Ruth Ann arrived at my doorway this afternoon about 4:00 (I didn't know she was coming) and asked me to go down town with her, Esther and Aunt May. So I did, and we went to Murphy's to get you some sheets.

And Honey, Mr. Sayre said the committee recommended me for a (music) scholarship. He seems sure I've got it. But I guess I won't be notified till July.

Oh, Honey, I feel so welcome at Alliance and I haven't even been there! Two places for me to stay – and we've been invited out to dinner. I think you're fitting into the congregation well.

I doubt that I'll be home before 6:00 p.m. home time. Then I'll have to visit with brother and sisters and Grandma and have supper. So I might wait until late, if rates are lower, and call about 10:00 p.m. I'll think about this and probably write again tomorrow. . .

With love,
Phyllis   Romans 1:8-12

July 2, 1962

Dear Verne,

   After describing the birthday party that I was in charge of for Allie that day, I wrote:

   Honey, I enjoy being with you so much. And thank you, Honey, for giving me your large picture. Carol Jean and Mother really like it, too. . .

   Yours with lots of love,
   Phyllis   1st Timothy 2:1-5

July 11, 1962
Dear Phyllis,

   . . . I wrote out my reports and a letter home between watching them put in the new water line. They finished the job about 4:30 p.m. So I now have water. The showers are sure nice. I took a long one this morning. . .

   I will bring my check book Saturday so we can get the dishes (if you have ordered them.) I think I will wear the shirt you made for me when I come up and we go to town. I will also bring my work clothes. . .

   With all my love,
   Verne Henry   Hebrews 11: 1-40

July 12, 1962
Dear Phyllis,

   . . . Phyllis, I don't know what you think, but I think we should tell your folks about our plans before we get the dishes from Warren on Saturday. I think it would be better to tell them right out than to make them guess and be uncertain about our plans. You can think it over and have your

answer ready Saturday morning. If you want to not tell, I suppose this would be possible also.
. . . I will see you Saturday morning. Until I see you, may God be with you. And you can decide about telling your folks of our engagement.

    With love,
    Verne Henry   Song of Solomon 8: 6-7

July 21, 1962
Dear Phyllis,

    If you agree, you will be playing the piano for church and possibly Sunday School on July 29 when Alliance Church is in charge of the worship services at West View Manor at 11:00 a.m. Esther is going to play their Baldwin organ, Winnie is going to bring a special number and lead singing and Leo is going to be in charge. Here are the hymns and responses. . .

    Honey, I wish I could be with you right now, but I can't. I'm almost tempted to come up, but it would be 6:30 or so before I got there. I would have such a few hours with you. . . I am really looking forward to the weekend.

    Yours with love,
    Verne Henry   Matthew 19: 4-6

July 31, 1962
Dear Verne,

    I just arrived at work. Junior is home. Anyway, I have no time to myself when he's here. He has more energy than my little sisters. . . he really has too much energy to be satisfied in the city. Junior is good as long as I keep him busy. He's anxious to play monopoly. As soon as he finishes eating breakfast, we'll play.

Today is kiddy's day at the fair, so I'll take the children. I've taken them other years and they nearly go crazy to pet the animals.

. . . Now we're back from the fair and I gave the kids cookies and punch. What an afternoon. I also took three neighbor kids. Well, we had a really good time. I didn't lose any of them. But it was sure hard to get them all persuaded it was time to go home.

"All things work together for good to them who love the Lord."

Yours with lots of love,
Phyllis

My job finished mid-August, in time for me to counsel at Camp Zion with Verne. After camp, we went to District Conference at Ashland and then traveled together to his home. Seminary classes began sooner than Defiance College classes, so I had a few days with Verne and Esther before moving to Whitney Hall.

September 10, 1962
Dear Verne,

, , , Your Dad came in. He had put up stakes in the south pasture for me to use to practice parking. . . Verne showed me how to park and then left me to practice. I parked for my first time at 2:33 p.m. Just after 3:30 when I had just taken the keys out and rolled up the windows, Verne came out and wanted me to back down the field. I backed pretty straight and then He had me pull ahead practicing shifting gears. He wanted me to shift from 3rd to 2nd. I couldn't then, but now I see how easy it is.

Anyway, to practice shifting, we headed south again. Soon we came to two <u>huge</u> thistles which were growing like cars in a regular parking place. Verne didn't think I could park between them but he said I might as well try.

So try I did and believe it or not, both of those thistles are still standing and I had your car between them (in one try).

I was ironing my black skirt when my iron started spitting minerals. So Esther suggested that I let it cool, (because I wanted to open it) and that I practice the piano. (Editor's note: I do not ever remember my own mother suggesting I practice the piano.)

I decided I should use my metronome. I took it out of the box and it ticked unevenly. Then it stopped. When I tried to wind it, the key would turn without getting any tension.

I showed Esther and just then the metronome made a noise that sounded like a window blind going up suddenly.

She suggested that I take it to the shop. Verne and I were just looking at it when Esther came out with my iron to also be fixed.

You know what Verne just said? I quote, "I still think she could pass her test if she could crawl between those things." (meaning the thistles) You'll have to see those thistles. Anyway, I'm not really too good yet. A couple times I parked with my two tires on the wrong side of the board which represented the curb.

But back to the shop. Verne fixed the iron first. He cleaned it out with compressed air. Also he made me a special screw driver because the iron takes a moon-shaped screw driver. Then he fixed the metronome. It didn't take him long to see what was wrong. He fixed it, wound it and it ticked evenly. Meanwhile, he opened the shop refrigerator to defrost it so that I might have the mineral-free water for in my iron.

Well, Honey, I miss you already. I'm sure I want to get married and I hope it can be June 22, 1963.

God be with you and give you strength sufficient for all your tasks.

Yours with love,

Phyllis   Philippians 1:6   James 1: 3-5

September 11, 1962
Dear Verne,

. . . Right after supper I practiced parallel parking. After I practiced parking, I came in and practiced the piano, mainly an 86 page Concerto by Mozart. (I played all my parts in this.)

So, for this weekend I'll leave it up to you as to when you want to come. . . Sometime, perhaps Saturday, I'd like to practice driving. My permit runs out October 28.

Well, good night, dear. . . May our God be with you and give you a safe trip home.

    Loving you,
    Phyllis   Romans 1: 8 & 9

September 13, 1962
Dear Verne,

    . . . Mr. Sayre says Mr. Chaffoo, the orchestra director, is planning for me to play the 1st movement of Mozart's Concerto in A with the orchestra in April. What an experience that will be!

    May God help you know and do His will.
    With my love,
    Phyllis   Acts 2:17

September 18, 1962
My Dear Verne,

    When I asked about getting a job in the cafeteria, they asked if I could work tonight – just that sudden. I said I had a class until 5:00. So I was told to come at 5:00. I worked from 5:00 – 7:15. I had 15 minutes out for supper, so I worked two hours. The starting rate is $.80 an hour.

    After seeing about work, I went to the registrar's office and found out that my scholarship will apply, whether I'm married or single, as long as I keep my grades up.

    Honey, I felt so close to you this weekend. I think we can make whatever sacrifices are necessary for us to be married.

So I will close for now. May God be always with us both.

    With my love,

    Phyllis   Matthew 6:33 & 34 New English Bible

October 1, 1962
Dear Wife to be,

    I don't know if you will have time to think about the wedding this week or not. If you do have time, I think it would be good to begin writing out our plans so we can know what we have done and also know what we need to do. If we don't start listing things, we may forget some things we need to do. . .

    Good bye dear, and don't accept too many more tasks at college because no matter how intelligent a person is, they have to study some time.

    May God direct all your thoughts and actions.
    With Love,
    Verne Henry

Verne's next letter is a long and detailed description of his work at the WTTW-TV station. I share just a small bit of his letter.

October 2, 1962
Hi Honey,

    I am writing this in the control room of studio 2 at WTTW-TV. Dr. Faw is now on the air. . . . While he is on the air I don't have anything to do . Most of my work with the program is before the telecast. . . As I am sitting here I can see six different pictures of six TV monitors. There is also one monitor that shows which picture is going over the air. So actually there are seven sets in front of me. There is also glass around the control room so that I can actually see what is taking place in the studio. . .

You know, dear, our wedding just can't come too soon for me. I am really wanting for the day to come. I love you very much because you are a big help to me.

Good-bye dear and may God guide you in everything you do and keep you safe until we meet Friday evening.

With lots of love,
Verne Henry   Philemon verses 4-7

I remember telling my children how I studied at the library every night during college and how I was back in my dorm by curfew and went to bed. I kept up with my homework and got regular rest. The letters I wrote to Verne Henry tell a different story.

Let me share excerpts from a letter I wrote on October 2nd & 3rd, 1962
Hi Honey,

I went to choir. Gary didn't come. (In a previous letter I had told Verne that the choir pianist had stormed out of the last choir practice after a disagreement with the director.) I had to sight read more music again. Then Barb (my roommate) and I ate supper with Miss Lewis, our dorm mother. After supper I lay down until about 6:30 when I was in charge of our dorm section meeting because Barb had to babysit. After the meeting, I took the choir music which I asked to have and went to the basement of the dorm and played. This relaxed me considerably. I went back upstairs and wrote a letter home.

Then I was going to write my Advanced Grammar stories, but two girls came wanting help with physics. Then at a quarter till nine Miss Lewis came wanting help with music dictation. So back to the basement till about 9:30. By that time I only felt like going to bed. So I did. I didn't accomplish a thing last night. We had several lengthy interruptions. I think I got to sleep by 11:00.

(Editor's note: This same letter continues about the following evening after a busy day of classes and hitting golf balls in phys ed.) I went to supper and ate without waiting for Barb because I had a lot to do and I didn't know how late she would be from lab. I wasn't alone long. . . A fellow from Creative Class joined me and shared his musical problems. I tried to explain to him how F sharp minor was/is related to A major.

Barb came from supper. She wanted to go to the library so I went too. I had hesitated because it was raining. Well, I was fortunate to get a desk in the stacks (6:30 p.m.) and at least while I was there I had only one interruption – one girl asked me how to do an explication – a question that puzzles me, too.. I got a lot done before Barb was ready to go back at 9:30.

Well, I wanted to write to you but my baby finger was awfully sore from writing so many pages of outline. So I decided to take my shower first. I left the restroom and was getting a drink of water when Pat Martin, one of my piano students, came around the corner on her way to my room. She had to write a one line melody and lyrics for an elementary education class so – she needed help.

Oh, Honey, I love you. It makes me feel good that you took time to write a card to my parents. They appreciated it, too.

I have not started reading the 459 page Iliad which is due next Monday. So it looks like I'll have a busy weekend.

Well, I think I'll say good-bye for now, Dear. And no matter how busy I get, I always think of you.

With Love,
Phyllis   Philippians 1: 3-6 NEB

October 8, 1962
Dear Verne,

Counting yours, I'll have four letters to mail tomorrow. I asked Everetts about the use of the church and about flowers. I wrote to Rev. Higelmire asking if he'd have the opening prayer at our wedding and I wrote to the Bristolville Church clerk asking for my letter to be sent here to Poplar Ridge. . .

I pray that God will give you all necessary wisdom and understanding as you prepare and take your mid-terms.

Love,
Phyllis

November 7, 1962
Dear Verne,

Dear, I wish you were here to talk to. I got a letter from home today which made me feel wanted. But I wish the letter hadn't come this week. I'm enclosing the letter.

We wouldn't probably leave 'till Saturday morning, if we go -- but should I work breakfast or should I not? If you wanted to come back to study Sunday night, maybe we could leave right after dinner Sunday.

Honey, I don't know what is the right thing to do, but I almost feel that now Mother's asked me, I should go, even though we can't stay long because of your finals. They are so important that ordinarily I'd say we should only spend the weekend studying. In fact, I wouldn't want to go anywhere if I were having finals.

I think I should work breakfast. We could leave – if you're willing – at 9:30 a.m.

I got my psychology test back. This time there were three A's. I got the lowest A, which I'm thankful for considering the amount I studied. I'm the only one in the class that has two A's.

Love,
Phyllis   1st John 5:4

99

November 13, 1962
Dear Verne,

. . . Darling, I hope I didn't cause you to get too far behind this last weekend. But this weekend really did me a lot of good.

Verne, I realize more and more how much I love you. It seems that my love for you has grown so much even since we've been engaged. I never imagined anything so wonderful.

May God be with you as you study, as you learn, and as you take finals, to help you. May He be first in both our lives.

Love,
Phyllis   Revelation 20:14

November 14, 1962
Dear Verne,

. . . I think now I'll quote you the first part of a note from Mom I received today: "So good to have had you two home. Dad said I put one over on him. So glad I did.

Amazing, but true, Grandma is so much better. Can walk, eat, and so far bowels O.K."

(Editor's reflection: I wonder if Dad thought that perhaps Grandma wouldn't make it and that we didn't care to come visit her. Anyway, Mom and Dad were glad we came home.)

Yours with love,
Phyllis   1st Corinthians 1: 3-8

November 15, 1962 (Verne will soon be done with
                        another term's finals and wants to go to
                        classes with me on his break.)
Dear Phyllis,

Honey, you didn't cause me to get far behind in
my lessons. Things are working out nicely,
especially since I will not have that one test. I am
realizing more all the time that God will take care
of us.

I have two schedules on other paper. If I would
attend classes Monday morning (before heading
back to Seminary in the afternoon), I would be
able to visit all your classes except piano lesson.

I have a question. When is the Messiah going
to be given? Where will it be given and what time
of the day? Please let me know as soon as you can,
Honey.

Honey, I love you and want to be with you as
much as possible.

With my love,
Verne Henry   I Thessalonians 5: 12-22

November 16, 1962
Dear Verne,

The Christmas portion of the "Messiah" is
being given in the lecture hall Tuesday evening,
December 11, at 8:00 p.m. I wonder why you want
to know that so quickly, but it doesn't matter.

At my lesson this afternoon Mr. Sayre and I
practiced (on the two pianos in his office) the

"Messiah" together. A Baldwin organ is being brought in probably next week.

Shagon, my new piano pupil is impatient to learn. He talked and talked tonight after supper. I felt caught with no way to escape. . . I'm having a difficult time trying to impress upon him the fact that I only take one lesson a week, but that I practice at the least an hour a day. He seems to feel the only way he can learn is to have more lessons. Oh, for some paying students like him! I'm beginning to feel that just because he's from Africa, he doesn't need so many favors.

By the way, he's flying home to Nigeria for the weekend. Cost = $1,500.00.

Thanks, Dear, for hearing an account of my frustration.

Yours with love,
Phyllis   Ephesians 3:20-21

November 17, 1962
Dear Verne,

Honey, I can't promise that I'll spend Sunday night at your house, because Esther will probably have my invitation written for Wednesday-Saturday. . . I might have to study Thursday night for Friday's classes.

I am looking forward to next week. Honey, I love you.

With love,
Phyllis   1st Peter 3: 1-15
November 26, 1962
Dear Phyllis,

Phyllis dear, I was thinking on the way back, which is a surprise. I think I gave you a very hard time this vacation. I was trying to have fun, but thinking about it now, it probably wasn't fun for you.

I think I made too much of a joyous event out of your getting a low C in Psychology. Honey, I'm glad to see that you don't always get A's, but yet I am concerned about the low grade. I'm sorry I made such a fuss over the C. I will try not to do this the next time. . .

Your Lover.

November 28, 1962
Dearest Verne,

. . . By the way Honey, your giving me a hard time once in a while keeps life interesting.

As for my C, I heard even more from Barb than from you. Every time anyone came Monday, she told them to guess what her roomie got. As far as I'm concerned, it's over. But I'm not going to get another C in that course. There's no sense to get a C when one could do better. . .

With my love,
Phyllis   Romans 8: 29-30

November 28, 1962
Dear Phyllis,

It looks like the choir is just about requiring all your time with the special programs and rehearsals. I will almost bet that you will not work in the cafeteria at noon on Thursday, December 17.

If you go to tape the TV show I'll almost bet you won't get back in time for your 1:00 p.m. Phys. Ed. Class either.

It also looks like you will be skipping several classes to go with the choir. With all of these activities, I don't see how you can even hope to get all A's this semester. . .

I pray that God will give you the strength to carry you through all your activities.

With love,

Verne Henry   II Timothy 1:4 Matthew 20:1-15

December 3 & 4, 1962

Good evening dear,

In the Sears catalog they have a 3 cell flashlight that has a 4000 foot beam. I was wondering if you wanted me to get it for Freddy for Christmas. You can either write or wait until the weekend.

Oh yes, I heard on the radio coming to Chicago that the Hammond Organ Company bought the Everett Piano Company outright for about five Million. I thought you might be interested to know this.

Dear, I have a question. Do you think it would be possible to go with you to Edgerton when the choir goes Monday morning, December 10? I could even drive and take you and would prefer driving if it is possible. . .

With my love,

Verne Henry   I Thessalonians 4:10b – 12

January 23, 1963

Dear Phyllis,

You sure have difficult rules at college. I am glad you can sign out to our place and then come on to seminary.

I have a note enclosed that you can give to Miss Ebel. It is from Carrie Simmers who is the girls dorm mother here. You can turn this in and use either signout slip or both if you want to.

Oh yes, Carrie Simmers is having a meal Saturday evening for the single students. She invited you specifically. Also Richard Bohn, the one we met at Gordon Bucher's this summer, also wants us to come for supper some evening. Also Professor Dale Brown asked in class this morning if you weren't coming. I told him not to rush the time because you aren't coming until tomorrow. So it looks like I am not the only looking forward to seeing you. However, I don't believe anyone is looking forward to your coming as I am.

I have a lot of possibilities of things to do. We can go over them when you get here. . .

I have permission from all the professors for you to attend classes.

Oh yes, be certain to dress warmly. It is really cold here in Chicago.

May God be with you on your final exam. I will say good bye and will look forward to seeing you tomorrow evening about 7:25 at the train.

With lots of love,
Verne Henry   Jeremiah 9:23-24

March 13, 1963

Dearest Phyllis,

Honey, I have an observation to make about your studies and your grades. Please do not take it as a criticism of what you are taking.

You really seem to be interested in music. In this you spend a great deal of your time for the hours of credit you get. This is spent in practice for yourself, choir, and playing for soloists.

Another observation is that you are becoming increasingly interested in religion and philosophy. Most of the papers you have written in connection with your other classes have been on this general topic. If you are studying English and literature, there is a possibility that the professors are not interested in the religious aspects like you are. . .

Here are some possibilities I see. You can think them over and we can talk about them together. As you know you can do your best work if you are really interested in it. . . There is also the possibility of majoring in music. You have given several reasons for not doing this and I think they are valid.

Another possibility is majoring or minoring in religion and philosophy. However, there are very few high schools that have a need for teachers in this area (religion and philosophy).

Maybe I have interpreted your feelings wrong. Maybe you are really interested in literature, but are having a hard time. Well, enough of those thoughts. . .

Good-bye, Dear.

With my love to you

Verne Henry   Daniel 1:8-16

April 24, 1963
Dearest Phyllis,

Well I know where I will have my pastorate for the summer. It will be about 500 miles from Bristolville one way or about 1000 miles round trip. So it looks like you will have to make all the arrangements for the wedding. I just won't be able to get to your place to help.

The church is the Lakeview Congregation in Brethren, Michigan. It is over near Lake Michigan. The nearest big town is Manistee which is a lake shore city. Brethren is located in the Manistee National Forest.

We can now start making some of our plans . . . We can talk this weekend. . .

With my love,
Verne Henry   Psalms 80:3

May 6, 1963
Dearest Husband to Be,

Hi! I was just Mr. and Mrs. Sayre's first official guest. Mr. Sayre asked me to come over for tea and wedding cake and then I had my lesson in their home. They are so happy! And did they ever have fun "taking the back roads" to make the arrangements.

I just wrote to Dad and Mom and encouraged them to come out and see us and our deep freeze, sewing machine, studio couch, etc. I told them how to get to your house in case I'm not here. I don't know whether they'll come, but while they seemed in the mood, I decided to coax. They've never been to your house. They've never seen Whitney (my dorm), either. .

Love from a future wife,
Phyllis   John 15: 9-17

May 8, 1963 After talking with my advisor in the
    English Department, Professor Ryan
Dear Verne Henry,

... I have been trying to decide on a program of study for the next two years. If it's alright with you, I am not going to take education courses or student teach. A long talk with Ryan has convinced me that I'll get more out of my education by taking more meaty courses ... The requirements for an English major are really being increased next year... Ryan has put French on my schedule...

Ryan says if I want to learn Education theory and methods, he'll give me a list of books I can read.

I think I will be more challenged now and more satisfied...

Love to my future husband,
Phyllis   Romans 1: 8-12

May 9, 1963
Dearest Phyllis,

You have made me very disturbed. I do not think any person can teach without education courses. . . If you don't want to take any education courses to teach, what are you going to college for? I thought you were going to prepare for teaching.

I had professors tell me not to take education courses also. I found that these courses are some of the most important I took. These courses have helped me a great deal in teaching in the church school . . .

And why French? I would say if you want a language, take German or Russian. Our church originated in Germany. A lot of books and material s are in German. Why not take a language that might be helpful? . . . I would even recommend Spanish before French because there are a lot of Spanish speaking people in the U.S. French is one of the last languages I would want.

Also, you do not learn education methods by reading. You have to have experience. The experience is more important than all the reading you can do. You didn't learn to drive by reading a book, did you? No, you had and have to practice. The same is true of the piano. . .

<u>Don't do any changing until I see you and talk to you. I may cool off until then.</u>

Sincerely yours,

Verne Henry.

P.S. And you're even giving up Creative Music. Just taking piano lessons? I thought you were interested in music.

May 14, 1963
Dearest Verne Henry,

I talked to Mr. Sayre today and he thought our schedule was good, but he thought I should have choral conducting. I showed him that this isn't necessary for a minor, so he thinks, like we do, that I should try to get it sometime, for he says it will be useful in church work.

Ryan changed Sue S's mind, too, and then Sue went to see Dr. Kurtz. She said that when she went to see Ryan to change her schedule, both he and Mr. Mitchell who shares the office "hit the ceiling." Well, I'll be firm this time.

Honey, when I was driving the tractor, I stood on my tip toes all the time. Stand that way and see what muscles pull.

May God be with you during this last week of school.

Loving you,
Phyllis   2nd Corinthians 1: 17-18

May 16, 1963
Dearest Verne,

. . . Mom and Dad will be here Sunday.
Loving you,
Phyllis

May 31, 1963
Dearest Verne,

While Mother was getting supper, I wrote to Carol Maddox. Mother says she doesn't want anything to spoil our day. We can invite Carol, but she shouldn't be in charge of the guest book because others wouldn't know her like I do. Also,

Mom says we'd probably leave from here to go home, and Dad won't have Carol here. – It's the old story of keeping peace in the family. Your family is different. They would accept Carol.

Mom thinks my girlfriend, Linda Sue, would be good to work at the guest book. But, I think that when it comes to unwrapping the gifts, we'd like to work with someone we both know. So, I'm going to ask your cousin, Gloria, and ask Linda Sue to help in the kitchen as I planned.

Carol and I did the supper dishes and straightened up and then we looked at recipes for cakes. Carol showed me a picture of a cross cake she'd seen and I like it. I'm sending you the picture and you can look at it and send it to Esther and then she can send it back to me.

I love you and wish I were with you. But I'd better stop wishing and read Amos so I can send you my ideas.

Oh yes! I have an appointment to get my hair trimmed Tuesday morning. . .

Loving you and wanting soon to be your wife,
Phyllis

June 2, 1963
Dearest Phyllis,

Well, I left your place at 2:55 Stryker time. I took the turnpike until Fremont, then took U.S. 6. I made the 202 miles in 210 minutes. There was hardly any traffic. I got home and unloaded your things and changed my clothes. I changed the oil, greased the car, and checked it over. Then I

111

backed it right up to the door and loaded all the things we had in boxes.

The next morning I packed my clothes and a few other things and left for Brethren at 9;30 a.m. I arrived at 2:15. It is 260 miles here from home. There are a lot of things I want to show you on our way here after the wedding. Start out in the morning and take all day getting here with a picnic dinner on the way. I drove all the way without a rest stop to get out of the car.

After I arrived I talked with the Brians for a while. Then he took me to the store where he introduced me to Jess Sturdevent who owns the store and several houses including the one I am staying in. I will only be staying here about two weeks until they finish painting and fixing the other house I will be living in . . .

Honey, Mother said she was asked when we want to have the shower at Poplar Ridge. I said Sunday or Monday night. Maybe you could write and tell her when.

I will close for now. I'll probably send a letter every other day. . .

With my love,
Verne Henry   Genesis 1 – story of
creation

June 4, 1963
Dearest Phyllis,

On the trip to Onekama I got the bark I am enclosing. See if you can find out what kind it is and I will check you when you write your answer.

They are off the same tree. The lighter, whiter bark is the underneath. I put a number 2 on that piece and the piece with the number 1 is the outside bark. I will send smaller pieces in another letter. If the kids want some more, I think I could get them some more.

I sent the picture of the cake to mom today. I told her to send it to you. It's O.K. with me however you make the cake. I think the cake in the picture was nice.

I am sure lonesome tonight. You just can't possibly know how it feels to be all by yourself alone in a house when someone you love is so far away. You have all your sisters, brother, mom and dad to keep you company. Here I hardly know anyone. Oh they are friendly and nice but it is different from being with your folks. I sure wish you could be here with me. . . I think this is the most lonesome I have ever felt. And here it is about 17 days until I can see you and 18 until the wedding.

About Carol Maddox. I'm disappointed that she won't be in the wedding. I was really looking forward to her. . . I just about give up. Go ahead and do what your folks want you to do. Mine will be satisfied with whatever is done.

To tell the truth, I thought we would leave for my place right from the church. I thought we would have your suitcases in the car before the wedding. . .

Please don't change any plans you have made with your folks about the wedding. I guess it is important to please them at the marriage of their first daughter. . .

Your husband to be,
Verne Henry   Philippians 4;1

June 4, 1963
Dearest Verne Henry,

Sunday night I had some thank you notes to write to people who sent gifts but weren't at the shower. I also wrote to Gloria and Larry (and sent it with their invitation), Ida Mae, my cousin Valerie, your parents, and Grandma and Grandpa Williams. I had nine envelopes to put in the mail Monday and none for you. It took a long time to do all the necessary writing. In fact, Mom wrote to Verne and Esther to describe the shower and I added a short letter to Mom's.

Sunday afternoon Mom and I figured that the cross will serve 91 people. We made a paper cross and marked out pieces on it. We did the same for the sheet cakes. A sheet cake will only serve 48 because it is only one layer high. I'll put a little flower and a leaf on each piece so the servers will know where to cut. I think I should make three sheet cakes – what do you think?

Honey, our cross can't be like the picture I sent because with the large third layer underneath, the cake would be too wide to fit in our deep freeze. (We've measured it.)

Carol Jean is going to work for Mrs. Force starting June 24. . .

114

Did I tell you or your mother that we can borrow white bells to decorate the basement for the reception?

Saturday night, June 15, at 7:30 is Alice's shower for us. This Saturday night we will go to Windham to celebrate Earl's (my cousin's) graduation from Kent State.

I'd better study Amos some more. I have gotten much from Amos by studying it that I never would have from just reading it. Yet, I probably don't help you like I should because I have little Old Testament background.

. . . I hope to hear from you tomorrow.

Loving you so much,

Phyllis

June 6 & 7, 1963

Hi Honey,

Well, Dear, my hair will probably look neater now that it has a permanent, but it looks shorter, too.

Yesterday, I made an apron and cut out and made the tops to another pair of pajamas. I'm sending you a sample of the blue pajama material and the tulip trim I used.

Mom says that Dad has to go back into town after he finishes chores and that I can go get our license then. . . Now I know why Dad and Mom are going to town in the morning. Dad bought a tractor tonight – a used Ford, I think.

Honey, I miss you so much. I wish we didn't have to be apart, but I am realizing even more how much I love you. . .

Love,
Phyllis

June 6, 1963
Dearest wife to be,

I have decided to try to write every day. I know it sure seems like something is missing when I go to the post office and receive no letter from you.

I went to Leo Parson's for some information. He is the church clerk and has the records. I got a list of the church officers. We found something strange. . . On the Board of Christian Education, I could only find 2 members. No one knew who the third member was. Leo and I looked over the records and found that Lois H is serving two terms. One expires in the fall of 1964, the other in the fall of 1965. Somebody was not observant when they made out the nominations for the elections. . .

I wish you could be with me. Please get your rest and don't work too hard.

Your future husband,
Verne Henry   Amos 4: 1-5 Sunday's Scripture, I think

June 7, 1963
Hi Honey,

How am I going to find out what kind of bark that is? When I opened your letter, Dad said that looked like old wall paper. I started to read your letter and I read about your working in the church basement. I almost thought you were sending me a piece of the basement. What a different kind of bark. I wonder if I've ever heard of that kind of tree.

Well, now we have a license to be married. Also we have a blank certificate that the minister will fill out. I was given a self-addressed card to be filled out and returned to the social security office with my new name after we're married.

Honey, I promised you I'd wear my wedding dress home after we're married and I want to. . .

Mom had been asking me if we would want to eat supper after the wedding and if so what she should have. She was going to invite your family, too.

To settle everything, I told Mom today (after I read your letter) that you would be here before the wedding so we will have time to pack my things in a car before we are married. Mom hadn't made any definite plans, and now she doesn't have to. That's one less thing to worry about while getting all the kids and Grandma ready. . .

Good night with love,
Phyllis   Ephesians 5: 21-33
especially verse 31

On June 8, 1963, each of the "three little kids" wrote letters and sent them to Verne Henry in the same envelope. Here are a few highlights.
Dear Verne,

117

Once before Phyllis went to college, she stuck her finger in the peanut butter and licked it. I said "the goops they lick their fingers" and Phyllis laughed. (She still laughs about it when I remind her.)

I get a front seat at the wedding if I want one. . . Love, Betty

Dear Verne H.

I am going to Vacation Bible School. It's lots of fun. Phyllis is scared to death of Purkey, our pet pigeon. When you are married don't get a Big Bird. I'll draw a picture for you now. On the side of Karen's letter are these words: Betty, Sharon, Karen would like to help decorate. . . Love, Karen M   P.S. I want some bark, too.

Dear Verne Henry,

Phyllis made a cake and I liked it.

Mom started to talk about love birds. Then someone said to put Perky, our pet pigeon, in the wedding cake. Phyllis said if they put Perky in the wedding cake, they would have to bury Perky up to his neck. Carol said at the wedding when you and Phyllis cut the cake, Karen, Betty and I would yell, "Don't cut the cake. Perky is in it!"

I would like to have some bark, too. Love, Sharon Mahan

Saturday night, June 8, & Sunday, June 9, 1963, Mailed Monday, June 10
Dearest Husband to Be,

Here's the surprise. Guess who met us at the door at Aunt Laverne's tonight? – Grandma Williams. She came by train. It was a complete surprise. Not even her sister Aunt Jennie knew she was coming until she called yesterday during her 17 hour layover in Washington D.C. to say she was on her way.

She plans to be here until June 24, so she'll be here for our wedding and you'll get to meet her. I'm so happy. Remember that you said Grandma would be here for our wedding.

By the way, she reminded me tonight that I'm her oldest grand<u>daughter</u>.

Grandpa didn't come. He said in his teasing way for Grandma to tell me that I didn't go to his wedding so he doesn't have to go to mine.

One reason that I didn't write more last night was that I felt irritable. That's why I cracked nuts. I missed you and little things my family did rubbed me the wrong way. I thought it best just to be quiet.

I can't describe how I felt. I just couldn't listen to anything Dad and Mom said seriously, because I thought I should use my own judgment as to what would please you and me at <u>our</u> wedding.

Last night at work Dad got me the aluminum sheets to put the cakes on.

I feel better today. One thing, though, Dear. If you have any suggestions for the wedding, tell me. I want to please <u>you</u> first of all.

I shall guess at the answer to my riddle. My guess is that the bark is <u>Grey Birch.</u>

119

Your letters take two days to get here, also. I figure that it's impossible for either of us to get a letter on Tuesday, unless I happen to get to Warren (which is unlikely) to mail one on Sunday. Mail doesn't go from Bristolville on Sunday.

Lots of Love,

Phyllis   Psalms 105: 1

June 9 & 10, 1963

Hi Honey,

. . . Oh, have you decided what kind of tree grew the bark I sent you? Also, I got a lot more of the same kind of bark from a dead tree. I got home from this hike and ride about 5:00. I wish you could have been with us. I wish you could be with me now almost more than earlier in the day. Then I was busy and someone was around. Now I am by myself with my thoughts of you.

Thanks a lot, honey, for the letters. I feel better now than when I wrote last night. So you don't know what kind of bark I sent you. Well, there is more in this letter. If you don't want it you can give it to the kids. I have some more that I got yesterday. It's a bigger piece and I'll bring it when I come June 21 to your place. Honey, you'll see lots of trees with that kind of bark on them. In case you haven't found out yet, it is off a birch tree. Have you heard of that kind of tree? Also I have 3 porcupine needles. They are really sharp. I got them off a porcupine myself. He was dead when I got them yesterday on the hike.

Just think. 12 days from now we'll be married. I should be at your place 11 days from now. . . I guess the days are passing, slowly. I wish they would hurry up a bit.

Wishing you were here,
Verne Henry

June 11, 1963
Hi Dearest wife to be in 11 days,

Only 11 more days. I was figuring. Nine days from now at this time I hope to be on my way home.

Did you get any extra napkins? I can't remember if we did or not. We should have more than 200 just in case. I believe they could be plain white napkins about the same size as those we got. However, if you think they should be decorated, it's all right with me.

Will your church have enough silverware?

Thank you for your suggestions on the sermon seed plots and your letters. And thanks for sending scraps of the material of things you are making.

Your husband to be,
Verne Henry

June 11, 1963 Tuesday morning
Dearest Verne Henry,

If this letter is short, it will be because we have company today. On the way home from work this morning, Dad stopped at Aunt Jennie's and got Grandma Williams. She will spend the day here.

Honey, do you have any suggestions for a gift for Gloria and Larry?

I'm sure I was in bed before you were last night. I went at 7:45 p.m. I wasn't sick. Between 6:30 and 7:00 last night while we were eating a late supper, we had a severe thunderstorm and our lights went out. The storm let up, but we still didn't have any electricity. That's why I didn't write anything to you last night.

The little ones had Bible School by candlelight. Dad lay on the davenport resting for work and I played the piano by memory and ear for over an hour. Then Carol and I went to bed before the others came home.

This morning I was the first one up. I woke up at 6:00 and got up and burnt the wastepaper and started getting ready for G. Williams. I did last night's supper dishes because we had electricity this morning.

Carol Jean got a pink dress yesterday for the wedding and Mom got a blue and white flowered one.

At the church shower, the church janitor's wife came up to me and said not to worry about cleaning up after the wedding because they'd take care of it. I told her we'd stay and do it. So Sunday morning at church the janitor himself insisted he would do the cleaning up.

Honey, eleven more days and we'll be married. We've been apart eleven days already. It has seemed like such a long time. I've been in church two Sundays without you. . .

Your future wife who wants you and cares for you more than you can believe,
Phyllis

June 11, 1963 7:15 p.m. and June 12, 1963
Hi Dearest,

. . . Then I went to Reuben and Mildred Coldesser's. These folks are Larry Taylor's aunt and uncle. . . Mildred said that Gloria and Larry didn't get any blankets or bedspreads at their wedding. Could you get one and wrap it and we could give it to them at our wedding. Also Mildred said we could do our washing at their place. . . Also we can use their deep freeze, so we will be able to bring meat along with us and some frozen vegetables if we want to do so.

Honey, it may sound like I am doing a lot of things and making a lot of visits. Well, I am. After we are married I'll still visit, but not for the same reasons. The reason why I'm on the go so much is so I don't get too lonesome. Don't worry, I'll spend time with you. I also want you to get in all the members' homes. Many of the folks want you to come. They ask about you a lot.

I think presently we will plan on coming back on Tuesday after the shower (on Monday night). I want to get back and on our own away from our folks as soon as possible. I like my folks, but I still want to be by ourselves as soon as possible. Don't you? I think we should be able to take care of all the business on Monday. . .

With lots of love,

Verne Henry

June 12, 1963
Dearest wife to be,

. . . Next week at this time and day I hope to be
traveling south. Eight days from now I hope to be
just about to your place. Nine days and a few
hours and you know what the event will be. I still
have about 8 more visits I want to make.

No, don't ask your dad for a lifejacket. If you
want one, we'll buy one for ourselves. . . In case
you are thinking of the canoe trip, I and probably
you, won't be going on it since it is Sunday. They
talked about having their own service.

Honey, if the janitor and his wife want to help
clean up the church that's all right. I don't think
we should leave the whole job to them, however, so
we will still plan on helping.

If we have to borrow chairs, do you think it
would be too much to ask your dad if he could take
them back? I could get them and probably even
help load them after the wedding if he would take
them back and unload them. If you think it's too
much to ask, I suppose I could take care of it
myself.

Yes dear, I believe you do want and care for me.
I just hope I can live up to your expectations for a
husband. I'll probably fall short many times but I
hope you will be able to forgive me and let me try
to do better. This marriage needs to last a lifetime,
so we want to do everything we can to be happy. . .

With deepest love,

Verne Henry

June 12, 1963
Good morning dear,

I just took our third sheet cake from the oven.
I froze the one I baked last night before I went to
bed. I can't bake any more cakes until we get more
eggs. Each recipe takes 6 egg whites. I am
freezing the egg yolks hoping to get time to make
noodles. . .

Now I must write to your mom and ask for
some paper tablecloth.

Aunt Jennie came just as we were getting ready
to go to the store. We came home from the store
and got supper. After this, I played several pieces
for Grandma and Aunt Jennie and visited more.

This is the first time for three years we've seen
Grandma Williams. Three years ago Grandma and
Grandpa were up when they celebrated their
golden wedding anniversary. Grandma says I'm
lucky that letters get to you in 2 days. She says it
takes 4 days for letters from Warren to Englewood,
Florida.

Dad said today that he thought I'd probably
never be home after I left. I told him we would.

I got this letter from Carol Ann Maddox today.
Carol says: "Now then, my bus leaves for Warren
at 9:30 a.m. Saturday the 22nd. So, it will arrive in
Warren at 11:05. Thus, dear friend Ruth Ann or
V.H. will be treated to the sight of that paragon of
virtue – you guess it – Me! Hee! Hee!"

Mom asked me what I was going to do with
her. I said, we'll have to compromise. I didn't ask
her to be in the wedding so I think my parents
should give in enough to accept her coming.

By the way Carol mentions nothing about going
home, so I presume she wants us to take her. . .

Love,
Phyllis

June 12, 1963
Hi Dear,

I can't go to bed without writing a line to you. I
went to Bible School tonight to play because the
regular organist had a school board meeting. I
don't think the organ should be used for children's
singing. but it's no longer my place to have any
say here.

Tomorrow I must call to see if we can borrow
chairs from the Grange. . .

Good morning, Dearest,

The time has come to frost cakes. . . I hope I get
a letter today. It's been two long days between
Monday and today. . .

Loving you,
Phyllis

June 13, Thursday night
Dearest husband to be,

I was happy to get the letter that you mailed
Monday today. I also received one that your
mother mailed Tuesday. She says that the church

is going to have our shower Monday evening, June 24. . .

Tomorrow is the day I plan to frost and decorate our cross cake . . .I wish you could see our three sheet cakes. I put a light pink rosette and a light green leaf where each piece will be. I enjoyed decorating. I was tired of baking cakes.

Honey, you're probably so tired of cooking that you don't care to hear what I do in the kitchen. But I haven't done much else the last couple days except bake, frost and do dishes.

I was so tired of sifting flour. I sifted 24 ½ cups of flour at least two times. 1 Some I sifted three times. . . Aren't you glad that I probably won't be in the mood to make more cake right after we're married?

Yes, I really enjoyed your letter today. Maybe I wanted it so badly because I hadn't heard since Monday.

Goodnight Honey

June 13, 1963
To my dear wife to be,

A thought wave just struck me (as Ruth Ann would say). Did you make a list of 20 pictures you would like taken at the wedding? Larry wants this before the wedding. Honey, I would suggest that no pictures be taken during the service.

I guess we won't know what we have to say in the ceremony until the time comes. Rev. Coldren hasn't sent a copy of the ceremony like we asked him to do, has he? . . . I really wish we knew more of what he is going to do.

Dear, I was just thinking. I suppose Ruth Ann and I will be staying at George and Alice's Friday night before the wedding. I was wondering if you could stay there also. That way we wouldn't be separated for so long a time.

We could go to your place any time you wanted Saturday morning. I would like to get all the decorating and things done at the church Friday. There will be a few last minute details, I suppose.

Then since your folks don't care to have Carol (Maddox) at your place, maybe Ruth Ann and I could go into Warren and get her. We could show her around town a little and then eat a lunch at a drive in. From town we could go to the church until time for the wedding and meet you there. I think my folks had planned to eat along the way. I can just about see your place with everyone getting ready for the wedding. I don't think you should go to the extra work of having everyone for lunch. That's too much for before the wedding.

Honey, thanks for at least inviting Carol. If she is her usually self I think she will be the life of the wedding reception.

I just received your letter stating you didn't get a letter Wednesday. Honey, I've sent a letter every day this week. . . Honey, as a compromise for not getter a letter this last Wednesday and not being able to get one to you on Tuesday, I will try to call (phone) you Tuesday evening, June 18. I will call after 9:00 this time, 10:00 your time. I think the rates are cheaper then. You should have this letter by then and I want to make certain of plans for Friday night and for Saturday (i.e. getting Carol, lunch, and anything else that comes up). So honey, please try to be at home. . .

Until tomorrow's letter, good bye, dear.
With lots of love,
Verne Henry

June 14, 9:06 a.m. Friday
Good morning, Dear

I wonder how I'll feel a week from now. Probably pretty happy.

The notice to the Tribune must be sent this morning, so I'll hve to close and do that before the mail goes. Mom has it partly written.

Waiting longingly for you,
Phyllis   Romans 1: 8-12

June 14, 1963
Hi Honey,

In my lap is a certificate of appreciation for helping in Bible School. I really didn't do much, but I played for the entire closing program tonight. Mrs. Holko couldn't be there to play.

After the program tonight I counted every folding chair in the church. I counted 77 (seventy seven) chairs. I also counted 80 forks.

Honey, would you please bring all our forks when your come. We could use both our salad forks and our regular forks, if necessary. Mom has 22 silver forks in her good set. If your Mom has any she wants to let us use, maybe you could bring them also. I don't think I'll write to your parents any more before the wedding. I think it was yesterday that I wrote to them last.

I need to figure out how much punch we will need so that I can order it today.

I'll write letters to mail on Monday and Tuesday and then I hope to see you soon.

I'm getting a "little" excited!

Love and longing,

Phyllis

June 15, 1963 – Saturday 9:20 a.m.

Hi Dearest,

Since the Post Office closes at noon, I had better write now. Well, tonight is another shower for you. Actually when you get this it will be past. I hope you have or had fun at the shower. I'll probably be alone this evening thinking of you.

Be sure to try to be home Tuesday evening about 10:00 your time. Actually a little after. I will not call person to person and that will cut down on the cost. So honey, please try to be close to the phone so it doesn't use up a lot of our time with your getting to the phone.

I'll probably only write two more letters. One to mail Monday and one Tuesday. I hope to see you Friday about noon or a little there after. In case you are thinking of it, don't wait dinner for us. If anything, we could eat a sack lunch on the road so we have more time for decorating, etc. (Just being together.)

If your church only has silverware for 50, as Everetts thought, what about the grange? If you can't borrow from there, let me know Tuesday night, and I'll bring some from our church. I'm pretty certain we could use it. We will probably only need forks, won't we?

Remember 10:00 or after your time Tuesday evening.

With lots of love,

Verne Henry

June 15, 1963 Saturday evening.

Dearest wife to be,

Honey, I'm lonesome tonight. I'm thinking of you at the shower and having fun. And here I am setting on the davenport alone thinking of you. I'm listening to WOWO Fort Wayne. It is coming in good tonight on the radio. Some nights I can get one station good and the next night not at all. I can't get the Manistee radio station at night. I sure wish this was Saturday the 22nd instead of the 15th. An evening by myself sure can go slowly when I think how much I would like to be with you.

Honey, you may have to get in the mood to bake another cake when you get here if we don't have any left. Leo wants to try your cake with homemade ice cream. We furnish the cake and he will furnish the ice cream.

Honey, I don't think we will need to teach in Bible School. I believe we will have enough teachers and helpers. In fact, I don't think anyone will have to help in both programs. We will be counseling in the Day Camp program, especially in the evening for youth. So get your ideas ready because we will be having a meeting on Wednesday night after we get back.

About the forks. Ours are still packed away. I'll bring the church's (Poplar Ridge's). If I can't get them, I'll buy plastic forks. But I'm pretty certain I won't have to buy any.

Good bye dear and get your beauty rest. . .

Your husband to be in 5 days (3 or 2 days depending upon when you get this.)

Verne Henry

June 17, 1963 10:05 p.m.
To my dear future husband,

Today Carol and I washed living room windows inside and out, washed the living room walls and the woodwork, cleaned the kids' shelves and did this cleaning in the living room.

I read to Mom the part of your letter where you said that it would be too much for her to fix lunch for a lot of people before the wedding. Mom said something like this: "I love that man of yours!" She doesn't have to wonder about this. You got her out of some work.

Also <u>Mom</u> wouldn't care if Carol came. But Dad doesn't like the idea. . . I'm so glad that you're willing to help take care of Carol after she gets to Warren.

Honey, I was happy to receive three letters today – sent Thursday, Friday and Saturday.

Thanks for reminding me that we can have 20 pictures. I'd forgotten the number.

I'm so happy that I'll hear your voice tomorrow night.

Good morning, Dear,

The sun is shining brightly. I hope that four days from today it shines as nicely.

Today we will clean kitchen cupboards and do other kitchen cleaning.

Drive carefully.

With love and anxious desire to see you.

Phyllis

June 17, 1963 11:15 p.m.

Dearest wife to be,

. . . I'm just thinking. This will be the last letter I have to write to you for a while. It sure seems good to think that in a few days you will be with me here in Brethren and wherever I go as my wife: as Mrs. Verne H. Leininger. I wonder how many times you will sign your name Mahan after we are married. I suppose you will a few times after signing that way for over 19 ½ years. Honey, I can hardly wait until Saturday. But yet I think I am really looking forward to Friday more when I can again be with you. . . Honey, it will be almost 3 weeks from the time I saw you last until I see you Friday. I left your place on Friday about 3:00 and hope to see you by 1:00 or before (my time).

Tuesday, June 18, 1963 1:25 p.m.

Tonight I will be at the Coldessers for supper.
Then I make the phone call. When you get this
you will have already received the call. . .
Waiting anxiously to be with you,
Verne Henry

Letter writing, phase one is finally over. We are
about to be married.

Many more letters passed between us during the
following school year while I was a student at
Defiance College and Verne was in his last year at
seminary. To share all our letters would take an
entire book.   I hope you have enjoyed the snippets of
letters that I chose to include.

The Wedding

It was a beautiful, clear summer day on June 22, 1963. Verne had arrived at my Bristolville home the night before. With musicians, Rev. Coldren, Verne's family, and the best man coming long distances, we did not have a dress rehearsal- not Friday night and not Saturday morning. The morning consisted of trips to church, about a mile from home, taking wedding essentials, cake, punch ingredients, nuts, mints, paper plates, napkins, and aprons for our two church server/helpers. Then Verne and I went to Warren, Ohio to pick up Carol Maddox, my black college roommate from the bus station.

After we picked up Carol, we stopped at a fast food place and the three of us had hotdogs to eat. My father was not pleased that Carol was coming. He said something like, "the church will fall down or people will pass out if she comes." She came. Neither of these happened.

Verne's second assigned summer pastorate was at Brethren, Michigan, a long way up in Michigan not too far from the Manistee National Forest. He wanted to get married before he went there. I said I needed time to prepare. We settled upon June 22, 1963, my parents' 22nd wedding anniversary. He settled into "temporary housing" a Sturdevant summer cottage, and began his ministry there on or before June 1, while the "Tom Thumb house" a lovely small Sears and Robuck package home across the street from the church was being prepared for us.

He had a long trip to the wedding. His route was south through Michigan to his parents' home at Stryker, Ohio and then east about four hours to Bristolville. Enroute to his home, he started having car trouble. When he made it home, Dad looked under Verne's Studebaker's hood. There was a major problem; I believe it was a cracked block, something that would mean major repair. Verne borrowed his sister, Ruth Ann's Studebaker, and came on to Bristolville. No one could find Verne's car at the wedding and so we were spared any decorations.

My records show that I spent $105 for the wedding. That amount included beautiful, interlocking invitations, a bridesmaid gift, wedding napkins with our names inscribed, aprons for my two servers, a guest and gift book, small paper plates, helpers' corsages, Verne's ring, my gown, and payments for the musicians. The two most expensive items were each $20: the material for my dress and payment to the musicians.

The wedding dress pattern I liked best had a scalloped neckline, scalloped short sleeves and the bodice came down to a point in the front. I didn't like the gathered skirt, so I designed large box pleats for the whole skirt.

My white taffeta-like material had something like a brocade design. I liked it a lot. I also sewed a pair of shorty pajamas using some I had for the pattern.

When it came to the cake, I used a recipe for Bride's cake and "made it from scratch." It was in the shaped of a large cross. Training from my 4-H cake decorating projects was useful. I loved making frosting roses and was not bad at piping the cake edges. I set a bride and groom on top the cake. I worked on the cake ahead of time and kept the cake in the freezer until the wedding.

Our neighbors, the Everetts, always had a large flower garden right across the road from us. Ralph especially loved to work in the flowers. The Everetts supplied the flowers for the wedding.

Rev. Walter Coldren, former pastor of the Bristolville Church of the Brethren, came back from Canton, Ohio to officiate. We had met with Walter at Canton, Ohio and planned the service which was written especially for us. After the "Joyful, Joyful We Adore Thee" processional, Rev. Higelmire, Bristolville's current pastor, had the opening prayer. Then the congregation sang "Breathe Upon Us, Holy Spirit."

Our ceremony did not end when Pastor Coldren pronounced us husband and wife. According to the wedding script that Walter included with our Marriage Certificate, the service ended with a commissioning service which would be again confirmed about ten months later at Verne's ordination service in April 1964. Here is how the rest of our wedding service reads:

> Phyllis and Verne on this occasion you are not only being joined together as husband and wife but also this makes you a team working in the direct service of God.
>
> As a word of advise that comes to us from Paul, may I remind you that at all times you should present yourselves to God as one approved, a workman who has no need to be ashamed, rightly handling the word of truth.
>
> Are you willing at this time to dedicate yourselves again to this high calling of Christ? The Church has seen fit to call Verne into the ministry, and you have seen fit to invite Phyllis to be your helpmate and partner. Therefore I now ask the two of you these questions.
>
> Do you willingly accept the office to which you are called and promise to be faithful in all of the duties?
> WE DO
> Do you promise to live a life worthy of this entrustment, a life that radiates and exemplifies Christ in all you do?

WE DO

Do you promise to be creative, redemptive, brotherly, and cooperative with all others in the performance of your ministry?

WE DO

Do you purpose to train yourself by prayer, meditation, Bible reading, study, and heart searching to be fit at all times for the responsibilities that shall be yours?

WE DO

When the questions were finished, we knelt and Walter had a spoken prayer. At this point we had planned that the congregation would all pray "The Lord's Prayer." I don't know whether our wishes were not clear, or whether the pastor just forgot, but when it was time for this prayer, Pastor Walter said, "We will now sing "The Lord's Prayer." This was a surprise to us and a bigger surprise for our musicians, Lois and Denny Hornish, from Verne's home church. But they were great. Lois played and Denny led in the singing and indeed, the congregation sang The Lord's Prayer.

The benediction, the kiss and the introductions as Mr. and Mrs.____(I don't know what Walter called us as there is a blank line in our script) concluded the ceremony and we recessed with "Blest Be the Tie that Binds" being sung as a solo.

My Maid of Honor was my sister Carol. Verne's best man was his cousin, Roger Wyse. Church ladies served the cake and punch. Nothing else too unusual happened, except that relatives from Indiana, Aunt Ethelyn and Uncle George Titler and cousins Larry and Gloria Taylor, newlyweds who had just been married on June 1, all were an hour late and missed our wedding. Our 2:30 p.m. wedding time was 1:30 for them with Indiana on "slow" time and Ohio on daylight savings time.

After opening gifts, cleaning up the church, and loading cars, Verne and I set out for Cleveland, Ohio to take Carol Maddox home. This was 1963 and relations between blacks and whites in this country were quite volatile. I didn't realize how concerned Carol was about our safety or how glad she was to arrive home without us experiencing problems or confrontations.

Without our detour, Verne's parents and sister were home waiting for us when we arrived for a very late supper. Our "honeymoon" would begin at Verne's parents. First, there was church in the morning and then a shower for us at Poplar Ridge on Sunday evening. Monday and Tuesday were busy days of tearing down and rebuilding Verne's car engine. It seems like it was Wednesday before our delayed trip to Brethren, Michigan began.

Verne's dad told us to travel slowly as the engine wasn't broken in yet. We started out and hadn't gone very far when we saw Verne's Dad coming up fast behind us. I had forgotten my coat.

Finally, hopefully with everything we would need, it was just us and God as we set out to face the summer together.

The Summer at Brethren, Michigan

What warm hospitality awaited us when we arrived at the Tom Thumb house where we were to spend the summer! There was food in the cupboards and in the refrigerator. The bed was all made upstairs. Getting the bed upstairs took some strong effort. Let me explain.

The Tom Thumb house had two rooms downstairs: a comfortable kitchen with a back door and then stairs down to the basement, and a living room with a fireplace on the center of the outside wall. To the left as we entered the living room from the kitchen we came to a tightly winding staircase to the upstairs. No bed or mattress could be carried up this snug space.

Another look at the kitchen revealed a large panel in the ceiling which apparently was removed to take furniture upstairs. Going back to the living room we found that a desk and book case area had been arranged along the wall opposite the staircase and the front door was accessible to this "office." Other comfortable furniture completed the décor of the room.

Besides our bedroom on the upper level, there was another room where I often did my ironing. All my dresses and all Verne's shirts needed ironed. Ironing that summer seemed like a never ending job to this newlywed. There may have been a bed in that room, too.

We had been there a few days and Verne was back into the swing of ministry. One night, when there was no meeting he knew of scheduled at church, we saw people arriving there. The Brethren Church of the Brethren was just across the intersection from us. Verne figured out what was happening. People were waiting for us to go to bed so that they could come and wake us up with a "Belling." So Verne said, "We'll turn out all the lights, but we won't get ready for bed."

After our house was dark for a short time, we heard the noise makers coming. What a loud racket as people beat on pans, hollered, or made noise however they could. We turned on the lights and surprised them – we were fully dressed and wide awake! Tradition tells us that we should feed those who "belled" us. But these reveling guests brought an abundance of desserts with them and we enjoyed a late night party!

I remember a couple other special events of that summer. In addition to two weeks of Bible School, we had a week of day camp at one of the member's rustic and environmentally friendly large homestead. I can't remember the theme of that Day Camp or the scriptures we studied, but I remember the feelings that I, and I hope the campers, received from being close to God as we were surrounded by many awesome God-given gifts in nature that we explored and experienced.

As I recall another special event of the summer, I think that Verne must have planned this especially with me in mind. Verne took me, and I believe some church friends also went, to see and hear the famous pianist Van Cliburn in a recital at Interlochen Music Camp. What a treat!

This was 1963. Five years earlier, at the height of the Cold War in 1958, Van Cliburn—a 23-year-old Texan—won the first International Tchaikovsky Competition in Moscow, a contest meant to show Soviet cultural superiority. The judges had to get permission from Soviet leader Nikita Khrushchev before they could give first prize to an American. They convinced Khrushchev that Van Cliburn was the best. This winning American pianist who came home to a parade and instant fame is the pianist we enjoyed in Northwestern Michigan at Interlochen.

When I could or should have been packing to head south to Ohio, some church ladies invited me to go berry picking with them. I left Verne packing his books and went to pick berries, what kind I do not remember. I know they were wild and had thorns. I guess I was still a little independent, but it was good to feel included by the Brethren women.

It was time to say our goodbyes to all our wonderful friends at Brethren. Verne was looking forward to his last year of seminary and I would be returning to Defiance college as a Junior with a new last name. Verne would leave each Monday afternoon and return Friday nights. I would be staying with Verne's parents and commuting to Defiance.

Back to school

Since I had succeeded in getting my driver's license the previous fall, Verne's father blessed me with my own Studebaker so that I could commute to Defiance for classes during my Junior year. Verne and I had decided that we could save a lot on room and board by accepting his parents' generous offer to live with them during that time.

Bethany Biblical Seminary moved from Van Buren Street in Chicago to the beautiful new spacious site at Oak Brook, Illinois between Verne's second and third years. This, his third and last year, was at the Oak Brook site. Besides moving to a new location, the seminary's name was changed from Bethany Biblical Seminary to Bethany Theological Seminary. Again he traveled there on Monday afternoons and returned home to an excitedly awaiting wife (and parents) each Friday night.

I remember Friday, November 22, 1963. I was driving from Defiance on Route 66 toward home. Verne's mother, Esther, was with me. We had been shopping. Thanksgiving was coming the following Thursday, November 28. The radio was playing when suddenly we heard that our President, John F. Kennedy had been shot. That was shocking news to both of us. Ongoing reporting blurred my memories of our Thanksgiving celebration for that year. I can't remember whether Verne and I celebrated with his family or went to my home.

We enjoyed time with my family over Christmas and then celebrated with Verne's parents and Ruth Ann. On New Year's Eve we went to the traditional Poplar Ridge celebration in the school gym. Kids played basketball and other active games.. Adults played games or mostly talked. Gift exchanges were limited to 10 cent gifts. That was do-able back then. The New Year was brought in with worship.

Verne was so busy completing all his papers, sermons and radio programs to complete his seminary degree that in one letter to me he wrote that he wished classes and his work at the Radio Station would be suspended for a week so that he might get caught up. Meanwhile he was teaching the young adult Sunday School Class at Poplar Ridge.

I continued to teach my piano students. At least one family came to the house for lessons. Usually I traveled to the students' homes at Defiance. During this, my Junior year, I played percussion with the band. With Verne's encouragement, I had changed from an English major to a Music major with an English minor. Of course that meant that I had to learn to play every band and every string instrument. I was having the most trouble with the flute. I wasn't getting a sound. You don't blow into it like most reed instruments or buzz your lips as for brass

instruments. The seemingly simple little flute was
challenging me.

Verne's dad came to my rescue. He brought a glass
pop bottle into the living room and told me to blow
across it. As soon as I learned to "play the pop bottle"
I had mastered the technique for the flute. Dad loved
to tell people how he taught Phyllis to play the flute.

Verne had been licensed to the ministry on October
27, 1957, shortly after he began his college education
at Manchester College in Indiana. Now, nearly seven
years later, he was about to graduate from seminary in
May and accept the call to his first church. It was time
for him to be ordained. District leadership as well as
local Poplar Ridge leaders officiated at his Ordination
Service at Poplar Ridge on April 26, 1964. As his wife
and helpmate, I was included in the service.

As I count the individual pictures in his May, 1964
graduating class composite photo, I count 29
graduates with the Bachelor of Divinity Degrees which
Verne received, three with MRE (Minister of Religious
Education?) degrees and one with a MT (Minister of
Theology?) degree. I traveled with Verne's family to
the beautiful new Oak Brook campus for the
graduation ceremony. For graduation, I gave him a
black case with 4 individual communion cups, a juice
bottle, and a small container for communion bread
with a little serving tray on top of the bread container.
I also gave him a pen-shaped instrument for holding

anointing oil. Now all he needed was a church to serve.

Another task on his "have to do before graduation" list" was filling out his profile. This would be circulated to Church of the Brethren District Executives in districts where Verne would consider serving as pastor. Sometime around graduation time, Verne received a call from the County Line Church of the Brethren at Lafayette, (later Route 7, Lima) Ohio requesting an interview. The church was 65 miles from his home.   We went to the interview. Verne was called to serve at this first and only church where he interviewed. He would start on September 1st.

The County Line Church was one room upstairs and one room downstairs with the men's "restroom" across the road and the women's "restroom" behind the church. However, the church did have a lovely parsonage with an attached garage at one end and a study with an outside door on the opposite end. The large living room and as I remember also the bedrooms had hardwood floors.

The retiring pastor at County Line invited us to see the parsonage. He and his wife would not need most of their furniture in retirement. They sold us their bed, their white painted chest and dresser and their oak kitchen table and four chairs at $5.00 per group. We paid $20 total.

Note: Years later Verne stripped the white paint off the chest of drawers and several layers of paint, including a green layer from off the oak table and chairs and refinished these pieces. We used this table and these chairs in the kitchen at the Wawaka parsonage during our nearly thirteen years there. Shortly after Verne retired from Wawaka, the table and chairs moved to grandson Sean Dickason's family. When that family got new ones, our beginning dining table and chairs became the property of Dylan Leininger. The refinished chest of drawers resides at our son, John's, house.

.

Verne was finished with school. I was not. During the summer after his graduation I took summer school organ lessons, practicing at Poplar Ridge. I still had to complete my last year of college. For fall semester of my Senior year, Verne would be living in the County Line Parsonage and I would be living with his parents and coming home on weekends.

Reversed Commute

Our goals were in site. I was scheduled to graduate in May of 1965, nearly two years after our June 22, 1963 wedding. I was practicing the piano at College and at home, looking forward to my Senior Piano Recital in March. When we moved into the parsonage just before my school and Verne's employment began, one of the things we brought with us was a very large and heavy upright piano, a gift from the Kurtz family whose children I had taught and who had recently purchased a new piano. I would get to know my gifted piano inside and out.

After only a short time at County Line, we realized that Verne's serving County Line fulfilled a prophesy made when he was a baby. The story was often told that when Verne was born (in a snow storm that kept the doctor from getting to the delivery) on April 1, 1939, his family lived with his grandparents on a farm at Jasper, Michigan. One day, their pastor, a Rev. Guthrie, came to visit and carried the infant Verne out to the orchard. There Rev. Guthrie is reported as saying, "This baby will grow up to be the pastor of my home church." I never heard anyone say what or where Rev. Guthrie's home church was.

How surprised we were to learn that there were a number of Guthrie members at County Line- Will

Guthrie, Rose Guthrie, Faye Guthrie. These were older folks, single and living alone at the time we arrived. They were all related to the pastor who, years earlier, had proclaimed that Verne would be the pastor of his home church. County Line was his home congregation!

Verne was working hard at County Line, too hard. Sometimes his stomach would be in knots. Alma Long visited him privately one day and said that God sent her to tell Verne that he didn't need to prove himself. He needed to relax and let God lead him. Verne had struggled so, especially with Old Testament at Seminary, where he had to know which prophets lived at the time of each king. He was still trying to prove himself. He often shared in sermons how his stomach aches left when he let God have control of his ministry.

Back to my piano. We called a recommended piano tuner. My piano needed some "major surgery" inside. The technician would get me what I needed and I would perform the "operations." Several strong men of the congregation helped Verne lay the piano on its back. I was anxious to start on the repairs. Having a good sounding piano was a high priority for me.

First I put pin tight on the sound board where each of the strings attached. The pin tight needed several days to soak into the wood to hydrate the dried out sound board enough to hold the strings securely so they would stay in tune. I replaced broken hammers. I replaced the dried out and broken leathers and all the different sizes of dampers. When the men set the piano upright and the tuner did his job, I had a beautiful sounding piano with a full, rich tone due to the large size of its sound board.

Now I was the commuter. I came home to County Line after my classes ended on Friday. I returned to Defiance on Mondays for classes and stayed with Verne's parents during the week. This was the routine for the first semester of my senior year.

County Line had "Revival Services" for several days in October. I knew that Verne had company and I was anxious to get home. I pulled into the drive, took a load of my things into the house and went back for another load. Somehow I managed to lock myself out of the house. So there was nothing to do but sit in the car and wait for the evangelist and Verne to return from wherever they were visiting. I waited and waited. The church was at an intersection and blocked my view of the house on the other side of the County Line Road. When Verne and our guest returned, I learned that they had ended their afternoon visits right across the road. I could easily have walked there.

The last family of instruments I had to succeed in learning to play was the brass family. Verne knew that I wanted to start a family, but he said we needed to wait until I could play all the brass instruments. So I lugged a sousaphone home over Christmas vacation. I wasn't the only one "playing" it. Verne tried it out, too, and managed to do quite well getting a reasonable sound. I passed brass! Now I just needed to complete four more credit hours and a senior recital.

Dr. Sayre, my piano instructor for three years at Defiance, was on Sabbatical my Senior year. My new piano instructor, a Mrs. Ryan, and I spent the fall of my Senior year preparing to play together Mozart's Sonata IV for four hands at my Senior Recital. Verne's sister, Ruth Ann, herself a senior at Manchester, helped me prepare for my recital by making me a long black skirt.

At the end of the first semester of my Senior year, I needed just four credit hours to graduate. I could get the needed credits at nearby Bluffton College and transfer them back to Defiance to graduate. I took one music class plus viola and piano lessons at Bluffton. There I did final preparations on the rest of my recital, polishing the Sonata in E-Flat, Opus 31, No. 3 by Beethoven, Nocturne in F#

Major Opus 15, No. 2 by Chopin, Valse in E
Minor also by Chopin and Ostinato from
Microkosmos by Bela Bartok.

The recital was over. Spring break was here.
Time for a vacation. We left in a snowstorm for
destination, Englewood, Florida. We went to visit
my grandparents, Papa John and Grandma Edna
Williams as well as aunts, uncles and cousins,
some of whom I had never seen. I had never been
to Florida before. We sat down to eat with
Grandpa and Grandma. I don't remember the main
course, but I remember that Grandma had made
some kumquat jelly. They also had tomatoes.
Grandpa, who was often joking around, kept trying
to get Verne to try some kumquat jelly on his
tomato. Finally Verne said, "Well, I'll do it if you
will." So they both had kumquat jelly on
tomatoes. Grandpa asked Verne, "How did you
like it." Verne admitted he didn't. Grandpa said,
"I didn't like it either, I was just trying to get you
to do it."

Early one morning before the tide came in, we
went to the beach to pick up sea shells. I lost my
cookies, probably from lots of bending over. That
is the only time in my three pregnancies that I

remember being sick, and that was brief. Yes, I was pregnant and due in September.

Our foster child, Lee, joined our family a few weeks later on April 27. We were told that Lee was too energetic for the children's home. He soon became one of our family. He went most places we did. Once he said, "I thought I wanted to be a minister, but there are too many funerals." I remember that we got three things especially for Lee to use: ABC blocks, a used red wagon, and a puppy. I can still see Lee snuggled up with his puppy on the landing right outside our front door.

Finally, my commuting days were over. I graduated from Defiance College on May 23, 1965. Getting married had not stopped me or slowed me down. We celebrated at Verne and Esther's home. My parents came and I think that Elizabeth Everett, their neighbor came, too. Finally I would live "fulltime" at County Line together with my dear husband and pastor, Verne Henry.

Life at County Line

The summer after graduation brought a plenteous garden with vegetables to share. Lee learned where sweet corn came from. I directed the Bible School and Verne spent a week as a counselor at Camp Zion. When Verne went to District Conference at the end of August, we were concerned that our baby might come early, so I stayed with church members in Bluffton, the town where our hospital was, just in case. I wonder where Lee was.

In the process of getting the necessary documents to enroll Lee in first grade, we learned that his name was really Allen Lee Cook. (I don't remember how Allen was spelled.) Lee immediately learned to line up the ABC blocks to spell his whole name.

I was somewhat uncomfortable sitting on the hard pews at the church on Friday evening, September 17, 1965. We were at a long special council meeting. Our dear deacon, Will Guthrie, was adamant that the church was dedicated as it currently was and it shouldn't be changed. No addition should be attached to it. Even though to get to the bathrooms during a service, persons would have to walk up front to the exit door near the pulpit, the worship center and pulpit could not be moved – the front and back of the sanctuary could not be switched around. The congregation respected and listened to the old deacon. The council voted to build an educational unit with bathrooms not attached to the church, accessible from within through the door near the pulpit.

I just got Lee ready for bed and my water broke. So we called our planned sitter for this occasion and Verne and Lee were on their way. Verne Henry came back at about 11 p.m. and we headed to Bluffton Hospital. Less than four hours after the council meeting ended, our son, Verne Edward, entered the world at 12:43 a.m. on Saturday, September 18, a beautiful eight and a half pound, healthy baby boy! Verne and I were exuberant! We later learned that Lee went to school and excitedly announced that he had a brother.

Around Halloween Lee's social worker called us with these instructions: "Stop sending Lee to school and do not tell him why he can't go. We have adopted one of his siblings, a sister, into a family in your school district. We do not want Lee to see her." Ohio rules for foster children at that time seemed strange. As foster parents, the law at that time was that we could not consider adopting a child we had fostered. That weekend the social worker arrived and took Lee to meet perspective parents.

At the end of the weekend, the social worker returned with Lee. The perspective parents did not want him. That was so hard for me to imagine. Our blond haired, intelligent, loveable boy was returned. When we saw the arsenal of toy guns – rifles, pistols, and who-knows- what weapons, that his possible parents had given Lee, we talked with Lee. We told him that we were glad he wasn't going to live there because we don't believe in shooting and killing people or even pretending to do that. Then, Verne pulled down the steps from the ceiling in the hall, and took the guns up to the attic and put them clear back over his study.

According to my Christmas letter for 1965, Lee left us for good on November 9. He went to adopting parents who did not send him back. I continue to often wonder where Lee went and what he became.

As for the arsenal of weapons, we forgot about them. We never got rid of them or moved them. Other pastoral leadership lived in that parsonage through the years. Maybe 40 or so years later, we saw a couple of County Line members at Annual Conference and we remembered the toy guns we left in the parsonage attic. We asked Bud and Cleola if anyone ever mentioned finding the hidden toy guns, but they didn't know anything about them. Whether the toy weapons were ever discovered, is still my unsolved mystery.

I remember my father sitting on the worn linoleum kitchen floor playing with a small train set and a quiet four-year old boy. It was Christmas, 1965 at the house on Thompson-Clark Road, Bristolville, Ohio, before Dad built new homes on State Route 45. The little boy was our latest foster child, Ray, who came to us on December 20. We were glad to care for him, but I don't think we had him long.

We had kept a baby boy for two weeks in July, so I could get some experience with babies. As if all my younger siblings didn't give me any experience. The last foster child we kept was twelve year old Jeff. We didn't feel we bonded well with him. He came in the front door from school and we would ask, "How was school today?" He walked straight past us to his room and to his bunk bed. He was so withdrawn that it was only by chance – or God's prompting – that we discovered Jeff had an ingrown toenail that needed medical attention. I remember that even at 12 years old, Jeff thought he needed to wear a bib when he ate – like he had to do at the children's home. We shared with the social worker that we thought Jeff needed more experienced Foster parents.

Once during late winter or early spring of 1966 when Verne and I were playing ping-pong in the parsonage basement, Verne stretched to return a ball. Something in Verne gave way, and when the game ended, Verne had his first hernia. He always liked to say I gave him a hernia. He was scheduled for surgery at Bluffton Hospital the Monday morning following the April 10, 1966 Easter Sunday.

Verne's mother came and stayed with Verne Edward at the parsonage. I was still nursing him and had nursed him before we left. After his surgery, I had to hold the IV line in Verne's arm. I could not remember ever being so hungry. Verne was kept intentionally in the hospital until after church on Sunday, April 17, to keep him from going to church or over-doing. I remember that nurses took good care of him, once bringing him a meatloaf sandwich for a bedtime snack. Meanwhile, I scheduled a doctor's appointment for me. There was a reason I was hungry after surgery. Not only was I a nursing mother, I was pregnant.

Perhaps it sounds like Bluffton Hospital was a little primitive since I had to hold Verne's IV in place. However, the hernia repair done in 1966 without mesh inserted, lasted him for 50 years. Verne had four hernia surgeries over his lifetime. The fourth and last one was a repair of his first hernia. The surgeon for the fourth hernia was intrigued by how the original repair was made with no mesh and how it lasted for so long.

Verne was busy with the district camping program and the Bluffton Ministerial Association as well as his normal ministry tasks. He also served as voluntary chaplain at Bluffton hospital for a week at a time about once every six weeks. On October 18, Verne needed to go to Bluffton to see a Pastor Carter about Ministerial Association business. I was having a few cramps and didn't eat much supper. Verne thought that after we visited Pastor Carter, he would take me to the hospital. Verne Edward was at Grandpa and Grandma Leininger's house. Verne packed his bag and said he planned to go to tell Verne Edward whether he had a brother or sister. I insisted that he wouldn't know that tonight.

We went to Bluffton. But Pastor Carter was not home. There was no place else to go but to the hospital. We sat in the car in the parking lot and argued. I said I hadn't had enough pain to go in. Verne said I should go in. It's a good thing that Verne prevailed. We were hardly in the hospital until 8 pound, 1 ounce John Henry burst forth with the water at 8:45 p.m. I told Dr. Shelly that I had not had enough pain for him to be born yet. Dr. Shelly said, "Well, here he is!" Verne Henry did go to share the wonderful news with Verne Edward and his parents. He had two boys!

When Grandpa Leininger came to see John, John was lying with the baby bed mattress tipped as instructed to help him breathe more easily. Grandpa turned around, drove the 65 miles back home and returned with some Ready Relief which he put on a tissue near John. That helped to clear John's breathing which I think was somewhat affected by the gush of water that brought him forth.

Sometime during the summer, I had signed a contract with Ada Exempted Village School System to teach music to grades 1-3 for four afternoons a week, beginning on Monday, October 31. Thirteen days after John was born, I taught my first class. I nursed John before I went and when I got home. I remember seeing the wind moving a piece of farm equipment as I left school that first day in swirling snow. Going slowly I drove past Monroe Central Road and was lost on the way home. I don't remember how I got help to find my way. Verne liked to tease me about being lost so close to home.

On Tuesday, November 1st, that was supposed to be my second day of teaching, school was cancelled because of all the snow. But at least I was now on the payroll. The following school year – 1967-1968 – I added grade four and taught music all five afternoons each week. We had a baby sitter for afternoons. Although I enjoyed teaching music at Ada, I wanted to be home with my boys. I was getting known as a pianist and soon had at least 33 piano pupils. Some came in families. I taught four girls from one family. There was usually someone entertaining the boys while I taught. One of the young men I taught during this time later became a piano professor.

To help free up money for building at County Line and to fill a vacancy at Eagle Creek, Verne made the big decision in 1967 to accept the call to serve as pastor of Eagle Creek Church of the Brethren as well as the County Line Church. Now he preached two sermons each Sunday morning, had two of each kind of committee meetings, two youth fellowships, more people to visit, two Vacation Bible Schools annually, each two weeks long, and two weeklong series of evangelistic meetings. The boys and I rarely went to Eagle Creek on Sunday morning. I wanted Verne Edward and John to be in a Sunday School consistently.

We did go to special Eagle Creek events, dinners and sometimes visiting with Verne. Once Pastor Verne took the boys and me to visit an elderly Eagle Creek lady. I don't know whether John sat in her beautiful oak child's rocker, or whether she was just attracted to John. Anyway, she insisted that John should have her child-size rocker. (Thankfully, Verne Edward had my Great Aunt Jennie's cane-seated child's rocker.)

Since I had recently purchased a new Everett Studio Upright piano at a piano teacher's discount and was paying for it with piano teaching income, somehow our big heavy piano that I had worked hard to restore found its way to the Eagle Creek parsonage. I added more piano pupils, teaching at the Eagle Creek parsonage one night a week. Verne and John remember playing upstairs in the mostly empty rooms while I taught.

Verne had a workshop in one area of the County Line parsonage basement. He especially enjoyed building toys for his boys. The big red barn Verne built for them was big enough for both boys to be in at the same time. They often stored their growing collection of farm equipment toys in the barn. The date painted on the barn is 1967.

As anyone who has read this far knows, I grew up looking forward to church camp each summer at Camp Zion. As Northern Ohio Camp Board Chair, Verne led a number of discussions at the 1967 District Conference concerning the future of Camp Zion. He also shared possibilities for a new camp, which came to be called Inspiration Hills. Delegates voted with colored stickers for their least favorite option. Voting happened several times as least favorite options were eliminated. Finally it came down for voting on whether or not to sell Camp Zion. I was the only one who spoke against selling my beloved Camp Zion. Verne knew how I felt and was not upset with me. The timing of the sale must have been a "God thing." Camp Zion was in the Boliver Dam flood plain. The summer after Camp Zion closed, the area received record rainfall. The flood gates were opened and Camp Zion was under water.

The summer of 1968 is memorable for me. The last camps were held at Camp Zion that summer, but I didn't counsel there. The district offered a Primitive Camp at the site of the new camp. Verne and I, along with 3 other sets of counselors, each had ten campers in our units, five boys and five girls. When we and our campers arrived on Sunday, July 14, the grass and weeds were at least waist high. We needed to get our two tents set up and then get a fire pit dug and check out our cooler for something to fix for our evening meal. Our family unit set up our tents with pine trees behind them and fastened the two wide awnings together so that we would have a somewhat dry place to meet under in case of rain.

Wash stations were wood frames, with black plastic fastened around them and attached shelves inside around the perimeter to hold wash basins. We met the health Department requirements for large round tiles to hold stone, sunk into the ground for dumping the wash water. Portable toilets were brought to the site. An electric pole near the road provided our only electricity and serviced a milk cooler. We also had a well and five gallon water jugs, cooking utensils and dishpans. Campers brought their own dishes.

We had a camp director who kept busy purchasing our food each day and dividing it among the units. We took the entire camp to Wooster to swim in the pool. Showers were required to get into the pool. That was helpful. Camp was sometimes dirty work: getting firewood cut, building fires, carrying water, cooking meals. Units had Bible studies and units took turns planning worships for the total group. I remember our group of boys hunched over the Bible when they discovered the Song of Solomon. On Wednesday the District Executive and a couple parents visited us to take home anyone who wanted to go. None of the campers wanted to leave.

Camp Inspiration Hills was ready enough to have its first camp during summer 1969. I was at home and the phone started ringing. The question I was asked was, "Will Camp open this weekend?" I thought, "Why not?" Then I began hearing about the flood there. Verne and some board members were at Camp to help facilitate the opening. But that weekend, the area received eleven inches of rain in 24 hours. The Camp phones were down so persons could not call Camp. Verne and a friend finally made it through to Wooster to check on our Brethren Home there. Westview Manor did not have electricity and needed water to give residents medicines. Verne and crew in the camp truck took the home's frozen food to camp and returned with jugs of water. Camp had electricity. Enroute they had to clear tree limbs to get through and find a safe route when the water was too high to go through. One camper did make it to Inspiration Hills, but brought no boots, so he couldn't stay.

Books were very important at our house. I read to all my children soon after bringing them home from the hospital. By six months of age, they were showing appreciation and paying close attention to books. We signed up for a Dr. Seuss book club for them. On alternate months one of the boys could have their name in the book. Around this time, Verne Henry's sister, Ruth Ann, traveled to England. She brought back a beginning reader from Great Brittan. Verne Edward says this is the first book he remembers reading on his own.

In 1969, Verne Edward and John as well as many church folks enjoyed watching the bulldozers and cement mixers and the men working on the new educational unit. One day when the building had taken shape, Brother Will Guthrie came to take a look. Surprising all who heard, Will said, "Wouldn't it be nice if the new building could be attached to the church." That's all it took. Immediately workers quickly figured out how to make a covered, attached walkway from the educational building to the church. But the church worship center remained unchanged. The boys' building blocks were sanded pieces of two by four scraps from the building.

The moon landing on July 20, 1969 was an event that I wanted our children to see. Although John was a bit too young to remember, Verne Edward, who was two months shy of four years old, recalls that I made them watch it on our black and white television. I wonder if watching the moon landing led to this statement in our Christmas letter of 1969: "And both boys "go to the moon" in their space ship (their climbing bars) every time they play outdoors."

That fall Verne Edward turned four and John turned three. I wanted my sons to have the interaction and experiences provided by a nursery school. I teamed up with Joyce Risser from the County Line congregation, and we started one in the parsonage basement for three, four, and five-year-olds two mornings a week. We did all the regular nursery school activities: painting, stories, games, ABC's, songs, time outside, snacks, days of the week, and many other creative activities. .Verne spent Fridays, his day off, building a book rack, coat rack, cupboard-sink combination, rocking boat, and more – items for the nursery school.

Norm and Sandy Hostetler and their family lived around the corner from us and were members of another church. We enjoyed getting together with these wonderful non-County Line friends. Verne and John loved being with the Hostetler children, Bruce and Ginger. They used a field tile at the back property line as their mail box leaving in the tile whatever they wanted their friends to find. They loved playing in the big tree in the neighbor's yard. They may have been in the tree when their father was helping Norm Hostetler try to clear a fence row. There was a huge amount of concrete holding the corner post. The plan was to use dynamite to move the concrete. The dynamite moved the concrete – which made a memorable hole through the side of the barn – a hole that Verne Edward and John still talk about fifty years later.

Things seemed to be going smoothly with the yoked parish. At least that is what was reported early in 1971 at the joint meeting of ministerial committees from Eagle Creek and County Line. And then, without warning, at the spring church congregational business meeting at Eagle Creek, a board member moved that the relationship with County Line be ended. The question was asked, "Have you talked to the District Executive?" The Board member answered, "yes." What the board member didn't say was that he had not talked to the District Executive about this proposal. This member was either very persuasive or had been working behind the scenes. The proposal was passed. The shared pastor relationship would be severed. Eagle Creek would look for a pastor who would be theirs and live in their parsonage.

County Line members were not pleased with the decision. They told Verne Henry that they would love to keep him as their pastor, but with the current building debt, they couldn't afford to pay him as a full-time pastor. They shared that they felt he should continue in full-time ministry and gave him their blessing to look for a full-time position. County Line would find a part-time minister for the time being.

That summer the Church of the Brethren Annual Conference was at St. Petersburg, Florida. I was the delegate from County Line and I fulfilled this calling. Our friends from the district whom we had worked closely with at Camp, Bruce and Lorraine Bennett, were also going. I remember counseling with them one summer when Lorraine announced she was expecting a baby right after camp ended. She was not pregnant; they were adopting a baby boy. Now at St Petersburg, the Bennetts and we had three little boys. Since Bruce and I were delegates, we had to attend all the business meetings. Lorraine and Verne took the boys to attractions that interested the children. We all attended the evening worships.

At 6 p.m. on Friday, July 23, Verne's regular day off, we enjoyed time learning about our new congregation and having a meal with the outgoing pastor and his wife, Warren and Dottie Shoemaker. Verne had earlier accepted the call to serve this congregation, the Prices Creek Church of the Brethren in the Southern Ohio District.

On Sunday, August 15, the County Line Church celebrated Verne's time with them hosting a carry-in meal and farewell party. On August 23 and 24, a moving company loaded our possessions and delivered them to our new location at 8548 Monroe Central Road, West Manchester, Ohio.

Life at Prices Creek

I had plenty of reasons to rejoice when Verne was called to serve the Prices Creek congregation. Timing was great! Verne Edward was ready to begin kindergarten. I was offered a Middle School music job at the school a half mile from our home. Prices Creek was a country church which made both Verne and me feel at home and very welcome. The parsonage was a modern ranch style home, set back from the road with room for children to play in the front and the back.

Perhaps it was the day I had an interview at Monroe Central School. We were driving around getting a little acquainted with the area and stopped at a public park at Eldorado. The boys could run and play and we had a picnic lunch with us. (For years we never ate out except at church carry-ins or suppers.) Anyway, when they sat down – whether on a toy or a bench I don't remember- the backs of their nice shorts were covered with creosote which had recently been applied. It was still a good day. Later we learned that word had spread that we were in the area. We were not checking the place out as incognito as we thought.

As I mentioned in the previous chapter, the pastor and wife who were leaving Prices Creek, Warren and Dottie Shoemaker, invited our family to a meal. Warren had pin-pointed on a map where each of the church members lived, so that Verne would be able to find them. Of course, there was no such thing as Google map. Pastor Warren and Dottie were a prelude to the warm welcome we were about to receive.

Verne "hit the ground running" as they say. When I look at his schedule for that year's Christmas time, Verne already had a membership class meeting in the study, a youth group practicing a play for December 19, a Junior High Christmas Party, a Youth Party on the same December 22nd date as Ministry Commission, Christmas Caroling at 6:15 on December 23rd, a trip to my folks at Bristolville, Ohio to celebrate Christmas leaving after church on December 26, membership class again on December 28, Church Board on December 29 to choose their Annual Conference delegate, and a New Year's Eve party at 7:00 p.m. on December 31.

Teaching 7th and 8th grade music classes was challenging. Music and physical education classes separated girls and boys. The music room was next to the gym. When girls had gym, boys had music and when boys had gym, girls had music. So on Mondays, Wednesdays and Fridays, I could have classes of 7th grade girls and classes of 8th grade girls. On Tuesdays and Thursdays I had the classes of 7th grade boys and 8th grade boys who made it very clear that they would rather be in physical education. There was a closet off the music room where I put my coat. One day some boys hid it. I didn't know that until I looked for it to go home. I don't remember where I found it.

I tried to make music interesting for these disagreeable boys. I'm not sure I got them to love music. But I did have one joy to look forward to each day – the Junior High Choir. Looking at the list of choir members on a 1971 program, I was surprised to find 10 baritones listed along with 14 sopranos and 6 altos.

During the Christmas season during one of my two years teaching the Junior Highs, the choir was singing at the Christmas Concert and the band was also performing. The band director shared that he was going to wear a green velvet jacket for the performance and that I might want to wear something "Christmasy," too. I went shopping and purchased a red velvet dress with sequins. This is the only dress shopping trip that I ever remember doing on my own – the only dress that I purchased by myself! I remember Verne buying me clothes without me being present and I remember us usually shopping together. I wonder where Verne was when I went shopping. I think he liked the dress.

Prices Creek had an amazing number of musicians, pianists, organists and singers. A great variety of music, solos and duets, vocal and instrumental, followed the responsive reading, presentations, and act of dedication for the new piano and new pews and pulpit on January 30, 1972. I played in one piano and organ duet with Joellen Waltz at the organ and I played a piano solo before the closing hymn.

If Verne was going to get sick, it would be during advent or lent. The normally busy schedule was especially hectic during those times. His calendar for this year (1972) shows that he preached a series of evangelistic meetings at his home church, Poplar Ridge, from March 13-19. He had two weekly membership classes going, meeting when he got back on March 21st and March 22nd. The community Easter cantata practiced on Sunday afternoons. Community sunrise service was at 6:00 a.m. followed by breakfast at 7:00 a.m. at the West Manchester United Methodist Church this year. After Easter Verne needed to get rid of his bad cold.

I helped with the 2-week VBS in June prior to packing to go to Annual Conference at Cincinnati from June 27-July 2nd. Right after Annual Conference we served as leaders at Camp Sugar Grove. (I'll write more about Sugar Grove later.) And then it was time to prepare for Verne's sister, Ruth Ann's wedding to be held at the Beacon Heights church in Fort Wayne on July 22nd.

The weekend of July 21 and 22, 1972 was almost unbearably hot. The church must not have had air conditioning because the groom-to- be, Robert Cheeseman, went out after rehearsal on Friday night and purchased all the fans on stands that he could find. Meanwhile, we had arrived on Friday during the day so that I could practice the organ only to find that technicians were in the midst of installing a new digital Allen organ with memory cards, and many other new features. Finally I got to practice a little.

At the wedding I was organist, Pastor Verne was officiating minister and Verne Edward and John were sharing a cheap camera and were having fun taking pictures pretty much on their own. Verne and John were well behaved. (They had heard their father say enough times as they sat up front in Sunday morning services and I played organ or piano, "Now just don't make me come down from the pulpit.") The boys got some good pictures of their grandparents, and the bride and groom. I don't think they photographed the candles which softened and bent over in the heat and had to be extinguished.

Ruth's husband, Bob, had a son by his first wife who was deceased. The child, Bobby, was staying with his grandparents in Pennsylvania. He was not at the wedding. After the wedding Ruth Ann and Bob started out to go to Pennsylvania to get Bobby. They were in an accident in Ohio. They called Verne Henry. Fortunately, he had taken vacation after their wedding, although he would have helped his sister regardless. He now became the chaperone and chauffer for their honeymoon. Verne's picture of Bob and Ruth Ann with Bobby in Pennsylvania is a family treasure.

Verne officiated at a number of church weddings, at one time marrying sisters, Rosemary and Linda, a month apart. In September that year, 1972, we were at the rehearsal for my brother Fred's wedding as I was the pianist. The minister said a few words of instruction and left. I remember Fred and Nanci turning to Verne Henry with all their questions: How do we do this?. . . . How do we do that? . . . Verne actually walked them through a rehearsal even though he was not their pastor.

I watched both of our boys get on the school bus in the fall of 1972. John was now in kindergarten, turning six years old in October. John recalls that by the time he was seven, possibly following his first grade year, he was spending two weeks to a month each summer at his Leininger Grandparents, often driving the tractor to pull the hay wagon.

John had been driving tractor before he started to school. I stood with his Aunt Ruth and his Grandma Leininger near the back porch and watched one of his early tractor driving experiences. It was the spring of 1971. John was four years old. He was driving the tractor while his father and grandfather stood on the platform attached to the back of the tractor seeding the hayfield with a hand crank broadcast seeder. We saw that John knew what he was doing!

In the spring of 1973, I decided to take my choir to contest. I wanted the choir to be dressed alike. So I talked with the Home Economics teacher and we decided that the choir girls could make their matching dresses as their class projects. We got plenty of pink dotted Swiss fabric for all the girls. I made a pink dotted Swiss dress as well, although my pattern was slightly different. I was making a maternity dress. The young men in the choir wore shirts and ties. The choir not only looked good, they sang well at contest. They earned a top 1 rating.

On three Saturday mornings that May, their father took Verne Edward and John to the YMCA in Richmond, Indiana for introductory swimming lessons. A couple years later when they were old enough to attend church camp, they received more swimming lessons at Woodland Altars, our Church of the Brethren Camp at Peebles, Ohio.

That spring Verne Edward completed first grade and wanted to play T ball. We signed him up. Verne Henry helped both the boys learn to bat the ball off the T. At a game in mid June, Verne Edward collapsed on the field. He was a sick boy. His rheumatic fever story is told in another chapter.

Pastor Verne was busy in the ministry, but he continued to use his day off most weeks to do woodworking. He was making a beautiful large walnut cradle with turned oak spindles and inlaid walnut panels on an oak stand. I wasn't sure he would get it done before our baby came. When I knew the cradle's size for sure, I covered a two inch foam pad with heavy yellow plastic for a mattress and set about sewing about six white cradle sheets with mitered corners. When it was uncertain if the cradle would be ready in time, Verne would say, "Well, we could put the baby in a cardboard box." When he started rubbing in the linseed oil, I knew it was about done. Soon it sat in our living room waiting for a baby whose brothers could rock with their feet while they laid on the couch watching TV or reading.

The baby, our seven and a half pound daughter, Barbara Jean, was born at 10:44 p.m. on November 15, 1973. She was an individual, breaking her brothers' pattern of September 18 and October 18th. She didn't wait until November 18th to be born.

When Barb had learned to walk, she toddled down the hall toward the boys' room one day when they were cleaning their room. They saw her coming and as she got to the door, they (John says it was he) slammed the door shut. Barb's middle finger was badly cut.

We wrapped it up and headed to Greenville to the hospital. The doctor on call had a reputation of being rough. I didn't want him to stitch Barb's finger. I said I would wait for our doctor, Dr. Thuma, whom I had called and whom I knew was on the way. Verne Henry was not sure that I had made the right decision. He said something like, "What if we really need a doctor again and this one is the only one available and he knows you didn't let him help you before?" Dr. Thuma arrived and carefully put six stitches in Barb's small middle finger.

I loved music and wanted my children to enjoy it as well. I got books with stories and music on long playing records. One of their favorites was "Peter and the Wolfe." Verne and John both had violin lessons. John had banjo lessons and Verne had piano lessons.

At one time our entire family had spinning and weaving lessons at Greenville, Ohio. I remember having a sick headache on the night we learned the drop spindle, and missed that lesson. Verne Henry put together an Ashford Spinning Wheel and I got fairly good at spinning with the wheel. Then Verne built table top looms and the boys each had intricate designs in the threads on their looms. Barbara had a small toy loom.

Verne led two Bible Clubs, one for younger children and one for older children. I also directed two children's choirs. While he had the older students, I had primary choir and then we traded our groups of children. My friend, Linda Smith, accompanied the primary and junior choirs.

I needed six credit hours of continuing education to renew my teaching license. I signed up for Counterpoint and Advanced Music History, two classes at Miami University at Oxford, Ohio during a fall semester. I taped the classes and listened to them on my way home to help me remember what I learned. One day I was too tired to listen. I turned off the tape recorder and soon went to sleep, waking up when the car went off the road. I was fine. The car needed a little repair. Thankfully I was not driving the new green station wagon that we bought the year our daughter was born.

Verne Henry used my regular times away at the university to order a kit and put together a wonderful Christmas surprise for me. It was a large-sized present and he wrapped it to take it to my parents to give me at Christmas. I was surprised on Christmas to receive a beautiful folk harp. I think Verne had even worked to tune it at the piano. So it was ready to play.

Linda and I saw openings for a teacher and aide at a Nursery School near us at Lewisburg. We applied and got the jobs. We worked well together. The school was only for a couple of hours in the morning. I can't remember how many mornings a week we worked, but I remember feeling good about what we were accomplishing. One problem I recall. On a Show and Tell day, one student brought a rabbit and let others pet it. I had not before seen a child have an allergic reaction to a rabbit. I'm glad we called the parents immediately when the allergic child's eyes swelled. No more furry pets for show and tell. I taught at the Nursery School for the 1974-75 and 1975-76 school years.

Linda and I enjoyed visiting older members together. We enjoyed playing piano and organ duets. I remember that we were asked to play piano and organ at a National Church of the Brethren Evangelism Conference at Dayton, Ohio. We were going to move the piano so that I could see Linda better, but were stopped – not allowed. We had to let convention staff do the moving.

Speaking of evangelism, Verne had an evangelism group that met at the parsonage for years. These meetings were numbered in Verne's reminder. When he got to number 17, he started over again with number 1 – maybe with a new group of participants. We had a study time and then went out two by two to visit persons whom it had been suggested that we visit. I'm not sure where we got the suggestions, but there were names and addresses on cards. We kept track of who was visited and when. I helped with the record keeping for these meeting and also sometimes was able to go visiting.

We also had a marriage and family enrichment group that met at the parsonage. I always had crock cheese and crackers for this group. We studied Anna Mow's book, "How to Be Happy Though Married" and also a book by Tim LaHaye on marriage. The couples in this group became our very good friends: Linda and Ron Smith, Bonnie and Bill Jones, Jim and Karen McWhinney and maybe Meryl and Joyce Harden. When volleyball and softball games interrupted our meeting time during the summer, we got together at one of our homes about once a month and then got back on our regular meeting nights at the parsonage in the fall.

In front of the parsonage was a grassy area with a sidewalk that led to the church parking lot and the volleyball courts, 4-square, and shuffle board courts.. Behind the house the land sloped down to the creek. When we got a new dryer, the boys loved rolling down the hill in the old dryer drum. Barb was upset that they would not let her do it. Thankfully there was a fence at the bottom of the hill. There may have been some room on the far side of the church for a garden, but not enough space for what we wanted to plant.

Emma Snyder was the Clerk of Courts for Preble County, Ohio. We had a new couple attending Prices

Creek who were working to stay sober. Emma offered the wife a job in her office. Things appeared to be going well for them. The couple asked Verne to marry them. He did. One evening Verne decided to stop in and have a quick visit with this couple on his way to his Mental Health Board meeting at Eaton. I didn't bother to pray for Verne. As far as I knew he was just going to a monthly board meeting.

When Verne got to the couple's apartment, he found they were very drunk. The man was trying to hang the wife up in the closet with his belt. He was set off because he was pulled over that day by police for a minor violation – a light out or something simple. They were trying to break liquor bottles over each other. Neighbors heard the loud commotion and called the police. When the police arrived and saw that a minister was there, they said that he could handle it and they left. Now Verne had no backup assistance. Verne finally managed to get them to pour all their alcohol down the drain. Things calmed enough that Verne felt he could come home. I remember him going straight to his phone in the study. I don't know whom he called. Maybe he was sharing why he missed the meeting. Maybe he was reporting to the police. I don't know.

The next day when Emma went to work she found a note and an office key under her office door. The couple had left town. No one knew where they went. This story will continue years later.

Harlan and Emma Snyder offered us garden space at their place. Their gardens were meticulously weed-free. It was difficult to have a garden away from where we lived. But we were thankful for it. Barb remembers going to the garden and visiting with Verna Lee, a small elderly lady who lived in an apartment attached to the Snyder's home. She was allowed to go there by herself if she was good. She calls these visits her first solo pastoral visits. She was careful not to touch Verna's breakables, because then Verna would take her to the kitchen and feed her soda crackers with butter, which Barb tells me she still considers her comfort food. Verne and John liked to take breaks from working in the garden and go to Verna's for cool drinks and maybe some cookies.

Elderly parishioners were pleased when Verne Henry took Barb with him to visit them. He always had to make sure she was fully dressed. From very early days, Barb loved to "design" clothes, wrapping herself in leftover fabrics. My school ended at 2:15. In the winter the heat was turned off at 1:00 p.m. to save money, so teachers were encouraged to leave as soon as school was over. Being only a half mile away, I was home early and Verne was free to visit those he needed to visit without Barb.

For two or three mornings a week, Barb attended nursery school. A number of parents took turns driving. Verne's planner notes occasional days when it was his turn to drive for Nursery School during the 1977-78 and 1978-79 years when I was teaching music.

We did have a sitter lined up in case of a funeral or hospital visit that needed Verne to be present during a morning that Barb didn't have school. When she was home, Barb often sat under her father's desk in the study cutting out 3-D stand up alphabet letters out of his waste paper.

Mary Ann Booher was Barb's good friend at church and they looked so alike they could have passed for twins. One Sunday Mary Ann's grandmother looked at Barb and said, "Mary Ann, get in the car, it's time to leave." Barb just looked at Jeanette and said, "I'm not Mary Ann."

Verne and John earned tickets to Cincinnati Reds Baseball Games with their straight A report cards. There were tickets for the whole family. They enjoyed the rewards of their good grades and our family enjoyed the special outings they provided.

Summer Friday nights were for Darke County Church League volleyball games. Three teams played each night: the junior team that Verne and John played on, the youth team, and the adult team. Pastor Verne played in the adult games. Prices Creek was the only Preble County team in the league and most years got the sportsmanship award. In1979, our last year at Prices Creek, our Junior Team was really good and the best in the league.

During games at Prices Creek, children who were not playing volleyball were usually at the 4-square court. I did not play volleyball. I watched. I wanted to play, so I asked Verne Henry to help me learn. He tried to teach me and I tried to play. I ended up in the emergency room with a very swollen wrist. So much for my playing volleyball!

I enjoyed my children's choirs and playing the piano and organ much more that playing any sports. I began to have annual children's musicals which continued to happen at future churches where we served.

As I recall, the first children's musical that I introduced was the short one called "100% Chance of Rain," the story of Noah and the flood. However, the first musical for which I have a saved program is "It's Cool in the Furnace," presented on May 18, 1975. There were eighteen choir members, and six instrumentalists. We used oboe, guitar, string bass, drums and trumpet. Linda Smith had a full piano score. An area pastor played King Nebuchadnezzar and another adult played Daniel. A creative seamstress made costumes. Always supporting me whenever I did musicals, Verne Henry cared for lighting and sound.

By the time my children's choir presented "Jonah's Tale of a Whale" in March of 1977, we had 22 singers, a scenery construction crew, a stage crew, three clarinets, two flutes, a guitar, a string bass, percussion and of course my pianist, Linda Smith, and my greatest supporter, Verne Henry on lighting and sound. This musical was presented twice. The second time was a week later at Eaton Church of the Brethren.

We had not been at Prices Creek very long until Pastor Verne was called to serve on the Southern Ohio Camp Board. History seemed to repeat itself as he tackled the closing of Camp Sugar Grove. But I was not against this closing. It seemed wise to me to close this camp. Southern Ohio already had a newer camp, Woodland Altars. Next to Camp Sugar Grove was a cemetery. Records showed that some people were actually buried on Camp property and some of the cemetery belonged to the camp. This camp was also a fairly public place. When we took our campers to vespers, at least one counselor would have to stay near the cabins "on guard," watching for intruders. Once Verne as Board Chair was called from home when someone ran a dune buggy through a cabin.

After Sugar Grove closed, I counseled Junior Highs on Hogan Ridge with Verne. Then we counseled in specialty camps. I had a couple of articles in the book, *CAMP WOODLAND ALTARS – A PLACE FOR ALL SEASONS* edited by Juanita Huber Deardorff in 1988. My short article about Dulcimer Camps is found on page 37.

> "Verne and I offered dulcimer camps during two summers—1977 and 1978. Our intent in providing this specialty camp was twofold: to teach campers how to play the dulcimer as well as how to make a dulcimer. We always took plenty of dulcimers to camp with us, which Verne had previously made, so that there would be enough instruments for everyone right from the beginning, since campers began learning to play on Sunday night. During the week, as the campers were working on making their own instruments, they were also practicing playing in every spare moment! By the end of the week, the campers were proficient at playing the dulcimer; they were also able to put their strings on and tune their own instruments by that time. The climax of the week's experiences came on Friday night when all the campers gathered together around the campfire and played their dulcimers together."

When I was hired for the 1977-78 school year to fill a middle school music teaching position at Monroe Central, where I had taught previously, I resigned as teacher at the Lewisburg Nursery School. This assignment was to teach music to five fifth grade classes, five 6th grade classes, and an elective for 7th and 8th grade students. This was prior to the government order to mainstream students. So the five sections of each grade were divided according to abilities. 5-1 and 6-1 were the top students. 5-2 and 6-2 were very good students, 5-3 and 6-3 were supposedly average, and so forth.

I presented about five programs per year – basically for each season or holiday, featuring two classes per performance. I worked with the teachers, for I needed their cooperation to let students out of class long enough to practice with the class they were paired with. After the evening performance of a major musical, I would invite the teachers of the classes that were featured to my house for a party. I usually served hot sandwiches and trimmings. I may have done a fall or Halloween program putting together a number of songs or readings. The first major musical that year was "Tall Tom Jefferson," presented by the top two sixth grade classes on November 17, 1977. The instrumental director directed those playing trumpets, trombones, snare drum and chime and violins. Verne Edward was one of two violinists for the program.

"Tall Tom Jefferson" was an undertaking! The art teacher designed the program covers. Twin Valley North High School loaned us music stand lights, our

National Trail High School loaned us a chime, and Richmond Civic Theater loaned us costumes. I had a person in charge of slide projection and lighting, allowing Verne to concentrate on the sound. Verne had purchased a Peevey sound system with mixer, speakers and microphones for my use at school and church. It was heavy, but he brought it to all necessary rehearsals and performances. Barb enjoyed going to final rehearsals when she could with her father. She sang most of the songs at home.

The school janitor, also a member of our congregation, was very skeptical about Verne's bringing in the big sound system for my musicals. He said that the school's electric system wouldn't handle it. The Principal disagreed with the janitor and was glad for Verne's support. Whether or not this incident had anything to do with the sound system disagreement, Verne received an anonymous letter stating that his wife was wearing her dresses too short. This was in the 1970's and dresses were fairly short, although I was always well covered, or so I thought. I remember Verne buying me a pretty orange, button down the front polyester dress trimmed in white and then asking me to add a white strip around the bottom to make it longer. I did.

Two things helped me survive my busy school and church activities schedule. One was a portable dishwasher which we wheeled up to the sink and attached to the faucet to do dishes. The second was a neighbor girl who graciously consented to clean house for me. Of course I paid her and we both benefited. I don't recall having cleaning help or a dishwasher at our residence for any other congregation.

I remember Verne Edward showing award winning ducks at the Preble County Fair. I also remember entering a recipe contest and winning second place with my recipe for duck soup. How did we get into raising ducks? We purchased an incubator that held 120 chicken eggs, maybe not quite that many duck eggs as they are a bit larger than chicken eggs. Someone asked Verne Henry to hatch duck eggs for him. We would get half the ducks for hatching them. He filled the incubator and turned the eggs, twice daily I think. When it was nearly time for them to hatch, he sprinkled them with water regularly.

When the ducks hatched, two strange chickens hatched as well. When the ducks got old enough, they enjoyed swimming in Prices Creek. The chicks followed the ducks into the water and nearly drowned. Verne or one of the boys saved these weird chicks. One grew to be white with fluffy white feathers on its legs. The other grew to be a small size black rooster that looked like a fighting cock. It was mean. One day the cock went after Verne Henry and ruined his plastic feed bucket. Verne called to me, "Get some boiling water ready, I'm killing the rooster."

I never thought I was prejudiced. But I did not enjoy eating that rooster. Its bones were not the color of chicken bones that I was used to seeing. This black rooster's bones were a charcoal gray color. I've never seen any others like those.

We became increasingly aware of the importance of good nutrition. Partly this was Nurse Shirley Fike's influence on us as she shared health related information and Shaklee product information. We became Shaklee distributors in 1975. Verne also invited interested persons to join with us to place orders of organic and bulk foods. Verne had to drive to locations where he could meet a truck to receive our combined food order. Group members would get together and divide the order. During this time we enjoyed going to Alpine Alpa where we picked up orders of cheese to divide with our co-op friends.

In Verne's 1977 Brethren Reminder he had some search committee meetings entered. He had a couple meetings listed at restaurants. We were not interviewing for a church. Then I remembered. Verne was Woodland Altars Camp Board Chair and he and the Board were interviewing applicants for Camp Director. Verne Henry was Board Chair when Roger Cruser was hired. Verne was happy that Roger brought lots of administrative gifts and camp expertise to Woodland Altars.

That year's Christmas musical was the story of the writing of "Silent Night." The musical was called "A Song for Christmas." In April of 1978, the top fifth grade classes presented, "It's Music" and our John was a railroader and sang a vocal duet.

Our son, John Henry, was one of my top students. I knew it and I know he knew it, too. Yet I bent way too far backwards to be sure I did not show favoritism to my child, and I gave him a "B" once in music. That is one mistake that I wish I could undo. John has plenty of musical talent. But better yet, he seems to have a forgiving heart.

I continued to direct youth musicals at church. In March of 1978 my Prices Creek choir and community youth presented "Beginnings." I was blessed to have Miss Donelda Conrad, my school's band director, as the instrumental director for this church program.

For Christmas in 1978 the school musical was "The Small One" about the donkey that carried Mary. One of the fifth grade teachers built a gray papier-mâché donkey over a saw horse on wheels. After the final performance the donkey's creator gave me the donkey. What a blessing!

We had invited the Sunday School Bible Class to the parsonage for a meal on Saturday, December 23. The class members came in the noon daylight and I had prepared a big table and lots of food for them. They seemed glad to be invited and enjoyed each other's company. After the meal, our family acted out the Christmas story using the gray donkey which I believe Barb may have ridden.

The next day church members carried boxes of food and wrapped gifts for Verne Edward, John and Barbara from the church to the parsonage. I am not the only one in the family who remembers Christmases at Prices Creek..

Then came January and the severe blizzard of 1978. We had a lot of snow, even what was called a blizzard in 1977, and had missed some days of school. But this was a severe blizzard and we were out of school about four weeks. From January 25-27, up to three feet of snow fell in Ohio with winds averaging between fifty and seventy miles per hour. The snowdrift in front of our house curled up over our front porch roof. The temperatures hovered near zero and the wind chill was deadly, reaching 60 degrees Fahrenheit below zero.

I remember Verne almost not making it home from an out of town meeting. My memory recalled he was at a Camp Board Meeting getting through just before the highway was closed. His Brethren reminder lists a Mental Health meeting at Dayton at 6:30 p.m. on the night of January 25. I was glad he safely made it home.

When our electricity at the parsonage went off, the church still had power. Verne had to drain the parsonage heat pipes – so they wouldn't freeze – and we went out the garage door and around to the church where we spent at least one night. When our electricity was restored, I remember the challenging time we had trying to get all the air out of the water pipes.

Barb remembers not being allowed in the tunnel that Verne and the boys dug through the snow in the front of the parsonage. I recall a mail carrier in a nearby town coming across a dead body in a snow drift.

We were snowed in. The drifts on Monroe Central Road were impassible. In a week or so, a Wright Patterson Airforce Base Snowblower arrived to open our country road. Snow flew, past the volleyball court and the yard and clear back to our front parsonage picture window. After the road was opened, a bus was sent out to see whether or not it could run its route and we could have school. Buses could not turn corners because of the huge drifts. School continued to be closed. That is, public school was closed.

We had three sets of children's encyclopedias as well as the regular size Britannica Encyclopedias. I assigned report topics for our boys and they reported on their subjects at the evening meal. After a couple of weeks the School Superintendent, James Walker, a member of our church, dropped some textbooks off and we continued our home school.

The boys were working on their science fair projects while they were snowed in. John had a number of white mice. He fed half of them white bread and half of them whole wheat bread – probably some I made. White mice are less sturdy than regular field mice. He lost a few when the electricity was off and the house was cold. But some of those on whole wheat bread were healthy enough to reproduce. He had kidney bean sized baby mice in his science fair exhibit. I remember someone looking at his exhibit and saying, "Don't eat whole wheat bread, or you'll have a baby." Very silly!

Verne Edward was growing salt water algae. I sent to a friend in Florida (or maybe a relative) and requested they send us some salt water algae. Verne's job was to keep the correct saline solution for the algae to live and grow. That took some careful study and measuring, and monitoring. But with no school or extra activities, there was time.

The last Community Youth musical that I directed at Prices Creek was "Barbecue for Ben" on March 18, 1979. This is the story of the prodigal son. We borrowed footlights from the middle school. Again, this was a cooperative project with adults helping with props and instruments.

Verne and John attended camps for their age groups at Woodland Altars during our last summer at Prices Creek, as they had for several summers now. For our last counseling experience before leaving Southern Ohio and Woodland Altars, Verne and I counseled a Pioneer Camp at the old, seldom used log cabin at Woodland Altars. Following is my description of that Camp found in the afore mentioned book, *CAMP WOODLAND ALTARS, A PLACE FOR ALL SEASONS, page 32, "Highlights of Pioneer Camp."*

Sunday, July 22, 1979. Junior Highs are moving into the log cabin to be pioneers for a week. We are entering the home of eighteen nests of wasps, one snake, a family of mice, and a convention of flies.

Hands and feet take care of the wasps. But twenty fly papers seem insufficient for a week's worth of flies.

Will we shoot bear and deer and coyotes? No, our game is smaller and more numerous.

But how to survive? What can we eat? We'll grind wheat to bake bread. We grind the wheat several times to get fine flour. A camper suggests, "Let's use some coarsely ground flour to make cream of wheat for breakfast." I'm not sure this will work, but, to my surprise, it does! And the campers really like it! Meanwhile, bread tastes better with butter, so we churn. Our butter turns out golden and delicious!

Wednesday morning's job is choosing and preparing roosters for our supper. The great debate is: Shall we carry them home or walk them home from the camp farm on a leash? Chop! Chop! Eeek, don't look! There. The roosters' heads are in the pit. Now to scald them and pull the feathers. And who's going to take out the insides? Wow! These chickens are beginning to look like they came from a store.

Spinning, weaving, fishing. Survival uses a lot of energy.

We watch the snake that is either disturbed by all the activity or hungry for mice that live upstairs. It slithers up the wall by the fireplace to the loft of the cabin where the girls sleep.

I imagine the log cabin occupants will be relieved when their uninvited guests finally go home.

As a school teacher, I saw children who had to move frequently – some who would be in and out of the same school several times in one year. Verne and I wanted our children to have as few school changes as possible. Throughout our time in ministry, God honored this request. Each of our children experienced only two school system – one for their early grades and one for their upper grades.

In the spring of 1979, Verne Edward completed the seventh grade. John completed the sixth grade and Barb was old enough by Ohio standards to start kindergarten. We had been at Prices Creek eight wonderful years. Verne and I felt it was time to consider moving. Probably some Prices Creek members were ready for a change, but to my knowledge, Verne was not asked to resign. It just felt like the right time to move, even though it meant leaving a lot of friends here.

Verne Edward's Rheumatic Fever Story

It was mid to late June after our oldest son, Verne Edward, completed first grade when he collapsed with knee pain on the T ball field. He was not hit by a ball or bat. He was sick. As his mother I did some reading and thought he might have rheumatic fever. The doctor said he didn't see that much anymore but ordered an ASO titer test, probably to satisfy me. I don't remember what immediate action the doctor took, but I know that Verne Edward and his younger brother went to their Leininger grandparents the week that included July 4th as his father and I kept our commitment to serve a week as Camp Counselors at our Southern Ohio District church camp, Camp Sugar Grove.

Our doctor knew where we were. One of his relatives lived near the camp. On July 4th, the doctor called his relative and asked her to come to Camp to tell us that our son had rheumatic fever and needed to take penicillin every day until he turned 18 years old. Somehow through a series of phone calls, Grandpa Leininger was able to secure his grandson's prescription, and we did not need to leave our campers and make the trip to get this.

One of Grandpa Leininger's sisters was Orpha Wyse. She and her husband were members of the

Church of the Brethren at Wauseon, Ohio where Pastor Don and Shirley Fike were serving. When Aunt Orpha heard about Verne Edward, she told Shirley and also told us we had to talk to Shirley. Shirley taught us now to make yogurt by the big bowls full to help replace the good bacteria that the penicillin was killing. Then she got us started on Shaklee.

For the remainder of the summer we carried Verne Edward most places. Usually he rested on a child's recliner under a tree in the Prices Creek parsonage yard and read books. During July and August he read 310 children's books through the local library's summer reading program. (I recall that he won a prize for reading the most books.)

When school started he began going to 2nd grade for half days. Later when he went full days, he stayed in at recess. Usually he played chess with his 2nd grade teacher during recess.

About every two weeks we took Verne Edward to Greenville, Ohio hospital for a blood test. And the rheumatic fever persisted. Finally early in November, we asked the church to pray for him. (The church then didn't share as openly as our church does now.) On Thursday, November 15, 1973, we took him for a regular blood test. That night I entered the same hospital and gave our boys a baby sister. I stayed at the hospital a little longer than usual. The doctor came, sat down and visited with me on Sunday morning. He told me that Verne Edward's ASO titer results came back in the normal range. I hate to admit my first response to his news. I said, "Will it stay that way?"

Years went by with Verne Edward taking penicillin, Shaklee supplements and yogurt. We were told that there would always be tracers in Verne Edward's blood showing that he has had rheumatic fever. But by the time he was 18 years old, doctors could no longer prove that he had ever had this illness. We are thankful to God for his healing and for the part that Shirley Fike and Shaklee played in helping him get well.

Decisions – Oak Park

I didn't realize what an emotional impact moving from Ohio to Maryland would have on me. I think it is only in looking back that I can understand the number of changes I faced and how they affected me. For the first 15 years of our married life we had lived in parsonages close to the churches we served. Often there were meetings in the parsonage. I knew the people. I worked closely with Verne. His office was in the parsonage at both County Line and Prices Creek. I could run over to church anytime I wanted or needed to be there. I had a close friend at Prices Creek. We spent lots of time together, visiting the elderly, playing piano and organ duets, teaching at Lewisburg Nursery School together. My adjustment to living about eight miles from church had its ups and downs. But first to get there. . .

Did the boys and I leave school early on May 18, 1979? Did we drive straight through to Oakland, Maryland or stop overnight on the way? I am not sure. I do remember meeting the District Executive Sylvus Flora on Saturday and our family riding with him to see the area. This was our first time in Maryland. I think that Verne sent sermon tapes prior to this visit which is why Saturday night was an interview and then a meeting with the congregation. What I remember about late Saturday night is the children and I listening to how loudly Verne Henry snored. I thought for sure that he would be heard in the neighboring motel room. I had never heard him snore so loudly. He was exhausted.

On Sunday afternoon after his morning sermon, Pastor Verne received and accepted the call to serve as Pastor at Oak Park Church of the Brethren, at Oakland, Maryland beginning September 1, 1979. Now we had more decisions. Where would we live? Oak Park did not have a parsonage. If we bought a house, how would we pay for it? And what could I do with an Ohio teaching certificate in Maryland? God provided answers.

We found a manufactured house on Deer Park Road that had a separate garage, a small barn and a little over four acres. It had no basement, but the crawl space was pretty much high enough to walk around in. I liked the two stacked ovens in the kitchen. I could continue baking some whole wheat bread. There was no dishwasher and no room for our portable one. I could live without that. We borrowed money for the down payment from Aunt Orpha and Uncle Earl and settled for this house on July 9th.

Verne had a week's vacation – July 9-16- to give time for us to find contractors we would need to make our dreams a reality. We hired the basement dug out and the floor cemented. We had the basement divided into a bedroom for the boys, a storage room for our three-door refrigerator and freezer which would be temporarily in the garage, and a meeting room. An attached ladder went from the basement up to the living room through a hole in the floor.

We added a patio door to the basement, cemented the basement outside entry way, and bought a wood stove which we put just inside the door to the right as we entered. Inside the door to the left was firewood storage. The refrigerator and freezer moved to their new location on Thanksgiving Day, which that year was unseasonably warm and Verne's sister's family was there to help us.

Moving was a several day adventure. A moving company loaded our possessions for two days in August. On the third day we drove. Grandpa Leininger had Verne's heavy woodworking tools on a trailer that he pulled behind his truck. John rode with Grandpa. Verne's sister, Ruth Ann, who liked to drive, drove my Falcon as I didn't want to drive that far. Verne Henry, Barbara and I came in the green Ford station wagon. The moving company unloaded their van on the fourth day, August 16, 1979.

During the July vacation, I applied for a job in the Garrett County Public Schools. A music job, if available, would mean that I would need to go into a school, arrange the lunch room into a music classroom, have class, put tables and chairs back where they had been and go to another school and repeat the process. I probably could get a Maryland Teachers License for music, but that wasn't a job I wanted. So I took a job for our first year in Maryland as a Title I teacher's aide and worked with Anna Buckingham traveling to Crellin and Redhouse assisting students with learning difficulties. Anna was fun to work with and we met and took turns driving.

We enrolled our youngest, Barbara, in Kindergarten at Broadford Elementary. She was five years old and would be six in November. I taught all my children academic skills like reading and some math before they started to school. Maryland had a later cut-off date for starting school that Ohio had. So when it was discovered that Barb was old enough by Maryland law to be in first grade and that she could already read, she was soon promoted to Mrs. Wood's first grade class.

I took classes at Garrett County Community College in the evenings during the school year and at Frostburg State University in the summer. I got my credits needed for an Early Childhood teaching license in Maryland. I could then teach kindergarten through third grade. Classes kept me busy on "free" nights attending or doing homework. Summer classes meant I couldn't attend Annual Conference at Pittsburgh. I got "A's" in classes but they took a toll on my personal life.

Verne officially began serving at Oak Park on
September 1, 1979. Prior to that date, he had a
wedding rehearsal and wedding. I found it interesting
that the rehearsal was at 7:00 p.m. Saturday evening
and the wedding was at 7:00 p.m. on Sunday evening.
His second wedding at Oak Park was at 3:00 p.m. on
Saturday, September 15. Immediately following the
Friday night and Saturday District Conference, Verne
was installed as Oak Park's Pastor on Sunday,
September 23rd. A look at some of the events that
filled out the fall of 1979 gives an idea of the ongoing
program at Oak Park

On World Wide Communion Sunday, October 7,
1979, Verne led his first Love Feast at Oak Park, I
wrote about Love Feasts in a separate chapter. Suffice
it to say that Verne was worried he would be blamed
for instituting crackers for communion bread when it
was discovered shortly before the service that no one
had the communion bread. It was locked in a freezer
owned by a couple who were out of town. Thankfully,
there was a grocery store close to the church.

Five days later, Verne officiated a wedding Friday
morning at 10:30 a.m. on October 12. The next day,
Saturday, he had a wedding at 1:00 p.m. These
weddings were fit into the church schedule prior to the
6:00 p.m. October 13th, Harvest Banquet that night.
On Sunday, October 14, the youth met at our house.
Verne Edward and John had devotions.

There were day meetings and evening meetings of the Women's Fellowship. The day meetings mostly consisted of older ladies doing quilting or knotting comforters. They brought food to have lunch at church and insisted that Verne eat with them. They usually served one thing that he really didn't like and often more than one lady brought this: rutabagas. He told me he tried to be polite.

Bible Clubs started in October on Monday evenings at 6:00 p.m. That took some hurrying to get home, get a meal, clean up and get to church ready for children's choirs and Bible Clubs at 6:00 p.m.

According to their father's Brethren Reminder, Verne Edward and John needed Polio and Measles booster shots which they got on October 19. Barbara had seen the doctor in Ohio prior to our move for all her kindergarten shot needs.

Verne had a 10:00 .a.m. wedding on Saturday, October 27. A morning wedding meant getting up, having breakfast, getting dressed for the wedding and getting to the church long before the scheduled nuptials. The Quester's Class Party was Sunday evening. I remember how creative Jeannie Whitehair was at creating Halloween stories with props for the party. If she told you to reach blindfolded into her container and feel the eyeballs, you were feeling slimy peeled grapes. I also remember that she used spaghetti to represent the brains.

Verne and I attended the National Church of the Brethren Camp Leaders Meeting at Woodland Altars. These meetings were held at different camps in different years. The meeting was November 1-4, Thursday through Sunday. With Verne so involved in Camp Leadership in Ohio, I wonder if we had requested this time off when we signed our contracts for church and school. I remember Rex Miller taking about adding more cinnamon or vanilla when you cut the amount of sugar to make the campers healthier cookies. I remember Shantilah Bhagat from Elgin speaking about environmental concerns at that conference. Soon Verne would be serving on the Program Committee for the West Marva District Church of the Brethren Camps – Camp Galilee and Camp Hope.

After the Camp Meeting ended, Verne got back in time for Sunday night Youth meeting and Christmas play practice.. The next Sunday night, the youth would start making their traditional hard tack candy which they would take orders to sell. Play practice followed candy making.

The Community Thanksgiving Service was at Oak Park our first fall there. Verne had two monthly ministers meetings, one with the West Marva District ministers and one with the Oakland Ministerial Association. It was a good way for him to get to know local and district ministers. Although I enjoyed my work in the Garrett County School System, I felt shy, lonely and hung back because I didn't know any of the other ministers or their wives at the Community Thanksgiving Service.

After Thanksgiving came Advent and The Hanging of the Greens. The church was invited to Walt and Jeannie Whitehair's to collect greens. Creative persons turned greens into beautiful decorations for specific areas of the church. At the Hanging of the Greens service after the carry-in supper, the symbolism or meaning of each decoration was shared as it was hung or placed.

The Vietnam War was going on and a Community Service of Prayer for Peace was held at 12:15 on Monday, December 10. Besides counseling sessions and weddings, Bible Clubs and choirs, committee meetings, class meetings, small group studies, and youth play practices were frequent events.

The Golden Bible Class liked to meet and eat buckwheat cakes and sausage gravy. Buckwheat cakes were new to us. The person in charge of the cakes seemed to have mixed the batter well ahead of time. I wonder if it was a sour dough starter that she used. Our family quickly developed a taste for this class's specialty. They might have had some regular pancakes for those who didn't like the buckwheat cakes, but I can't be sure. I liked their buckwheat cakes.

I have always enjoyed Christmas Caroling – so much so that I wrote an article about Christmas Caroling for our church magazine, "Messenger," and was paid for it to be published. Then a important church leader, M.R. Zigler, died and that Christmas issue became a tribute to him. My caroling article was not published.

At Oak Park I remember dividing up the carolers with each group going to a different geographical area. When they had caroled everyone on their list, groups would meet back at the church for hot chili and cocoa. My group went to the nursing home where Jeannie's mother, Nina, was. She was in bed and didn't appear to know any of us. We started singing a carol and stopped after the first verse. Nina kept going through all the verses. I learned that people can sing familiar songs when they may not be able talk to you. Another Oak Park caroling experience I remember is going through a farm kitchen to the living room where the older couple sat in their chairs. She was reading the Bible.

At 9 a.m. on December 16 the children presented their Christmas Program. The youth practiced their play at 2:00 p.m. They also practiced after school on Tuesday and at 2:00 p.m. on Saturday before presenting their plays that evening, December 22nd.

After worship on December 23rd we traveled to my folks. With Saturday so busy, I wonder when we packed. On Monday, the 24th, we went to Alpine Alpa and picked up cheese. We had Christmas at my folks on Christmas Day. The next day Verne's "little book" says we went toward his parents traveling to Columbus, Dayton and West Manchester. We must have stopped and delivered cheese in the West Manchester area. Dayton is where we picked up natural peanut butter and nuts. We celebrated Christmas with Verne's family on Friday, December 28th and traveled home to Maryland on Saturday.

During the summer of 1980 we considered what kind of animals we would like on our little acreage. To help us decide we went to the Garrett County Fair. After looking at a number sheep breeds and talking with persons, we decided that poled Dorsets looked to us to be a gentle breed without horns. One of the early sheep we purchased probably from the livestock auction, was not a Dorset. We named it "Jumpy" which described its behavior.

One of our first years found me dressing chickens that we raised in part of our little barn. Verne chopped off the heads, we dipped them in boiling water to loosen the feathers and then the family pulled feathers. It was my job to take out the insides. I think we dressed about 12 chickens a day. We were not speedy professionals, so this project lasted several days.

Instead of building furniture at Oak Park, Verne's woodworking was closing in part of the barn where the loading dock was and then adding an addition to the barn. Earlier he had closed in the carport section of the garage. Our number of sheep and our knowledge of how to care for them grew during our Maryland years, until we had 50 head to sell when we were leaving Maryland after eight years there.

The Personnel Director had told me that if I had an early children teaching certificate, he could give me a job. He was true to his word. For the 1980-1981 school year I taught Kindergarten in the same building where Barbara was now in second grade.
Kindergarten was lots of fun. I used the Alpha-Time characters to teach the alphabet letters. I taught math, social studies, science – you name it. Once I counted 13 different subjects that kindergarteners had. Kindergarten lasted all day and my children went out for special classes on different days - library, music, art, and physical education. These were my planning times. The first semester they also had a rest time in the afternoon on their own mats, followed by snack time. Parents took turns sending snacks.

Parents were very willing to help put up bulletin boards, help children make crafts, and make Indian and Pilgrim costumes – hats and collars – for our Thanksgiving program. I had a kindergarten student, the daughter of the Middle School Principal, who could read at third grade level. She had been babysat by a retired teacher/aunt while her mother worked. The first day of school Maria returned from recess and told me that the kids didn't understand when she was talking with them about Beethoven's symphonies and additives to cereals. She talked on the Kindergarten level after that experience.

Since Maria was a good reader, I wrote the Thanksgiving script for her to narrate while the rest of the class acted out coming over on the Mayflower (parents made the ship, too) and finally eating the first Thanksgiving Dinner together. I wish I had saved that script. With parents' help, our class also had a Thanksgiving meal in our classroom.

On Friday and Saturday, March 6 and 7, 1981, our family traveled to Ohio to see my mother. I took off school on Friday, wondering whether I should or shouldn't. I didn't know how much longer my mother would live. I am glad we went. She was on strong pain medicine in the hospital and some of the family and friends were staying with her round the clock. I felt like an outsider as far as knowing how to care for her needs. She managed to ask me to read scripture and sing. I could read scripture, stopping as necessary for composure. But I did not trust myself to sing. Since then I have sung for at least two church persons right before they died. But this was my mother. John spoke to her and she opened her eyes. That was the last time I ever saw her eyes open. She didn't open them for me. I think John's changing voice surprised her enough that she had to see him. We drove home on Saturday. I had a musical practice Sunday afternoon. I am glad I went to see mom. Probably I should had stayed longer, but I didn't know she would be leaving this earth on Wednesday, March 11, 1981.

Dad hired a long limousine to take him and his six children to the funeral and cemetery. I remember that it was an open casket funeral and Dad had to help pull Fred away from the casket after the funeral. I remember even the young pastor weeping prior to the service. Mom was sixty years old when cancer overwhelmed her body.

The boys had been in 4-H in Ohio, so it was natural to look for a club for them in our Maryland area. Barbara was eligible for 4-H a year earlier than she would have been in Ohio. She joined the Country Kids 4-H when she was seven. She took sewing projects and learned sewing basics. One time Barb came home from the Country Kids 4-H Club and told us that a family at the meeting wanted to give her the pony that their children, who had grown quite tall, were now too big to ride. They would also give her the saddle, the bridle and other pony necessities. A few days later, Cricket was delivered. Cricket was not use to being around sheep. Also horses' hooves carry tetanus. Should Cricket be put in the pasture? Well, we could give sheep tetanus shots. Cricket checked out the pasture, chased the sheep and injured at least one. Should Barb get to keep him? Her father decided. Cricket would stay. Cricket got used to his new surroundings.

By February, 1982, our children were active in two clubs.   Monthly Garrett County 4-H Shepherds Club meetings were happening in our basement. We were into sheep, shearing, docking tails, worming, trimming hooves, preparing to show. We had trimming stands and a show box painted with a picture of a Dorset on the lid. I made sheep blankets to keep the sheep clean after they were washed and prepared for showing. A number of our 4-H members attended a sheep workshop in Howard County in March that year.

Sheep need to eat. We bought the acre beside us and grew hay on it. We also baled hay on some property up the road from us and stored it in a barn near there. We bought a baler with some friends who also raised sheep. We and the Fulks each used the baler we purchased together. I enjoyed having Ron and Debbie Fulk eat meals with us when we were working together.

The Garrett County Fair was a big event for our family. Verne Henry always took fair week as a week of vacation. All three of our children had entries in many categories at the fair. They entered vegetables, baked goods, flowers, clothing projects, and of course breeding sheep and market lambs. Verne Edward was in the fashion revue with his brown wool suit. Barb wore her red wool jumper at a fashion revue she entered. She took sewing and learned to sew in the Country Kids 4-H Club. She made many wool outfits and as well as other clothing for future entries. One year Verne Edward cut all his green beans the same length and layered cut beans standing upright in rows in the jar. He really impressed the judge and received a blue ribbon on his green beans. The next year he repeated the process and the judge said he spent an impractical amount of time canning the beans so carefully and she marked him down for doing so. I soon realized that often the awards won at the fair, whether for showing sheep or other projects, depended upon a judge's opinion.

Here is how I became a judge one year at the Garrett County Fair. It is not a proud moment in my memory. A young girl who had just completed seventh grade was chosen as one of the judges for the Washed Lamb Contest. I expressed my opinion that I thought she was too young to be a judge. Thinking back I realize that this young lady had grown up with sheep. She had shown sheep and lambs from the time she was old enough to be in 4-H. She had much more experience with sheep that I had. And 4-H is supposed to develop leaders and leadership skills. But, my statement was taken seriously. The next thing I knew I was a judge in the arena watching contestants clean lamb's ears and hooves and card these animals for show. These lambs had just been brought in from a field and washed. They were not tame. I learned to trust youth; they have more talents and abilities than I sometimes realize.

About four days after the fair ended in August, 1982, Verne Henry, Verne Edward and John were on their way to the Church of the Brethren National Youth Conference (NYC) that happens every four years. Pastor Verne was a West Marva District Youth Advisor and so he was in charge of a busload of youth from our area, including Verne Edward and John, heading to Estes Park, Colorado. Each youth was supposed to take a pillow to sit on – preferably one they decorated, designed or made. I don't remember what pillows Verne Henry and John took. But I remember that Verne Edward made his pillow with many inset (not patch) pockets. He had learned to make inset pockets when sewing his suit, and he was good at making them. I will not describe the great events and speakers that I heard about after the trip, as I didn't get to experience them. In fact, I am the only member of our immediate family who never attended a Church of the Brethren National Youth Conference.

What I remember about the time of NYC is that my carpel tunnel syndrome was really uncomfortable. On the Saturday night that the guys were gone, I was awake nearly all night with painful wrists – pain that went on up my arms. Then I had to get up at 5:30 to do sheep chores and get ready to go to church. Sunday evenings I often made homemade pizza for the evening meal. I could not straighten y fingers during this time. My hands were usually in a good piano playing position with rounded fingers. That meant that I had to use that backs of my hands to spread out the pizza dough on the pans.

I did not want to have any surgery on my wrists. I was and am a pianist. So I did my research and found that for getting rid of carpel tunnels, Dr. Jonathan Wright recommended staying away from nightshade vegetables. These vegetables include white potatoes, tomatoes, eggplant, peppers and tobacco. Since I've never smoked or eaten eggplant, the diet was simple for me. I eat lots of sweet potatoes. Dr. Wright was in the state of Washington. I needed a doctor who was closer and who would treat with natural remedies.

I discovered a Dr. Conte in Pennsylvania. Verne took me there and I filled out a very long questionnaire prior to seeing the doctor and getting some helpful supplements. I took some niacin once instead of the recommended niacinamide. I turned beet red and was taken to Oakland hospital from the lunch room where I was on duty at school. I don't know where Verne was. He couldn't be reached. By the end of the day, I was no longer red and felt fine. It was probably a niacin flush. We made several trips to see Dr. Conte at Beaver Falls northwest of Pittsburgh. My wrists, fingers and arms are pain free.

Life continued to be full in 1983. We met in February with other families who would also be hosting a German Exchange student during this school year. Verne Edward's student was a great fit for our family. Lutz's father, as I recall, was a church leader in Germany. A number of field trips and outings were fit into the short three weeks that the exchange students from Sulingen, West Germany were in our midst. The students and their hosts went to Washington D.C. They went bowling. They had parties for getting acquainted, a pizza party, and then a farewell party. I remember our student being surprised when the school opened each day with the pledge of allegiance to our flag. He said that if that happened in Germany, people would think that Hitler was ruling again.

About this time one of the Oak Park youth was playing table games with his family one night and complained of a sore throat. His mother took him to the doctor the very next day. This teenager was taken to the hospital.

His throat shut off his breathing and he died. This was during a bad snow storm. Verne and the undertaker from the funeral home had to ride in a snow plow to the family's home to make funeral arrangements.

During warmer weather a young boy from our congregation about four or five years old was outside playing with the funeral director's child next door. That night we got called that this little one was in Oakland Hospital where his grandmother was a nurse. The child did not survive. The family didn't find answers in the autopsy that was done and the funeral director worried about whether or not his child would become sick. That was the second difficult funeral for a young person that Verne had at Oak Park.

For at least two years in a row, 1983 and 1984, our Shepherd's Club won 1st place in the Amateur Division and the Grand Marshall award for the over-all best float at the Autumn Glory Feature Parade, even beating out commercially made floats for the top award. Often we used two 18 foot wagons for our float. Our Club was getting a good reputation which made selling lambs at the Fair Auction easier. Buyers then began buying lambs and donating them back to our club to serve at our annual lamb dinner.

On November 5, 1983 our Garrett County 4-H Shepherds served perhaps our first of several annual lamb dinners for the community at the Oak Park

Fellowship Hall. We had crock pots everywhere it seemed. Our goal was to promote the eating of lamb. We used every part of the lamb. The ground up liver went into spaghetti. An area lawyer who liked to make curry came and made lamb curry for us. We had lamb chops, lamb burgers and my favorite lamb dish – Scotch broth, which was a delicious lamb soup.

We got a call from Verne Henry's father, Grandpa Verne, that my mother-in-law Esther had a stroke at 11:00 p.m. on Saturday night, November 19, 1983. She was in the hospital. On Thanksgiving Day, November 24, Esther spoke in sentences. Then on November 29th she was moved to North Crest Nursing Home. Dad kept us up to date on Verne's Mom's progress. On December 9 Mom walked with railings and on December 23rd she was walking with a walker. We went to the nursing home to see mom over the Christmas holidays. It was bitter cold, well below zero. There was a nurse or visitor whose car wouldn't start because of the frigid weather. Verne's dad, the mechanic, went out and got it started.

On January 2, 1984 Mom walked to the bathroom just with the nurse's arm. On February 3rd, Dad was able to take Mom home from the nursing home and she never returned to it. Esther called us on February 12. Dad had purchased a long phone cord so that the phone could be wherever Esther was.

Verne Henry was instrumental in starting Hospice in Garrett County. His Brethren Reminders note Hospice meetings, Hospice trainings for volunteers, Hospice graduations, Hospice Volunteer Dinners, Hospice fundraisers, Hospice Memorial Services and even a meeting with the Garrett County Commissioners about Hospice. As the spouse of the Chair of the Board, I went with Verne to a Doctor's home on Saturday evening, March 3rd where the wife prepared an elaborate meal for the Board members and spouses. There was before dinner wine and after dinner wine. Verne and I did not have wine either time. I was glad that there was no smoking and the conversation was pleasant. That same night Verne Edward was out with a group of seniors celebrating the last night of the Senior Class play. He came home early. There was drinking at that party and he wasn't partaking. We compared our evenings.

Verne Edward had put a lot of hours into working for that play. He and John both spent all day at school on Saturday, January 28 building the Senior Play set. When it was way past midnight and Verne and I couldn't sleep because the boys weren't home, Verne got up and went to school in the night and found them still working. Verne Edward and John came home at 2:35 a.m. And didn't miss church the next day – neither did their Father!

April 1, 1984. Working behind the scenes with many people and writing letters and invitations, I surprised Verne Henry with a "This is Your Life Program" for his birthday and 20 years since ordination (April, 1964). After a carry-in meal many people shared. District Executive, Sylvus Flora, had devotions. Bill Baker pinned a boutonniere on Verne and was Master of Ceremonies for the program. Representatives spoke on Verne's service to Bible Clubs, 4-H, Ecumenical work, Youth, Hospice and other groups in the church. Others read letters from persons from previous congregations who couldn't attend. My helpers and I totally surprised Verne! His Brethren reminder for that April 1 simply notes Musical Practice 2:30-4:30 and Youth Crazy Dinner in the evening. It was a full day!

On Palm Sunday, April 15, I directed the musical, "Beginnings" by Buryl Red and Ragan Courtney. For accompaniment I recruited two percussionists, an organist and a pianist. The musical shares the beginnings of the world and ends with Jesus and new beginnings. That was probably a better weather day than the following Sunday. On Easter Sunday, trees and lines were heavy with freezing rain and the lights went out several times during the church service.

As I looked toward the day when Verne and soon John, also, would be going to college, I began to fast and pray over my lunch break in the workroom off my classroom, praying that they would have the money needed to attend. I didn't turn on lights, and persons were seldom in my room over lunch. Part of my journal entry for April 22, 1984 reads: Answered prayers so far this year! V.H.'s very itchy rash is gone. V.E. money for college! John – has broken up with Dove. Phyllis- God was present and got us through "Beginnings." (Two of our practices had been snowed out.)

One of Verne Edward's sheep ate some Mountain Laurel which is poisonous to sheep. Instead of burying the animal, Verne somehow got a 50 gallon drum cut in two lengthwise, filled it with the now skinned carcass and water and cooked it day and night over a 3-burner gas plate outside until the meat fell off the bones. Then he carefully picked out the bones and reassembled the sheep's skeleton. Part of the time a school friend helped with this lengthy assembly process. The last I heard, the skeleton was still being displayed in Southern High School's science room.

On May 27 of Memorial Day Weekend, 1984, Verne Edward graduated from Garrett County's Southern High School as valedictorian. I had not seen or heard his valedictory address prior to his presentation, and I was impressed. He received several awards. I was not surprised that one of the awards was the Bauch and Lomb Science Award.

By this time I was teaching first grade at Broadford Elementary, after three years in Kindergarten. My first grade teacher friends knew that I was having a lot of company for graduation weekend, and volunteered to help fix food. I think that is the first time I ever had fruit pizza. It was delicious. I don't know where we put all the people who came. It was a wonderful celebration with Verne's sister Ruth and her three boys, Aunt Carol, Uncle Johnny and their children Lisa and David. My father and Marion also came. After graduation I served ham sandwiches, macaroni salad, chips, relish tray and dip, punch, cake, and mints that Ruth Ann made. This is the only family celebration I can remember for which Ruth Ann didn't make the cake. I purchased it from a lady in Crellin.

I missed my first graders' last two days of school on June 14 and 15th. I took personal days. After taking Barb to her Leininger grandparents on Thursday, the two Vernes and I went to Manchester College for Verne Edward's orientation. He picked his roommate and took placement tests. We came home on Sunday and my last day of school, a teachers' work day, was Monday, June 18.

On Sunday, June 24th, I went with Verne Edward who drove the green station wagon to Frederick, Maryland to receive his $700 State Elks award. His sports coat was in the back seat. When we arrived, he got his coat and locked the vehicle. He had locked the car with the keys in the ignition. We went into the building and someone gave us a hanger. Verne unlocked the station wagon driver's door with the hanger and got his keys. It is a good thing that he did. It was really raining after the luncheon and awards were over. We both missed church that day.

Since Annual Conference of 1983, Barb had planned that she would stay with Grandma Leininger during Annual Conference of 1984 and learn to do embroidery. None of us were counting on Grandma Esther having a stroke in November of 1983 and being unable to do embroidery, cook, or do the many things she did prior to her stroke.. Looking back, I wonder if we should have changed our plans and taken Barb to the 1984 conference at Carbondale, Illinois. Barb stayed with her grandparents. She was 10 years old. She did some cooking with their microwave. Things with grandma were different than she had expected when the plans were made. Verne Edward and John went with us to Carbondale. We got a lot of exercise walking to and from meetings and lodging on this large university campus.

We came home from conference on July 3rd. Both Verne Edward and John went back to work at My "O" Tire on July 5th, John in the warehouse and Verne in the office. Barb was happy to have a young lady from Oak Park as her cabin counselor for the week beginning July 15 at one of our two district church camps, Camp Galilee.

The next Sunday, Pastor Verne and I went to be counselors at Camp Hope, the more rugged, wilderness style of the two West Marva District Camps. We had counseled there a number of summers and enjoyed the rustic beauty there. Once Mama bear and little one drank out of the wash basin at Verne's boys area. One year when our boys were junior high age, they pooled their money and bought lots of heavy yellow rope which they used with a pulley to haul equipment and food supplies up the mountain. A truck was left in the strip mine area and girls cleaned out the bed of the truck to make the floor of their sleeping area. Then the animals returned at night and found other residents in their home. It didn't help that the boys laid a trail of chicken bones to the old truck attracting the wild animals. This year, only one camper showed up for our week of camp. On Monday morning, we had a staff meeting, and we and the other counselors packed up food, cleaned up and closed and locked the camp.

The same day that we were on our way to Camp Hope at Belington, West Virginia, Verne Edward drove a My "O" Tire company car to Pittsburgh and flew, along with a lady from work named Doris, to Atlanta, Georgia for computer training. We surprised John and Barbara when they came home after John got off work and I had supper ready. Barbara had stayed with

Evelyn Biser while John worked. She seemed to have a great time there. Verne Edward sent us a letter to Camp Hope which we didn't get until later. In the letter he shared about the day's lesson: "most of the class (there are 10 of us) had trouble with it, but I got it right away. It was just like learning another computer language. Then his P.S. "I could get a job in Kentucky or California if I wanted one." Then writing to us who are supposedly at camp he adds a P.S.S. "Remember to brush your teeth, comb your hair and worry Mom. Ha! Ha! Auf Wiedersehen." Of course he didn't accept either of the job offers; he was going to Manchester College in less than two months.

While the rest of the family was gone that July 22nd John and Barbara finished putting together the new Heath kit computer. This was the second Heath-Zenith computer that Verne and John made. When visionary Jeannie Whitehair told us that computers were going to be the thing of the future and that our children were intelligent and should be learning about them, we listened. The High School shop teacher was a member at Oak Park and had built a Heath-Zenith computer. Our boys could do that, too. And so, by the early 1980's we were learning to use a computer.

There was no internet yet and mail was still a major way of communicating. One day Pastor Verne received a letter with a return address of Florida and names that he did not recognize. The couple whom he married at Prices Creek (see the account in the Prices Creek chapter) and who disappeared after the night he broke up their fight when they were attempting to kill one another, were writing to apologize. They had joined Alcoholics Anonymous and had been sober for a number of years. They shared that Verne had married them under assumed names. That is why he didn't recognize the names on the envelope. They were asking his forgiveness for the ways they had acted. Verne and I were glad that their story had a good ending.

On September 2nd we took two vehicles to move Verne Edward to Manchester College after going to Grandpa and Grandma Leininger's to get the car that Grandpa had purchased for the boys to use at college. John would share it next year. There were no computers for daily use and no cell phones. I had the college phone numbers and the Ikenberry phone number or extension. We called every two weeks at first. Verne Henry didn't think we should bother Verne Edward too much. So I asked Verne Edward how often we should call. I recall that he said we should call as often as we wanted; he liked hearing from us.

In one phone call, Verne Edward shared that he was bringing a friend home for Thanksgiving vacation. The friend was Ferran from Catalonia (Spain). Ferran enjoyed our Thanksgiving dinner which he said had so much "variety." He took a picture of the dinner. On

Friday after Thanksgiving we took Ferran to Washington, D.C. He was impressed with the Library of Congress. We also had a great tour of the Capital building – Senate and House. Verne Edward picked up students enroute and had a carload of people and luggage on Sunday going back to Manchester.

Before Christmas John was already accepted at Manchester and Rose-Hulman – both in Indiana and was busy applying for scholarships. From the time John turned 16 years old, he had worked at My "O" Tire in retreading tires after school until about 7:00 p.m.. Thankfully Garrett County usually had a late spring and early fall because John and Verne also had lawn mowing jobs. It seems strange to me that Verne Edward was sent for computer training by My "O" Tire shortly before he was to go to college. During his senior year of High School, it was John who spent his last hour of work each evening at My "O" Tire backing up the company's computer. His boss approved of John's doing math homework during that hour.

Oak Park Church of the Brethren was a fairly young congregation. It celebrated its 25th anniversary while Verne was pastor. The founding congregational leaders were no longer the only leaders and they may have felt they were losing their power. Some of the founding members who were in Florida when Verne was called to serve, now decided that they should look for a new pastor. The Church Board wished to have a vote to determine whether Verne should stay. Verne would have quietly resigned, but our District Executive, Sylvus Flora thought that there were only a few "making waves" and that Verne should let them take a vote.

On January 6, 1985, we worshiped elsewhere. Sylvus Flora preached at Oak Park. The vote was taken. There was a strong majority for staying. Again Verne considered leaving, but Sylvus said, "No. Then the small minority would be the winners. You need to stay." Verne used to say that after that vote, he had some of his best time in ministry at Oak Park.

John's German exchange student from Sulingen was Matthias. It is interesting to me that the three weeks the exchange students were here in 1985 was over Easter. The welcome banquet for the German guests was the Thursday evening, one week before Maundy Thursday's Love Feast. The Garrett County Field trip was the Tuesday after Easter. When Matthias went home to Germany, John looked forward to seeing him in the summer, as John chose to go to Germany as an exchange student and spend three weeks with Matthias' family.

John graduated from Garrett County Southern High School on Sunday of Memorial Day weekend. He managed to graduate at the top of his class even with his full early morning to late night work and activities schedule. He knew how to manage his time. One night a week, he would come to the church after work, arriving shortly after 7:00 p.m. and eat the supper that I was keeping warm in the oven prior to attending adult choir practice at 7:30 p.m. Other nights were 4-H or lawn mowing. Then there were always the sheep chores.

John made the decision. He was going to Manchester College. We repeated the orientation process and the moving in process. Now we had two sons at Verne Henry's Alma Mater.

District Conference was Friday evening and Saturday, usually around September 20, my birthday. This year, 1985, it was at Oak Park, September 20-21. Pastor Verne's Brethren Reminder, notes that together he and I were to have devotions on Saturday at 1:00 p.m. on the theme, "Called to Make Disciples." It was a joy for me whenever we were working together.

As 1985 was drawing toward its end, Verne and I were again working together with our club's members and parents to do another big lamb dinner for the community on the first Saturday evening in November. This year, our sons were not home to help. At almost twelve years old, Barbara was an able worker.

A program from December 7, 1985 lists Pastor Verne as giving the blessing for the Hospice of Garrett

County Volunteer Luncheon at the Will "O the Wisp, a classy restaurant. Verne's Brethren Reminder has meetings stacked on meetings throughout the fall until Christmas Sunday, December 22nd. The Christmas Cantata that night at 7:00 p.m. is the last listing for 1985. The rest of December is blank. He must have been exhausted. Where and when we celebrated family Christmases is not noted. My journal is also blank for that time period. Our lives needed to slow down.

An Epiphany rehearsal and the January 6th Community Epiphany Service were a couple of the events added to the list of regular meetings in January 1986. Verne has written Nappanee, Indiana in pencil on Friday, April 25. The Northern Indiana District Office of the Church of the Brethren is located at Nappanee. Working closely with our West Marva District Executive, Verne likely went to Indiana to meet the Northern Indiana Executive and talk about churches that might be opening up in Northern Indiana and possibly look at church profiles. This was an unannounced meeting.

Our entire family went to Norfolk, Virginia for the Church of the Brethren Annual Conference from June 24-29, 1986

The Garrett County Fair overlapped National Youth Conference, but Verne did not need to chaperone the

West Marva contingent this year as he had at the last conference in 1982. Buyers donated lambs back to our Garrett 4-H Shepherds club and we had plenty of lamb to serve at the 1986 annual lamb dinner on the first Saturday in November.

Our school system hosted a Japanese teacher for the 1986-87 school year. Teachers signed up to host Kaomi Tanaka in their homes for six weeks at a time. Kaomi was a hard and very conscientious worker. When she was preparing her talk for one of our local service clubs, she asked me to read it and check her grammar and use of words. When she spoke to my first grade class, I remember her telling my students that if a student was sick or missed school in Japan, a parent had to go to school and learn the lessons for the day and teach the child at home. I also remember Miss Tanaka giving each of my students a piece of Japanese candy and telling them that they could eat the candy with the wrapper on it. I never understood how the wrapper could be edible.

Miss Tanaka was with us during the time that our choir was practicing the Christmas Cantata. She was not a Christian, but she loved to sing the songs of the Cantata. Verne Henry did some research and found a Japanese New Testament for Kaomi.

It was the spring of Barbara's eighth grade year when I realized that her Gifted and Talented math class was only about half way through their math book. I had two first grade students who were well into the second grade math books. All my first graders would complete first grade math I called the middle school. I sounded hypothetical when I asked her math teacher how Barb would survive in math, having so much uncovered, if she moved to another school. I also shared that all my first graders would finish their math books. I knew we were probably moving; although I tried not to come right out and say it.

In July of 1987 we took our daughter for a week of camp at Woodland Altars in southern Ohio. Even though she also attended Camp Galilee in the West Marva District in Maryland, we still appreciated the programming and leadership that we had known and served with at Woodland Altars. During the week that Barb was there, we hosted two Nigerian Church of the Brethren leaders.

A two page typed letter we sent to Barb at camp tells that Yamtikarya was the first woman to graduate from the seminary in Nigeria. Joel was a church leader, but not Yamikarya's husband. They each had spouses and children in Nigeria. Verne and I took them to the Farmer's Market and got them fruit and candy. We showed them the church and Swallow Falls and the local department store. I didn't know what they would like to eat for lunch, but I had put a roast in the oven. Joel had three helpings of the roast beef.

Yamtikarya slept in Barb's bed when she stayed overnight. Joel stayed overnight at the Whitehairs after the evening carry-in at church.

That spring we had traveled to Milford, Indiana. Verne had studied the Bethel profile and knew that the church had split. He had also talked to a former pastor and wasn't sure he wanted to go to Bethel. Verne preached his "trial sermon." The vote to call him as Bethel's pastor was 100%. He still had to say whether he would accept the call. What could he say to such a strong call? Verne accepted the call. We would be moving from Maryland to Indiana that August, 1987.

Memories of Bethel

Verne accepted the call to serve Bethel. It was a long ways between Bethel at Milford, Indiana and our home in Garrett County, Maryland. The next time we came might be the time of our move. We needed to use our short time at Milford, Indiana to look at possible housing. Kate Doty was a real estate agent and a member of Bethel. We visited with her Sunday afternoon and looked at what properties were listed. We had to act quickly so that the children and I could get back to school on Tuesday. We picked out the properties that we would visit on Monday morning.

We looked at a house with a barn and a little land. Maybe we could bring some sheep. But. . .we could see through the barn. The house was run down as well. We looked at an older home in Milford that Verne saw had a lot of flaws poorly covered over. Then we went to see a brick home on 900 N just off State Route 15. It was listed for more than we had hoped to spend. The lady of the house was there when we went to see that property. While we were looking at the pole building/garage, she let it slip that they might settle for less than had been advertised. Kate was working for the seller. When we went back to her home to talk things over, her husband said, "I don't work for the seller. Offer them $68,500. We did and our offer was accepted. We also learned that day that the Christian Church School in Milford was looking for a teacher for grades 1-4. That turned out to be important to know.

By this time we had 50 head of sheep and lambs. On Saturday, May 9, we sold the entire flock to one buyer. Our border collie went with the sheep. Verne Edward and John who owned many of the animals were at college. Barb's pony, Cricket, had died of old age earlier and was no longer with us.

One summer day I got a phone call from the John Deere Implement Company that had for years loaned Verne their best tractor with a cab to pull our Garrett County 4-H Shepherd's Autumn Glory Float. Someone else was asking for a tractor and the company wanted to be sure that we had what we wanted first. I shared that Verne wouldn't be driving a tractor this year as we were moving to Indiana.

Choosing a house was such a hurried process that I couldn't remember the layout of the inside of the house we were purchasing. So with the realtor's and homeowner's permissions, John was able to drive over from Grandpa and Grandma Leininger's. take pictures of the rooms of the house, and send them to us in Maryland. John was working construction with Mike Britenracker and staying at Grandpa Leininger's in Ohio that summer. Now I had an idea of what we were purchasing long-distance.

Russell Sines put John back on the payroll so that John would be insured to drive a My "O" Tire truck to help us move. Many Bethel members drove all night and arrived at breakfast time with a rental truck as well as other vehicles. I had breakfast for everyone. It was a long trip and late at night when we pulled into the driveway of members Raymond and Lura Hoover's home. (They are both now deceased.) After a little rest and breakfast, we headed to the bank. This was a little complicated because the survey of the soon-to-be our property didn't match the fenced area and the lawn building was not entirely on the property shown by the survey. Our wonderful farmer neighbor said, "Where the fence is, that's the property line." The contract had to be written to shown the correct acreage.

The church helpers were anxiously waiting for us to arrive at our new home so that they could begin unloading. They also wanted to return the rental truck as soon as possible. The Hollars were still moving out when our trucks arrived. The former owners took their last items out, as we were driving in from the bank. This was a Saturday in August. We slept in our new home that night and then attended the New Salem Church of the Brethren just a little way down County Road 900 from us on Sunday morning. Bethel was saying farewell to their former Pastor.

Monday morning we each needed to be a different place. I needed to be at the Milford Christian School to meet officials, sign a contract, set up and prepare for teaching grades 1-4. I had to promise that if a public school opening occurred, I would not leave the Christian School during the school year. Verne Henry and John had to go back to Maryland and return the My "O" Tire truck. Verne Edward was working in Florida that summer and could not help with the move.

Barb needed to register at Wawasee High School. Raymond Hoover volunteered to take Barbara to register. We had just moved from Garrett County Maryland where students did not have any book fees. I was shocked when Barb shared that it cost Raymond a couple hundred dollars in book fees to register her for classes. I had no idea we were supposed to send money to register her. Of course we repaid Raymond and were appreciative for his willingness to take her to her new school.

A day or so later, Morey Beer, Barb's school bus driver stopped by to share that he would be her bus driver and to let us know what time he would be picking her up.

It seemed to be a very welcoming community. Now it was time for us to be a part of our Bethel Church and the Milford, Indiana Community. We invited the congregation to an open house from 2:00 – 5:00 p.m. at our new home on September 20, (1987) following Verne's installation at the morning service and a carry-in meal. I baked a variety of cookies and purchased ingredients for punch and used my big punch bowl and snack sets. It was an enjoyable way to work at getting to know people and to make them feel welcome in our home. I remember people sitting in the living room visiting and others walking around upstairs and downstairs talking a look. I wonder if I realized that this was my 44th birthday.

The Christian School at Milford was in the Christian Church. The Pastor's wife was the pre-school teacher. I taught grades 1-4. It was easy to get to know the Christian Church staff; I worked with them. The Youth Pastor was the principal of the school. He also taught phys ed in their gymnasium. That was my planning time. His wife cared for lunch duty. I enjoyed teaching Abeka material. I had one rule in my class. A student was not allowed to answer a question directed toward another grade's students. That was important. There were two doctors in Milford and I had both of their oldest children, Allison and Glenn in first grade. They were quite intelligent. They could listen and learn from any class's presentations, but I only allowed them to answer questions directed to their class. Later as seniors each of these doctor's children was valedictorian of the high school in which they chose to attend, Bethany Christian and Wawasee respectively.

I enjoyed my freedom to be creative at the Christian School. During the morning opening, we worked at memorizing portions of scripture. At Christmas we memorized Luke 2. Allison loved to script and direct plays. She brought dress up clothes. When her work was completed she worked on creating plays which our class enjoyed. I had a science fair for my 12 students. They put a lot of work into their research and displays. I wish I had pictures of their exhibits. A Fairfield High School science teacher was a compassionate and encouraging judge.

I taught the music. We preformed the short catchy musical about Noah called "100% Chance of Rain." We walked to the public library once a week. We wrote poetry. We had math contests at the chalkboard. I still have my copy of our small yearbook. I did occasionally have to squelch the sentiment of some of my students that they were better than those who attended public school.

It was a fun and memorable year. The school board had even purchased some equipment including a microscope for my classroom. The church decided to vote on whether or not to continue the school. They had spent $10,000 that year on my salary and also funds for the pre-school teacher. They wanted a 75% vote to keep it open. They had well over a majority vote, but not the requested percentage. The desks, text books, equipment and the new microscope were all sent to an Indian reservation.

During that first fall while I was enjoying teaching, Barb was getting involved with a Milford 4-H club. She was also in the County Junior Leaders 4-H. Verne was gone a couple nights in early October to Church Leaders Conference at Manchester College. He returned in time for the 24 hour New Pastors' Retreat at Camp Mack.

People of the Covenant prayer and study groups were starting and meeting in members' homes. I was going to the People of the Covenant meeting at the Waggys on one of those nights that Verne was gone. The railroad crossing as I turned off Old 15 onto 1150 N had not yet been widened. I misjudged the width of the road and my Falcon's tires went between the rails and I was stuck in the railroad tracks. Suddenly someone – an angel? – appeared and said, "You get behind and push and I will drive you out." I pushed. The helper drove me out and then disappeared. I don't know how he or she came and I don't know how that "angel" left. I don't know my helper's name. When I got to the People of the Covenant meeting at the Waggys, the only proof I had of what happened were my very muddy shoes.

Different locations have different time traditions. We got used to 11:00 p.m. Joint Christmas Eve services with the First Brethren Church. Parents brought little ones to these services in their pajamas. It was usually a well-attended service with participants from both congregations. I remember being the organist for a Christmas Eve service at the First Brethren Church.

February 5, 1988 was Verne and Esther Leininger's 50th wedding anniversary. On Sunday, February 7, Verne and his sister, Ruth Ann, and I had open house for them at their home as Esther didn't move around easily after her stroke. Ruth Ann baked a beautiful cake. I made ham salad and egg salad sandwiches and punch. Ruth and I made various colors of jello squares. We also had coffee and tea. We got the folks a 50th anniversary guest book. Around 70 persons came. Mom and Dad seemed to really enjoy seeing all these friends and family.

I overheard Verne and Kathy talking to Ruth Ann about the beautiful cake. They had a reason for learning about the cake. So as not to take away from the 50th anniversary celebration, Verne Edward and Kathy Martin arranged for their coded letter announcing their engagement to reach us the day after Verne Henry's parents' celebration. To get the real message of their letter, you had to read down the left edge using the first letter of the word in each consecutive line. If you caught on, you would read, "We are engaged." Ruth Ann would make their wedding cake.

In just about three months we had another celebration. Verne Edward graduated from Manchester College with highest distinction. Baccalaureate was at 11:00 a.m. on Sunday morning. Bethel told Verne Henry to take the Sunday off, and so we were able to attend baccalaureate. The West Manchester Church of the Brethren had a lovely lunch for their Manchester graduates and their families. That was so much nicer and quicker than waiting in a long line at a restaurant. We did not have to rush to get to graduation on time.

When a month had a fifth Sunday, four area Churches of the Brethren met together for a special service. Once a year, when the service was at Bethel, I often directed a musical that children and youth from all the area Churches of the Brethren had practiced together for weeks.

As we had in previous churches, Verne began Bible Clubs for younger and older children, and I traded him age groups of children for children's choirs. I found quality children's music that suited our tastes and needs available from Chorister's Guild in Texas.

As a High School Sophomore in 1988, Barb was in drama and art clubs, choir, speech team, and the musical Oklahoma! Barb drew a very complicated house which got a blue ribbon at the school art show! Her self portrait received 3rd place. Pastor Verne helped with the Wawasee Speech Club because their teacher was expecting a baby. Verne went with students to contests on Saturdays.

On June 4 (1988) Verne and I took Kathy wedding dress shopping. Actually we took her to Shipshewana to Yoder's General Store where Kathy bought the pattern and material for the wedding dress she would make. Barb went along and bought fabric for 4-H projects.

Bethel had a Birthday Party scheduled for June 9th. The Melloaires, a local singing group, sang many love songs and wedding songs including "I Love You Truly" and "Let Me Call You Sweetheart," among others. Then we went down to the basement for birthday cake. One of the members, Phyllis Sorensen, announced that they were also celebrating a 25th anniversary – ours! Then she pinned flowers on Verne and me. Naomi led the congregation in singing, "Joyful, Joyful, We Adore Thee." The words for this hymn were printed in the lovely program they created especially for our anniversary event. Did the ladies know that was the processional at our wedding? The church gave us a 25th anniversary plate and a card shower. Also they had a special round cake for us to take home.

Bethel was in the process of looking for a new piano and I was on the piano search committee. One Friday night I got home about 9:30 after looking at pianos in

South Bend and Elkhart. Verne thought that Verne, Kathy and Barb had gone miniature golfing. Actually they had been grocery shopping.

The next morning the kids were up early. Verne and I were told that we were not allowed in the basement. About noon we were called in from the garden where we had been working. Our "children" had a table cloth covered table with flowers and lit candles set up in front of the family room mural. Yellow and white balloons hung from the ceiling. Verne, Kathy, John and Barbara cooked and served tossed salad, iced tea with lemon slice, homemade bread – little loves served warm, shrimp – Kathy made the breading and Verne Edward fried it – freshly picked garden peas – John shelled them, fried rice and homemade cheesecake made with five large packages of cream cheese and fresh strawberries. John had taped the background music. So in candlelight with lovely music and a beautiful setting we ate a delicious meal. They hung a sheet between the kitchen and the family room and they ate in the kitchen. This was our 2nd wonderful 25th wedding anniversary surprise celebration. What wonderful children we have!

Each summer Bethel had a Saturday-Sunday camp out at Camp Mack. We took our fold-out camper and enjoyed God's great outdoors with our Bethel friends. Everyone took something to add to the Saturday evening stew. We had campfire on Saturday night and worship at Vesper Hill on Sunday morning, along with meals together, lots of visiting, and swimming for those who wished to get in the water.

With over 10 years of teaching experience, I was too expensive to be hired to teach (one principal truthfully admitted that) when new graduates were available for less money. About August 22, 1988 I accepted an offer to work in the office at Camp Mack, thinking this would be like a year of Brethren Volunteer Service (although I did get paid) for me, while I continued to search for a teaching job. I retired after twenty-five years at Camp Mack. My wonderful years at Camp are a long story which I may share in another chapter. We celebrated Christmas with Verne's folks on December 23, 1988. From there Verne Edward and Kathy left to go to Florida to celebrate Christmas with Kathy's family. They invited Barbara to go with them and she enjoyed her first trip to Florida. Verne Henry and I were back at Milford in time for the annual joint Christmas Eve service with the First Brethren at 11:00 p.m.

In 1989 a new Church of the Brethren program, called "Passing on the Promise" was introduced. A couple of coordinators would work with Pastor Verne to plan the activities recommended. The program looked exciting. I really wanted to be a coordinator. Of course I was disappointed. I was chosen to be the adult Sunday School Teacher for the program. That was probably a God-thing. I gladly used the creative ideas offered in the adult material and I don't think anyone got bored. I was always creating props or illustrations. At least once I taped items for class under the students' chairs.

My first piano recital using the new Everett piano at Bethel was May 7 at 3:00 p.m. I don't know how I managed to have so many students without advertizing. I had students from church and from the Christian School and neighbors' children and even the First Brethren Pastor's daughter. I always served cookies and punch after the students finished playing. I did learn to ask parents to bring some cookies or brownies so that I didn't have to do all the baking to serve the many family members, friends and relatives who came.

Verne Edward and Kathy were married at the West Manchester Church of the Brethren, not far from Manchester College, on Saturday morning, May 20, 1989. Verne Henry's Brethren Reminder notes that he was scheduled to pick up two five-gallon hand crank ice cream freezers at 7:30 a.m. that morning at Shipshewana, I believe. Pictures were taken before the wedding. Verne Edward and Kathy had juice and donuts for those who came for pictures. The night before we, the groom's parents, served Pizza Hut pizzas, tossed salad, apple sauce, Oreo cookies, pop and milk at the rehearsal. Invitations encouraged guests to dress casually or to bring clothes to change into for outdoor activities following the wedding.

The wedding was beautiful. Bruce Young decorated with lilacs and dogwoods. Railings and windows had potted plants that Verne and Kathy bought for gifts to the wedding helpers. The dress Kathy made was lovely. Verne wore the pleated shirt he had made in 4-H without a coat or tie. Four pastors were part of the service: the current West Manchester Pastor, Debbie Roberts, Joan Deeter who did the actual vows ceremony, Kathy's grandfather, Rev. Kenneth Long, and Rev. Leininger, the groom's father.

Jan and John Long played hammered dulcimer and banjo for the prelude. I joined with the Appalachian dulcimer for the processional. Many of their friends formed a long line across the front and sang "Friends" during the ceremony. Clowns did the ring ceremony. Children threw balloons from the balcony during the recessional and clowns threw candy. Jane Hunn threw a frizbee which Verne Edward caught on the way out. Kathy's Uncle Joe Long set off fire crackers outside the windows. Guests brought carry-in salads to go with ham and turkey and cheese sandwiches. Frizbee and softball games and making ice cream in the five-gallon freezers followed lunch. Then it was time for cake, ice cream and presents, which children helped to unwrap. My father instigated the raising of Verne's car up on cement blocks.

We celebrated again the following day, Sunday, May 21, as our son John and our new daughter, Kathy, graduated from Manchester College. We like to say that we had cake for Verne and Kathy on Saturday and cake for John and Kathy on Sunday. The Martins and we shared in a graduation reception at Wampler Retreat Center at Camp Mack.

Wilderness camping was a comfortable style of church camp leadership for Verne and me. During our first summer after moving we counseled together at a "regular" Junior High Camp at Camp Mack. We had to work to keep the campers engaged. The girls loved to stay in the cabin and talk or write graffiti. So when Verne was asked to direct or be team leader for Mildly Wild, he accepted the call and led that camp a week each summer for years. Campers completing grades 5 and 6 lived in cabins but cooked all their own meals over a campfire. They heated water and washed their own dishes. They did all the other camp activities as well, including Bible study, swimming, nature activities, challenge course activities, worship services and more. Campers working together grew close in camp family units.

Soon after our week as counselors at the "regular" Junior High Camp in August 1988, I began to work in

the Camp Office. Each year when Verne directed
Mildly Wild, I often helped with his camp after work,
usually playing my guitar for campfire singing.

The year, 1989, continued with the usual class
meetings, study groups, Bible clubs and Children's
choirs, school performances for Barbara, and meetings,
meetings, meetings. I don't think I wrote about the
surprise I had when we went to church to go Christmas
Caroling our first December at Bethel. I wondered
why Verne parked his car instead of leaving it in front
of the church ready to be loaded with carolers. He had
always been one of the drivers at past churches when
we went caroling. I took my soup down to the church
basement where a couple older ladies who were not
going caroling would have the food ready when we
returned. Soon Verne said, "It looks like we are ready
to go. The bus is here." The bus? Yes, a school bus.
Bethel member, Herb Reuter, was a Wawasee School
bus driver who for a number of years got permission to
use the bus he drove to take our church members
caroling. We enjoyed singing on the bus and singing
at shut-in's homes. It was a fun way to go caroling.

I remember the family focused ad, "Do you know
where your children are?" Keeping track of them was
getting more difficult. Barb was interested in working
for peace and had been part of a Peace Pilgrimage
through parts of West Virginia and Virginia in the
summer of 1989. This group presented services in a

different church each evening and walked to their next destination during the day. This was just a prelude to her travels the next summer.

All of our family went to Milwaukee, Wisconsin for the 1990 Church of the Brethren Annual Conference. Barb was seldom home that summer before her Senior year of high school. I needed a calendar to know when she was a delegate to Indiana Hoosier Girls' State, when she was serving as a counselor at the 5th and 6th Grade Wilderness Camp her father directed, and when she was at Youth Camp at Camp Mack. She made sure that I was aware of her schedule for National Youth Conference in Colorado and the Shalom! Peace Pilgrimage in Iowa that she did right before school began.

That summer Verne and Kathy served as naturalists at Camp Mack and stayed in a room in Wampler Lodge. When I had peas picked that needed shelling, I sometimes took them to Camp for Verne and Kathy to help shell if they were free in an evening. John was working as a computer programmer in Indianapolis. I "sort of" knew where he was – quite a ways from the peas!

Working on health issues must have been in Verne Henry's DNA. As I look back I remember him going to Home Health Board meetings when we served Prices Creek. I remember him working to help start

Hospice Care in Garrett County, Maryland. In the 1990's Verne's reminder lists Home Health Board meetings frequently. Another volunteer activity that kept Verne Henry busy on Saturdays was judging speech contests. He continued to help with Wawasee's Speech Team during Barb's senior year on the team.

June 2, 1991. Barb graduated ranking third in her class from Wawasee High School at 2:30 p.m. on a Sunday afternoon. She was amazing. If you've read this far you know that Barb was only in kindergarten a few days. You also know that her Maryland gifted and talented eighth grade class completed only half of their math book. Barb entered Wawasee's Gifted program without having had the Algebra 1 that her new classmates had. She says her brother Verne helped her understand some basic Algebra principles when she took Algebra 2 with no Algebra background. She was surprised when it was announced that she, as the female in her class with the highest grade point average, was receiving an unexpected $500 scholarship from a local women's group.

Barbara worried her parents, especially her father, very badly right before graduation when she was out much later than she said she would be. Verne grounded her which meant that she missed her friends' celebrations. We had an open house for family and church friends for her. I intervened and Verne agreed that Barb's grounding would end when her 75 thank you notes were written. Barb got right on them. Soon her grounding was over, but so were her friends' open houses.

Barb worked in programming at Camp Mack the summer after she completed high school. She was on her way home in our van to get an iron, needed for whatever she was doing. A new culvert was installed on 1150N covered with gravel. The gravel was loose and full of ruts. Barb lost control, hit a utility box and ended up in a soybean field. She was not injured. A tire needed repaired. The next day the county put up a warning sign about the loose gravel. Barb was not cited; the farmer said the soybeans lost would be considered natural attrition, and we were not charged for the utility box. Verne took Barb to State Farm to explain what happened;   I do not think our insurance was raised due to this incident.

 In August we helped our last student move into East Hall (she soon moved to Oakwood) to begin her college years at Manchester College. I remember what she wanted instead of cake for her 18th birthday her freshman year of college. To fulfill her request, I made and Verne and I delivered two fruit pizzas to her.

Day Camp for a week each summer from 9 a.m. to 2:00 p.m. took the place of Vacation Bible School at Bethel. Verne worked with a committee to plan Bible Studies and field trips. I was working at Camp Mack during Bethel Day Camps, and I did not experience the fun of the day camps. I remember campers telling about a trip to some former missionaries who talked about the need for water and building wells in Africa. I know campers had a lesson and a trip each day to go along with the lesson.

Verne and Kathy were both working on graduate studies at Penn State University when Sarah Elizabeth, our first grandchild, was born on October 29, 1991. Arden Ball, the Camp Mack Director, purchased a train ticket for me to go to see my new grandchild and her parents. I left from Nappanee which since has closed their train station. Verne Edward met me at the Altoona station. I enjoyed holding Sarah and seeing her beautiful crib with the colorful hanging parrot. Verne was digging glad bulbs and I helped him meticulously sort the gladiola bulbs according to size. I took some pictures to show Grandpa Verne Henry our precious little one. She didn't weigh much over six pounds.

Even with Barb in college in 1992, Verne Henry continued to work with the Wawasee Speech Team. His reminder shows that about every other weekend from early January through the NFL Regional on April 11, Verne went with the Wawasee team to contests. He and I also volunteered at what was then called the Centre-In Food Coop in Goshen (now with a different name, Maple City Market, and a bigger store along

State Route 15.) Verne often helped unload trucks and take food to storage in the basement of this crowded store. Verne and I worked together doing inventory at that cooperative.

My ministry gift was often in the area of music – playing organ or piano, directing children's choirs or occasionally adult choir, and directing a musical most years. The Children's musical in 1992 was presented at the meeting of Bethel, New Salem, North Webster and Syracuse Churches of the Brethren on May 17 at Bethel. That year we did "Kids Praise – An Explosion of Happiness" and the Pastor of the North Webster congregation, Tim Waits, played the main character role of "Psalty."

At the four-church gathering at Bethel on May 23, 1993, we had an even more ambitious musical, "The Story-Tellin' Man" by Ken Medema. Again Tim Waits played a leading role as the "Story Tellin' Man" who, of course, was Jesus. This year I had musicians playing percussion, electric bass and piano, all friends of our son John who again cared for sound. I also had a flute player and seventeen singers. I enjoyed having John's friends with us to practice, eat and share time with us. Having a musical each year was becoming a tradition.

In August of 1993, I received a new ministry. I went with Verne to Loyola University at Baltimore for two weeks of intense Stephen Ministers training. We had lectures, discussions, reading assignments, role plays and worships. The way the Stephen Ministry Leadership cared for both the spiritual and physical needs of participants was in itself a lesson in hospitality. When we broke into small groups and needed to find our group's meeting location, a leader with a tall stick and a sign attached took us where we needed to go.

Here is a portion of the letter I sent to Bethel members and to Camp Mack:

Thank you for allowing us to be gone from Bethel to take this Stephen Leaders Training. This is one of the greatest experiences of our lives.

The conference (or training) is so well planned. Livelier activities and sessions are planned for when persons are tiredest. There is no dull or boring speaker here.

There are 501 persons registered from 44 states and 4 foreign countries – Canada, Taiwan, Korea and Japan. Thirty-three denominations are represented. We sing about 5 minutes before every session. Since participants sign up to lead singing and play the keyboard, our variety in songs, choruses and hymns has spanned Christendom. . . .

The only disappointment I had in Baltimore happened when we chose to go to the closest church to the University on the Sunday between our weeks of training.. That was fine. But I went expecting to hear great organ music. That may have happened at an early service. The musical instrument used at the service we attended was guitar. It was a contemporary service. I guess that was a learning experience, too.

While we were in Baltimore, we received a coded letter from our daughter, who was spending her second summer working for On Earth Peace at our service center at New Windsor, Maryland. By spelling the musical notes elegantly drawn on the decorated page, we discovered that she was engaged.

After I was trained as the Stephen Minister Leader, I led a training class for persons at Bethel to learn to give distinctively Christian care to individuals in crisis or problem situations. Usually the Bethel Stephen ministers were assigned persons who needed care. But one very windy rainy night we were having our Stephen ministry meeting in the Bethel Basement when the tornado siren went off. We heard the church door open and a lady and some of her family members from a nearby house trailer entered soaking wet. Our Stephen ministers sprang into action. They found comforters to wrap and warm the wet persons. We talked with them and discovered that especially the mother had a lot of needs and health problems. God sent us this family and our Stephen Ministers had a long, caring relationship with these wonderful people.

On the night of December, 12, 1993 Verne's and my schedules allowed us to accept an invitation to go on the Holy Walk at Bremen, Indiana. For one and a half hours we were a Biblical family from Hebron going to Bethlehem, the city of our ancestors, to be counted and to pay our taxes. We each had scrolls of identification which we presented whenever the brusque Roman soldiers demanded. We encountered shepherds with their sheep, angels, the innkeeper, all kinds of shops and wares, fishermen mending their nets, the Bethlehem synagogue where a "priest" read from Isaiah the words, "For unto us a child is born, unto us a son is given. . ." We found Mary, Joseph and Baby Jesus, the wise men and also the Cross of Calvary. The 3000 residents of Bremen hosted 10,000 persons in three evenings. Three hundred persons worked to put on the production. Yes, we did get our scrolls stamped when we were numbered and our family head, Hosea, who was also our guide, paid his taxes.

I continued to accumulate memories of work, family and community events in 1994. I added financial responsibilities to my job description at Camp Mack and took an accounting class at Ivy Tech in Warsaw to help facilitate this increased responsibility. I did less curriculum writing as Camp began purchasing curriculum.

The postcard I got from England was held with a magnet to our refrigerator for a long time. It was from our son John who was doing computer consulting there during January and February.

In March, Verne and I fulfilled all county and state requirements for having a home business. We began sharing with others more explicitly the benefits of these natural Shaklee products that we had learned about when our son Verne was diagnosed with rheumatic fever about twenty years earlier.

April 1st was Verne Henry's birthday, Good Friday, and our daughter Barb and Rob Dickason's wedding rehearsal. After the rehearsal we celebrated Verne's birthday with Dickasons at a bed and breakfast in Syracuse where they were staying and looked at pictures of the wedding couple from their younger years. Earlier that day Rob's mother, Lowie, and I sat next to each other on our living room couch each hemming a section of the very full skirt on the silk wedding dress that Barb had made.

The wedding was at 10:30 a.m. on Saturday in Wampler Retreat Center at Camp Mack. Pictures of family members of other generations set on the fireplace mantle symbolized the "cloud of witnesses."

Potted spring flowers were decorations. Barb carried white calla lilies. Barb and Rob wrote their own vows. The unfamiliar vows did not bring my father's favor. He even thought they weren't married, because he didn't hear the traditional words. My stepmother, Marian, was not feeling well. She stayed at our house and didn't come to the wedding. Grandpa Verne Ernest and Esther came with Esther in her wheelchair. This was her last trip away from home.

Because of the Dickason family's missionary experiences living in India, Lowie made some Indian dishes for the noon meal and I made "American" food. Ruth Ann made the lovely wedding cake decorated predominantly in fresh orchids. After the celebration the newly weds had a challenge getting into their car which their brothers had wrapped securely in plastic wrap.

That night and the next morning I tried to call my father to be sure he was home safely. He didn't answer. Later Easter evening we learned that my dad had taken a wrong turn and instead of heading toward Warren and Bristolville, Ohio, he drove to Detroit. I was very glad to learn he and Marian were finally home safely.

Some of our family members were soon together again. This time we were at the Poplar Ridge Church of the Brethren near Defiance, Ohio celebrating the life of Esther Leininger, Verne Henry's mother and my wonderful mother-in-law who passed away on April 25, 1994, just 23 days after Barb and Rob's wedding. Years before, I learned lots of things from Esther. I learned how to make some of the family's favorite recipes: navy bean soup, boiled dinner (I loved it but never could make it like Esther did.), acorn squash and sausage, and cereal cookies, Verne and I lived with her and Grandpa Verne, and I commuted to Defiance College while Verne Henry was in his last year of seminary and came home on weekends. Esther and I had time to talk and also do things like occasionally shopping together.

At that time, Verne and Kathy lived at Sunbury, Ohio and Verne was working on his doctorate in math at Ohio State University. We enjoyed having our granddaughter, Sarah, with us during our vacation the week before her brother, Caleb John, was born. Caleb arrived on Saturday, May 28, 1994. On Sunday the 29th we and Sarah visited the rest of her family at the hospital and then preceded them to their home. Sarah thought that her baby brother could use the doll cradle that her grandpa Verne had made for her. Her parents showed her how he would fit, but that wasn't his bed.

Sarah also stayed with us much of the time later that summer when her parents and her Uncle John were leading a Junior-High age wilderness camp at Camp Mack. These are probably the longest time periods I had with Sarah until she entered Manchester College (now Manchester University) and I became her piano accompanist when she performed with her clarinet.

The Home Health Care Services of Kosciusko County presented their second Annual Festival of Trees as a benefit for the Home Health Care Endowment Fund from November 30-December 4, 1994. As a member of the Board of Directors, Verne helped to find the necessary persons to make this happen. Each of the 51 tress at the Festival had a designer, a theme, and a sponsor. A number of tree judges were also needed. This was a beautiful and creative display of trees with many different themes. I enjoyed being able to enjoy the trees when it was Verne's turn to greet guests.

In 1995 Pastor Verne added the Northern Indiana District Church of the Brethren Board to his list of responsibilities and continued to serve on the Home Health Board of Kosciusko County.. During the year Verne began a drama club at church and we were challenged by dramas at least once a month. I continued to direct a musical each year. On November 12 we presented the musical, *Beginnings,* for a full church audience. Members of our four area churches sang, acted and played instruments for the telling of beginning in the Old Testament and new beginnings with the New Testament and the story of Jesus.

Verne's mother had been gone about a year when his father, Verne Ernest, became seriously ill. He stayed with us from the end of May through most of August except for his two hospital stays. Ruth Ann, his daughter, who was a teacher and out of school for the summer came during the week to help with her father while Phyllis was working.

Barbara graduated from Manchester College (now Manchester University) in May of 1995. She sewed a little black cap and gown for Sean Garrett. Sean had been born at Kosciusko Community Hospital in Warsaw, Indiana on October 5, 1994 to Barb and Rob during Barb's senior year of college. His parents were living at a house in North Manchester at the time and Barb planned and prepared food for a lovely reception there after her graduation. She, Rob and Sean lived in our basement during June and then moved into the home they purchased at Cassopolis, Michigan on July 4th. That summer our house was home to four generations. The youngest member kept us entertained as he loved to dance.

On Saturday, September 30, Pastor Verne came down with a high temperature. I used what he had prepared and preached for him the next day. I do not remember what I preached, only that I got it delivered. On Monday the X-rays showed that he had pneumonia. He was still tiring easily by the end of the month and missed four-year-old grand-daughter Sarah's birthday party.

Thankfully, Verne was well enough to go with me to his father's where we and our children and grandchildren celebrated Thanksgiving. The family worked to help Grandpa Verne cut wood. Verne Henry was well enough to run the buzz saw to saw wood to supply his dad for the winter. His dad was also well enough to enjoy being at home.

Life continued to be full in 1995. Verne especially enjoyed working with youth on short dramas for worship. I limited piano lessons to Tuesdays by starting to work at Camp early so that I could be home to begin my evening of ten lessons at 3:30 p.m.

I always loved going to Church of the Brethren Annual Conferences, seeing friends from across the country, and enjoying great music and great speakers. Some business was necessary also. Conference was the most fun when all, or at least some, of our family members were there. Conference in 1996 at Cincinnati, Ohio was a special one. Our son, John, and his friend, Alice Ann Peters, came to conference, found us, and shared that they were engaged. The wedding would be on my

birthday, September 20, 1997, at Saint Ignus,
Michigan, Alice's (we call her Allison) home area.

Early on the morning of August 8, 1996 Verne and I
headed to Saint Joseph's Hospital at Mishawaka,
Indiana to pick up Sean whom his parents had taken
with them to the hospital when Barb went into labor
with our granddaughter, Morgan Greer. The nurses
seemed surprised that Sean was there and probably
were relieved when we whisked him away. Later in
the day we took him back and we all marveled at his
beautiful sister.

Meanwhile, whenever he could eek out some time off,
Pastor Verne worked with Barb and Rob at remodeling
their house in Cassopolis, Michigan and getting it
ready to sell. Barb and Rob were moving to Syracuse,
New York after Christmas as Barb received a full
scholarship to Syracuse University for graduate study
in philosophy. Classes were to begin January 14, 1997.

I remember sanding drywall with gloves on and still
ruining my fingernails. Carleta Jay, who lived in staff
housing at Camp, had opened a nail business and gave
me a free manicure. I chose to have clear polish.
Soon after getting my nails done professionally for the
only time in my life, I put on gloves and helped sand
drywall at Cassopolis. Even through the gloves, my

nails were ruined. I don't even think they were pretty for 24 hours.

Our fifth grandchild, Micah Timothy, was born to Verne and Kathy on February 10, 1997. Like his brother, Caleb, Micah was born while the family lived at Sunbury, Ohio. His father, Verne Edward received his doctorate in Mathematics from Ohio State University on June 13 in the first-ever rained out, or should I say flooded out, ceremony at Ohio State. It was a "wade in the water" day. It is a good thing that Verne Henry and I didn't try to go.

Pastor Verne completed ten years of ministry as the Pastor of the Bethel Congregation in 1997. To celebrate this milestone, Bethel Church held a big celebration on Sunday, September 14, with much reminiscing.

Our son, John, and Alice Peters' wedding invitations invited guests to their wedding on September 20, 1997 at Saint Ignus, Michigan. The invitations also stated there would be a mystery event between the ceremony and the dinner reception. What was the mystery event and where would it be? John and Allison did an extraordinarily good job of keeping this event a secret.

The bride was beautiful in her lovely dress with a lace bodice and lace continuing to the hips. Long sleeves were of matching lace. The material of the skirt and train had a design similar to the design of the lace. Allison's niece, Jennifer, and John's niece, Sarah, were flower girls. The flower girls went with the bridal party and got their hair done in the morning, quite a first for our granddaughter, Sarah. The flower girls and bridesmaids wore hunter green gowns.

The wedding colors were hunter green and burgundy. Satin bows in alternating wedding colors were at each pew. I made a burgundy colored dress and jacket to wear for the wedding. To make it possible for Allison's mother, Freda, to attend the wedding, John and Allison hired her mother's nurse's aide to help her.

At the close of the ceremony in the beautiful Catholic Church at Saint Ignus, the priest shared that the couple had an announcement to make. John announced that all guests (220 or more) were invited to a cruise on Lake Huron. As we left we received maps directing us to the ship. The ship was decorated with balloons and banners and candy kisses were at the tables.

The reception dinner was in the hotel where our rooms were. I was able to care for little ones in my room when it got late. I cared for Sean and Morgan. I don't remember whether Kathy took her little ones to their room early. Grandpa Leininger came in when it was probably past his bedtime. I thought he was going to bed. No, he just came for a pit stop. He stayed at the reception until the very end. Grandpa Verne Ernest was enjoying every minute.

For a few days after the wedding, Verne and I enjoyed some relaxing time in Michigan. We visited Tahquamenon Falls, walked through an Indian village, explored trails, looked at lighthouses and shopped at a woolen outlet. We were away from most responsibilities and were having a wonderful time together.

Something new this fall was a series of five "End of Life Decisions" meetings. For one of the meetings we met with the Funeral Director from Mishler Funeral Home.

Another first that fall was the youth's crayon melt down fundraiser. The youth collected crayons, peeled off their papers, sorted them by colors and melted crayons of each color separately in the top of a double boilers. The melted wax was then poured into Disney character molds and other molds to make fancy crayons. The youth sold these to make money for National Youth Conference.

A committee was formed in 1997 to look at ways to grow the Bethel Church. The committee came to the church with some ambitious ideas. One recommendation from this committee was to ask the District to request young couples from area churches to make Bethel their church home and to bring some young energy and hopefully some youth to Bethel. There were also suggestions for things that the Bethel members could do to reach out. It seemed like the response to the committee's recommendations was positive. A congregational business meeting was held on October 27. I don't remember how the vote was at that meeting. My gut says that it was positive and didn't change until the "parking lot business meeting," where persons recognized that growing Bethel would take a lot of work.

Church Board met for its reorganizational meeting on November 11. It was now clear that the Bethel congregation did not feel they had the energy to tackle the committee's plan for growth. About this time Pastor Verne suggested that Bethel consider merging with another congregation. He had in mind a joint pastorate with the Milford First Brethren as they and Bethel worked together annually on Sunrise and Christmas Eve services. The Board picked up on Verne's idea, but they wanted to see whether or not the Bethany Church of the Brethren would consider a merger with Bethel. The Board set November 24th as the date for another Congregational Business meeting. It was unusual to have two congregational meetings in two months. Usually there were two Congregational

Business meetings in a year - one in the spring and one in the fall or at the most one a quarter. Change was on the horizon.

As I share in my chapter on my 25 years at Camp Mack, I was blessed with numerous opportunities for travel and spiritual growth and inspiration. The 1997 Christian Camping International Conference was at Orlando, Florida. It was a great week with many of the Camp Mack Staff also at the conference. Speakers presented wonderful Christian messages while workshops dealt with new ideas in our areas of service.

We were on vacation the week after Christmas. Still we went to our food co-op in Goshen to help with inventory on December 30, 1997 beginning at 5:30 p.m. Once in September and a couples times in both October and November Verne had volunteered at the co-op from 9:30 a.m. to 3:30 p.m. on his day off. I was at Camp and so it was just Verne volunteering those times. We both liked to support the effort to bring healthy, natural foods to our community at a time when organic foods were not as available in grocery stores as they became twenty years later.

January 26, 1998 was the night of yet another congregational business meeting. After this meeting a merger committee consisting of members from Bethany, Bethel and the Northern Indiana District

Leadership began working to chart the course for a merger of Bethany Church of the Brethren on U.S. 6 and Bethel Church of the Brethren in Milford, congregations barely five miles apart. Betty Smith and Elmer Sorenson represented Bethel and worked with selected Bethany members and also the Northern Indiana District Board Chair, Ray Barkey, to work out details of merger. Years before there had been some talk of merger and a suggestion to build a new building between the two existing ones. That merger did not happen. Both congregations had since made improvements to their own facilities.

TWO BECOME ONE

From September through May, Bethany had worship prior to Sunday School and the 9:30 a.m. Worship usually ended about 10:30 a.m. Bethel had Sunday School first and would be having announcement time in Worship around 10:30 a.m. It was decided that both congregations would have special council meetings and each would vote on the merger of Bethel and Bethany close to 10:30 a.m. on May 17, 1998. The votes were both affirmative. The two would become one.

The merged congregation would meet at the Bethany location where the sanctuary, fellowship hall, offices and restrooms were accessible without steps. Bethel had lots of room, but the only things on the entry level were the pastor's study, the restrooms and a secretary's room. There were steps up to the sanctuary. There were steps down to the basement, kitchen and fellowship hall. The education addition had an upper and lower level each accessible only by steps.

The closing services were scheduled for June 14, less than a month after the vote. What an amazing amount of work happened in that short time. Written memories and pictures were collected from former and current members and compiled in a fifty page, 5 ½ by 8 ½ inch booklet. The cover design was like a quilt with each square noting a group or activity at Bethel. This cover design was also used for both the morning and afternoon closing services.

Let me share one unique contribution to this memory booklet, something I didn't share earlier in writing about Bethel. This contribution was written by Donna Angle, Children's Librarian- Milford Public Library. She writes:

> In August 1994, the library was remodeling and looking for a home,
>
> So the books, videos, computers, staff, and shelves set out to roam…
>
> To a place on the corner of Catherine and East, called Bethel Church.
>
> It was there that the library found a temporary perch.
>
> The church family obliged and was more than gracious,
>
> To provide an area that the collection found quite spacious
>
> There was a "parson type" person by the name of Verne,
>
> Who remained ever calm and never seemed to squirm

When invaded by the public and visits of the kids. . .

Always accommodating and accepting of the situation he is.

The library dwelt there for more than a year,

When renovation was finished and time came to disappear.

And move back to the Carnegie building that the public holds dear.

So kudos to Verne, board, and congregation members. . . thanks for the pleasure.

You gave a gift that will forever be treasured!

I do remember that moving the library into and out of the church was a huge undertaking. I also learned many interesting things about members and former members by reading the Memories booklet.

A memory room was set up on the lower level of the educational wing. Photos, snapshots, mementos, programs of past happenings were displayed and arranged by Annabelle Replogle and Betty Witman. The corner stone was opened and its contents were on display.

Camp Mack staff provided child care during the morning worship and the First Brethren Youth provided child care for the afternoon service.

According to the day's programs, I was organist for both services. The District Pastor, Herman Kauffman, spoke at the 10:30 worship service on "The Journey from Bethel." Susan Weybright sang "Go My Children," and the Bethel Choir sang "Let Us Serve Him. About 120 persons attended the morning service.

Guests continued to arrive after worship. The basement was full as persons enjoyed the carry-in meal. The afternoon service was a time of sharing of memories – memories from former members and memories from current members. To assure enough hymnals for the estimated crowd of 150 persons, both red and blue hymnals were used with hymn numbers listed for both. Bertha Moneyheffer and Juanita Yoder (both no longer living on earth) sang a duet, "But This I Know." The Bethany Choir led by Andy Gall, sang "I Will Give Thanks."

After Northern Indiana Moderator Elect, Ray Barkey, the Chairperson of the Merger Committee, made comments on merger, he, District Pastor Herman Kauffman and Bethel Pastor Verne Leininger led the service of communion. Communion was served by Bethel Deacons and Bethany Ministry Commission Members.

We sang "Blest Be the Tie That Binds" for the closing hymn. After the benediction in unison, I played Stickles "Triumphal March" for the postlude.

Following the afternoon service each person received a carnation and each family was presented a memory booklet. VCR tapes could be ordered.

The two congregations were now one. But like a marriage there was a lot of work to be done. Bethel would need to be appraised to be sold. The church building would need to be watched over as it sat empty. The men of the church would continue to do the yard work for this summer. The date for the sale of items from the Church for Bethel members was set for Tuesday, June 30, at 7:00 p.m. The box containing persons' requests for items would be opened and the items sold. .Persons worked for two weeks on Tuesdays and Thursdays putting things to be sold on tables. Then there was the question of how to distribute the church's assets when the building sold. And letters of membership would need to be sent mostly to Bethany or another church of the Bethel member's choice.

Although I have many memories and pieces of information about the merger, I had forgotten this detail until I read it in the June 3rd edition of Milford's newspaper, the Mail-Journal. In extensive coverage of the merger, I read "Final approval for the merger cannot be given until the Northern Indiana District

Conference the third week in September. In the meantime, the churches will start holding services together later this month."

I should note that Verne and I did not move our memberships to Bethany at that time. And soon Bethany's Pastor Steve Durr resigned from Bethany. That gave the combined congregation opportunity to search for a pastor together. It would not be "my pastor" or "your pastor" but "our pastor." That may be one reason that the merged church thrived. Members worked together and grew the church.

The After Ministry of Bethel

Bethel was not empty or for sale for long. Word of Truth Ministries had been looking for a permanent worship facility and the Bethel building met their needs. By winter they had purchased the building and were worshipping there.

From the proceeds of the sale, Bethel gave donations to the National Church of the Brethren ministry, the Northern Indiana District, and to Camp Mack According to Herb Reuter, the former Bethel members decided to give $70,000 to Bethany where many of them were now members. Bethany installed air conditioning and applied the remainder of the Bethel monies to the new classroom addition. Bethel also provided the money, about $35,000, I'm told, for materials to build a Habitat for Humanity house in Milford. Betty Smith shared with me that Elmer Sorenson headed up the Habitat building project in Milford.

I will always remember our time at Bethel. Bethel's legacy will not be forgotten.

What Next? – 1998, Part 2!

Bethel and Bethany were now one. Verne's last date of service to Bethel was scheduled for June 30, 1998. Verne wrote a final newsletter describing the closing celebration and sharing the time for the auction of Bethel items for members. He cleaned out his office.

On Monday, July 27, he began as Interim Pastor at Columbia City Church of the Brethren. From my perspective, this was a good time for the Columbia City Church. Verne, knowing his time there was limited, could lead them without hesitation to look at themselves and discover why a number of their pastors had stayed for very brief times, sometimes less than a year. Verne also sought help from a reconciling –type person (I forget her credentials) who led meetings helping the members uncover and learn from their past. After Verne served just over a year at Columbia City as Interim, Columbia City called Pastor Dennis B. who, at this writing has given wonderful leadership there for over 20 years.

The Columbia City Church building had steep steps to the entrance. The restrooms were in the basement. I remember the basement walls at the bottom of the stairs as crumbly. But the people were joyous, loving and welcoming to us. Verne worked there part-time, with one of his days being Wednesday. He would come home and get me when I got done at Camp and we would go together to Columbia City for the evening meal and evening children's and Bible study activities. Verne led Love Feast there on October 4 and had a baptism on October 11. I remember singing in the Christmas Cantata – yes singing – not accompanying and not directing. I enjoyed the music with no pressure of responsibility. I want to share that the Columbia City congregation built a beautiful and truly accessible addition within the past five years. They are thriving.

On Saturday, July 31 we went to Sunbury, Ohio to help Verne Edward and Kathy pack to move to Timberville, Virginia. Verne had accepted the offer to teach math at Bridgewater College, our Church of the Brethren College at Bridgewater, Virginia.

Earlier that summer, Verne Edward received his doctorate in Mathematics from Ohio State University in the university's only rained out ceremony where students and guests waded in deep water only to find out that the electronic systems were also rained out and the ceremony was cancelled. He received instructions for going to a room to pick up his doctoral stole and robe.

Verne called his father with a question whenever he was considering a job offer. His question was, "Is there a Church of the Brethren nearby?' Then his father would get out his yearbook of Churches of the

Brethren and he and V.E. would calculate how far away from a teaching post the nearest Church of the Brethren would be.

There are many Churches of the Brethren and also Mennonites in the Bridgewater and Timberville area. Kathy's Uncle Joe called the Linville Creek Church because he knew someone there. Two men from Linville Creek helped them move in. But I am ahead of the story.

Because of Pastor Verne's new responsibilities at Columbia City, we could not be a part of the caravan that left their home after Sunday's worship service. Verne Edward drove the rented moving van and John drove his own vehicle pulling his black enclosed trailer loaded mostly with Verne and Kathy's plants.. Verne and Kathy were initially purchasing ninety-some acres (they purchased additional land later). Verne Edward's grandfather, Verne Ernest, thought they needed a tractor. So he loaded one on a trailer he would pull behind his truck and joined the caravan to Virginia.

Verne and Kathy had warned drivers, especially Grandpa with his heavy load, that their driveway was very long and steep. They were moving to the Shenandoah Valley and the mountains.

When they finally reached the driveway, Grandpa led the way down. His "slow" was not slow enough and his truck slid in the loose gravel and came to rest against a post by the apple orchard. John had stopped to see how grandpa made it down. John helped unload the tractor and Grandpa was able to go. Kathy shares that she was afraid there would be a big pile up. She thought that the moving van brakes wouldn't stop them in time. But God heard prayers for their safe trip. There was no pile up and there were no injuries. Verne Edward rode back to Ohio with John the next day to get his car.

After a long and tiring trip, they had reached their destination. Kathy shares that I had sent soup which they had that evening. Their new church friends wouldn't leave until baby Micah's swing was securely hanging from a tree. Verne and Kathy and their children have been very active in many areas of ministry in the Linville Creek Church ever since that day in 1998 when they moved to Timberville, Virginia.

Grandpa Verne Ernest turned 80 years old later that August on the 21st. Verne Henry's sister, Ruth Ann, and Verne Henry and I planned an 80th birthday party for Grandpa Verne on Saturday, August 22nd. We had plenty of space for the crowd of relatives and church friends who came to celebrate as we held it at his church, the Poplar Ridge Church of the Brethren near Defiance, Ohio. I don't remember what all we served, but I do remember that Ruth Ann again made the beautifully decorated cake. Dad seemed thrilled to see everyone.

Verne and I enjoyed an awesome experience together at the Shaklee New Supervisors' Convention in San Francisco, California from November 19-22, 1998. Shaklee arranged for us to travel on American Airlines from South Bend to Chicago and then from O'Hare to San Francisco. They met us at baggage claim, loaded our bags and us into a motor coach and we went to the very fancy Fairmont Hotel. Our bags soon arrived at our room with no effort by us.

The welcome reception was a taste of San Francisco. Following a map, we went from room to room where each had a buffet set up representing a local area. Each food area had entertainment as well. We went first to the Fisherman's Wharf. I really liked the smoked salmon. A street band was playing there. When we went to the China area I chose duck and vegetables. Acrobats were performing there. At the Mexican station there were dancers and music. We saw the "spaghetti lady" outside the door to Italy, but we did not eat there. Japan's station had fortune cookies and tea and a koto player whom we enjoyed. Chiradelli Chocolate was the dessert station. A harpist played relaxing music there.

This was just the first night, and the only time we moved from area to area to eat. There were healthy breakfast buffets with many kinds of fresh fruits, Shaklee shakes and other options. One day we had an interesting hour-long meeting about how Enfuselle skin care was developed and tested. Then we went on a tour of San Francisco from 10:30 – 2:30. We stopped at Treasure Island. We looked at the Oakland Bay Bridge. For lunch we had box lunches with chicken breast, macaroni salad, fresh fruit – melons, etcetera – roll, brownie, a mint and bottled water or juices.

Saturday evening was a sit-down banquet done in two seatings and two recognition programs. Three Community Caregiver Awards were given, An award of $5, 000 was given to each of the three winner's project or charity. Shaklee Care Packages were also being sent to Shaklee distributors who requested them to distribute in areas of hurricane damage.

When we arrived back at our hotel room on Saturday night the bed was turned down and there was candy and also a package on the bed. This may have been when we received the wind up snow globe music box that played "I Left My Heart in San Francisco." Sadly, years later I dropped it and broke the globe. I still have the little red, black and gold colored cable car that says San Francisco Municipal RY. That was a gift another time.

When we learned that we qualified for the San Francisco trip, we asked Shaklee if we could stop at the Shaklee manufacturing plant at Norman, Oklahoma on our way home. Shaklee agreed to arrange the transportation, but we would need to pay for the extra travel. After conference we flew to Dallas Fort Worth on a Boeing 767 and then on to Oklahoma City. We rented a car and drove to Norman where we ate supper at a Cracker Barrel. I remember the waitress talking about some of her relatives who work for Shaklee and how the longevity is so great there that it is difficult to get a job. People don't leave.

Monday we toured the plant. We were impressed by the face masks and hair nets, especially on one man who was watching a machine that reminded me of a clothes dryer putting the coating on the vita-lea pills. We saw other reasons why people liked working there. Employees could go to the dining room and take as many Shaklee supplements as they felt their body needed. They just could not carry them out or take them home. They could also use the provided exercise room.

Our travel itinerary from Shaklee shows us leaving Oklahoma City at 5:42 p.m. and leaving O'Hare at 8:25 p.m. arriving at South Bend at 10:15 p.m. Monday evening, November 23, 1998.

After the rush of Christmas events, hanging of the greens, cantata, and children's program, 1998 was soon just wonderful memories.

Beginnings and Endings – 1999

The familiar Ecclesiastes passage describes this year: "For everything there is a season and a time for every matter under heaven: a time to be born, and a time to die; . ." Chapter 3: 1-2a.

On February 26, Leah Elizabeth Leininger greeted her parents at 9:45 a.m. Leah was John and Allison's first child and our sixth grandchild. I was invited and honored to spend the second week of Leah's life helping to care for her and Allison, as John had taken off work during the first week of her life.

Verne Henry and I arrived at John and Allison's on Sunday afternoon and Verne left Monday morning. On Monday evening Allison received the very sad news that her mother had passed away. After I helped them pack for the long trip to Michigan's Upper Peninsula for the funeral, Verne met us on their way on Wednesday.

And so it was that I was home the next evening, Thursday, March 11, when I received the call that my father had passed away. This was eighteen years to the day after my mother's passing on March 11, 1981. That bothered me to the point of wondering about requesting an autopsy. But what good would that do? I did not pursue the autopsy route.

My father had changed through the years. At the time of my wedding he was adamant that no black girl friend of mine was allowed to come to our house or be a part of the wedding. Years later he was placed in a hospital room with a black preacher. They must have had some good discussions, because my father thought this preacher was really great. Once when we went home for a visit, Dad took us to the black church where his hospital friend preached. Dad also looked forward to Jehovah witness visits. He would invite them in to sit with him while he pointed out scriptures to them. Dad also did prison ministry with a Christian friend.

Verne Henry preached my father's funeral, a difficult task indeed! John took the new mother and the precious infant home from their long, sad and tiring trip and came on to Bristolville, Ohio to be a pall-bearer for his Grandpa Mahan's funeral.

Two of our children moved in 1999. Our daughter, always an advocate for peace, accepted the challenges of her new position as Program Coordinator for the On Earth Peace association. I had to change the address for their family in my records from Syracuse, New York to Mount Airy, Maryland. John and Allison purchased a lovely large home at Beavercreek, Ohio in June when Leah was four months old. They have lived at this home over twenty years. That address change has lasted a while.

301

Verne Henry completed his interim pastorate at Columbia City Church of the Brethren on August 15. He had served there just a couple weeks over a year. We had continued to live at our home at Milford, commuting to Columbia City. We both enjoyed the ministry and the wonderful people at Columbia City. While we waited for the Lord's leading as to Verne's future ministry, Verne began drawing some of his retirement. It seems that our Lord knew that Verne Henry would be needed with his father in September and also would need a lot of time to help sort Dad's "stuff."

Verne Ernest Leininger, Verne Henry's father, loved visiting his grandchildren and great-grandchildren. On the weekend of September 18-19, Grandpa Verne was at Verne and Kathy's home in Timberville, Virginia. John's and Barb's families were there. All our children and grandchildren were together and Verne Henry and I couldn't be there because we were at our church's District Conference.

On Sunday afternoon, Grandpa, or Dad as we call him, wanted to see all of Verne Edward and Kathy's ninety-some acres. We were told that he didn't want to ride a tractor; he wanted to walk. We heard that he seemed to have a great time. We later saw many pictures taken that day of him and his six great grandchildren, ranging in age from Sarah, age 8 to Leah, a little over six months old.

Dad had lots to see. Besides the fields and garden, Verne and Kathy have a cave on their property registered with the Virginia State Registry of Caves. They also had the remains of an old homestead and barn and some very old farm equipment – interesting things for Dad to explore. At that time their animals included three head of cattle, three goats, three sheep, a Chesapeake retriever, ducks, chickens, guineas, cats, guinea pigs and a bird. Their acreage and their number of animals would increase over the years.

The next day, Monday, September 20th, Dad was too sick to get out of bed. He refused medical treatment and declared that he was going back home to Ohio with our son John and his family on Tuesday morning. John called us to meet Dad because Dad was too sick to care for himself. We stayed with him at his home on Tuesday night.

On Wednesday morning, Verne Henry made arrangements with the neighbor to continue doing chores and we brought Dad to our home. He continued to grow weaker and Verne and his sister, Ruth Ann, took Dad to Goshen Hospital on Friday night. He lay hooked up to a respirator and a number of monitors.

On Tuesday afternoon Verne called me at Camp Mack. They were going to remove Dad's respirator. Did I want to be there? I said I was coming. He and Ruth would wait for me before letting them proceed. I left Camp immediately and drove to the hospital. When I arrived and greeted Dad, who had been lying still and not moving, he reached his hand up toward the respirator and indicated he wanted it off. I think he may have done that earlier when Ruth Ann arrived but I wasn't there then.

The hospital chaplain, Clare Hostetler, came and read scripture and had prayer. Then from memory he sang all the verses of "My Life Flows On." When he finished the last verse, the monitors were flat. Dad was gone, quickly, quietly, peacefully. He died of pneumonia. He was 81 years old.

New that fall was the first annual Camp Alexander Mack Festival. I had been working with a steering committee and ten subcommittees for two years to birth this Festival. (See the chapter on my time at Camp Mack.) It was scheduled for the first Saturday in October. The first Festival celebrated the 50th anniversary of the painting of the mural history of the Church of the Brethren. Six fifteen feet wide mural sections hang on each side of Quinter-Miller Auditorium at Camp Mack for a total of 90 feet per side. Verne's dad grew a beard over 50 years before to help the mural artist, Medford Neher, get the beards painted realistically. Dad had been re-growing a beard for the past year and was planning to share his story of the painting of the murals at the festival, scheduled for

October 2nd. At his death, Dad had a long white beard.
The family graciously held Dad's body until after the
festival. Dad's visitation was Sunday, October 3 and
the funeral was Monday, October 4th.

Another first for 1999 was my not being home to cook
Thanksgiving dinner for whoever could come. Verne
and I and twelve other Camp Mack staff attended a
very inspirational Christian Camping International
Conference at New Orleans from November 21 to 24.
That was not my first CCI Conference. The new
experience was traveling with many of the staff to
Lillian, Alabama after conference to the home of
Arden and Charmaine Ball. Arden was the first Camp
Mack Executive Director that I worked for when I
began at Camp Mack. Verne and I stayed in the Ball's
travel trailer. Some staff stayed in the house. We
enjoyed seeing Arden and Charmaine. We worked
together getting the meal and had a wonderful
Thanksgiving celebration there and flew home on
Friday.

Through joys and sorrows, birth and death, and all life
in between, God was with us in 1999 and is with us
still.

North Liberty

Verne and I wondered what God's plan for Verne's ministry was now. He had been busy with gardening and our Shaklee business and camp events since he completed his interim at Columbia City in August of 1999. Should he look for full-time ministry or another interim?

Verne was called to serve as Interim Pastor at North Liberty beginning May 1, 2000. As I recall, this was at least a 35 minute drive, maybe longer. North Liberty had a parsonage next to the church. I would come home from Camp Mack, if I worked on a Saturday, pack clothes and food quickly and we would go to North Liberty. Furniture was provided at the parsonage. Verne's office was in the church.

Verne's gifts were needed here. There were disagreements among members over various things, like the constitution that was being revised. Verne always listened to each side of an issue. I feel his biggest compliment while serving at North Liberty was from a member who was a business owner. The man said that he was amazed that Pastor Verne was not political. In other words, Verne didn't take sides. Verne did expect persons to listen to God and to each other at meetings. He told me once that when an argument was getting loud at a meeting, he raised his voice (very unusual) and exclaimed loudly, "Be quiet; let's pray." He says that everyone "got very quiet."

North Liberty had a number of gifts as a congregation. One was their elaborate Vacation Bible School. They put a lot of time and energy into decorations, skits, crafts, recreation, music and snacks to highlight the year's theme. North Liberty also provided leadership frequently through the years for Camp Mack's Colony Camp for families. The North Liberty men also made and donated a number of picnic tables to Camp Mack. Verne continued to direct Mildly Wild Camp for a week in the summer while serving at North Liberty.

Another unique event at North Liberty was their Saturday Super Singing Extravaganza. This was a 5:30 p.m. carry-in followed by all kinds of music. I played my folk harp for this meeting, the evening after my breast biopsy.

I was surprised that North Liberty had no choir. I set out to interest the congregation in having a Christmas Cantata. They were willing to try, but it was difficult for the choir members who had never sung together. Most did not read music. But, mission accomplished. They stuck with it.

During our time at North Liberty, on New Year's Eve, December 31, 2000, our seventh grandchild, Dylan Leininger was born to John and Allison. The doctors decided he needed to come early to protect his mother's health. On Friday, January 5th, Verne's sister, Ruth Ann, drove and we went to John and Allison's. Ruth went to the hospital with John to see Dylan that evening. Ruth's son, Kevin, had been premature and Ruth was encouraging. Ruth stayed all night and went home on Saturday.

Saturday afternoon, while John and Allison went to the hospital to see Dylan who was hooked up to medical equipment and IV's, I worked on laundry and bathed Leah after her nap. I don't know how John and Allison kept going. John was sick and Allison had just given birth. They were both worn out. That evening I went with John and Allison to see Dylan. Leah also went. Dylan had a value that needed to close to his lungs. So he was taken off his mother's milk which he was receiving through a tube down his nose while he sucked his pacifier. He instead received medication to constrict vessels to close the valve. That night Leah was sick. Allison called me in the night to help with Leah while she expressed milk for Dylan. I was happy she felt fee to call me.

I got plenty of healing rest at John and Allison's. John was still sick on Sunday, so we didn't go to church. I had to be quiet if anyone was sleeping or resting. So there was no running the dryer or anything that made noise. It was good to be able to rest on Sunday.

Leah and I played together while John and Allison went to Allison's doctor's appointment on Monday morning. All three of the family slept that afternoon, so I had a forced rest. I could read and pray and do the chi and fir. When Leah awoke from her nap, I played with her again while the others continued to rest. We read many books, put together puzzles, built with Lego blocks and even had a "tea party" while Grandma was visiting.

Ginger, the family dog, and I got along well when I took her out mornings and evenings. I think we both enjoyed our time outside. It gave me some fresh air and exercise and another focused conversation time with God. God answered prayers for the closing of Dylan's valve without him needing surgery.

I was glad for a long phone conversation with Verne Henry on Monday evening. His Wednesday was really full of appointments and meetings at North Liberty. He hoped to come on Thursday.

I have special memories of our time at North Liberty. Since the church was in town, we could walk downtown to shop and we could walk to visit members whose homes were close. There was a specialty shop with many novel gifts. I got a beautiful Angel Christmas tree topper like I'd always wanted at that store. We bought special gifts for grandchildren there like a rooster puppet and a chicken puppet that had little chicks.

Another reason that I am thankful that God called us to North Liberty is that I was wonderfully supported through my cancer ordeal. Ladies who had lived with cancer seemed to "come out of the woodwork." The church supported me as I ate a very restricted diet and didn't push me to eat sweets or foods at carry-ins that I felt I shouldn't eat.

One dear lady, told me about a book that had helped her on her cancer journey. Esther wished she could loan me the book by Bernie S. Siegel, M.D. called *Love, Medicine & Miracles.* But she had loaned it to someone else and didn't get it back. Well, I happened to have that book at home signed by the author whom Verne and I had heard speak once at Manchester College. Esther was right. It was a very helpful book during this time of my life.

North Liberty cared for their children with a Kids Fall Festival from 5-7 p.m. on Halloween. It provided fun, games, contests and candy. Not only did the children have fun, but it kept them off the streets. As I remember, the church also had a Christmas Project where children could purchase gifts for very little money for their family members.

Verne had office hours at North Liberty on certain days and we spent Saturday nights there. But we still lived at Milford. I continued working at Camp Mack. Verne was still on the Health Care Foundation Board and still volunteered at our natural foods co-operative in Goshen.

Verne's last day as Interim Pastor at North Liberty was January 14, 2002. I had been on my cancer journey during our North Liberty time and Verne had dealt with prostate issues. We are thankful for our experiences and the caring people there.

An Unwelcome Visitor

Discovery and Diagnosis

On September 24, 2000, my wonderful husband discovered a lump in my right breast, perhaps as big around as a dime. At 6:30 p.m. on the evening of October 3rd I had an appointment with my family doctor. Dr. Weybright said, "Yes, there is a lump. What do you want to do? Where do you want to go?"

I appreciated having a choice of where to go for treatment. My answer to the doctor's question was, "The Cancer Treatment Center of America at Goshen, Indiana." His office would make an appointment the next morning. (This was during the time when the Goshen Hospital was affiliated with the Cancer Center of America at Zion, Illinois.)

The next day, October 4, Dr. Weybright's nurse called me at work and said if I could get a mammogram at 11:30 that morning, Dr. Morris of the Cancer Center could see me tomorrow. Verne was at North Liberty. I called him and told him I was going; I took off work and went.

Interestingly, Goshen Hospital had just purchased a new machine for doing mammograms and was using it for the first time that week. Usually when I had mammograms, they were never right the first time and I had to have that "small amount" of radiation twice. Consequently, because I always had to have them done twice, I quit getting them and hadn't had one since 1991.

This was a sensitive machine. The technologist could not get the machine to snap the last picture of my right breast. (I think in the past that would have been a do-over.) In checking, the pressure needed tightening on the breast and the picture took. No do-overs!

On October 5, 2000, our Grandson Sean's sixth birthday, I met with Dr. Laura Morris, a very wonderful, young looking 40ish year old cancer surgeon who had taught at one of the Michigan Universities and was now pursuing a more natural approach to cancer care. She did an ultra sound and determined the lump was not liquid. She tried doing two needle biopsies; one with a small needle didn't work. One with a larger needle only produced red corpuscles. We scheduled surgery for 8:00 a.m. on October 13.

I was told to stop taking Shaklee Cor-Energy and Moodlift, so that the herbs Ginsing and St. John's Wort wouldn't interfere with anesthesia. Also, I chose to stop EPA and Garlic until after surgery as they are blood thinners. Per doctor's orders, I also stopped taking Shaklee Vita E three days prior to surgery.

October 13, 2000. Kathy Leininger's birthday. I arrived at the Goshen Hospital shortly before 6:30 a.m. All other others being prepared for surgery at that early hour were babies, toddlers and young children. I had registered by phone so I only had to sign a paper and let them copy my insurance card.

I took a Shaklee Bestwater bottle full of a quart of water and told the nurse that it was for after surgery. That was fine. I had not eaten or drank anything since midnight. I would not sign the surgery consent until I was certain that only the lump and some surrounding tissue would be removed.

After a nurse tried to start an IV and punctured a vein in my left arm, the anesthesiologist came in and offered to do it. He did it easily in my left wrist. I told the anesthesiologist that I wanted him to know three things: 1) I weigh 98 pounds; 2) I normally have low blood pressure (80/50 is good); 3) I have a low temperature.

Then my surgical nurse came in to meet me. He looked at my chart and asked, "Were you born Sept. 20, 1943?" I said, "Yes." He said, "So was I." So I smarted off, "And do you do Shaklee?" "Yes," he answered. So I continued, "Do you know Shirley Fike?" He said, "I've been to some of her meetings." His name is Leroy Cross. He would be back when it was time to go to surgery.

When Dr. Laura Morris came into my room, I told her about Leroy Cross. This was only her 2nd day (2nd Friday, also) of surgery at Goshen. She had not yet met Leroy. He came back about 7:50 a.m., I think, and pushed me on my bed to surgery. When we got there, Dr. Morris told Leroy she knew all about him and she had to put up with two of us Shaklee people!

After surgery I was back in my room and Verne was there. The clock showed 9:03. I sat in a big comfortable chair with my legs up and all cuddled in with blankets. The nurse brought my water. I drank nearly the entire quart. Verne had to keep adding water to my hospital mug.

I got dressed, used the bathroom and was wheeled by staff out of the hospital to our car at about 10:20 a.m. As I passed the anesthesiologist in the hall when I was leaving, he said, "I took into account the three things you told me." I hope I told him Thank you.

On the way home we stopped at Walmart. While I stayed in the car, Verne bought me some Tylenol and a beautiful pink potted miniature rose with 13 blooms. I took two Tylenol upon arriving home. Verne fixed lunch. At this writing all I remember is that it was something I'd fixed ahead. He and I fixed the evening meal together. By bedtime Friday night, I had used 6 Tylenol.

I did not go to work at Camp on Saturday. I took a total of four Tylenol on Saturday, to be sure I felt well for the evening at North Liberty's Super Singing Supper Sale Extravaganza. I fixed vegetables for the meeting: green beans, corn and a sprout salad that I made earlier in the day at home. At the silent auction we bought a lovely bowl made out of many kinds of wood and a doll swing. As I noted in my North Liberty story, I played two numbers on my folk harp for entertainment that evening.

On Sunday, I went to worship and Sunday school, had choir member, Goldie, over for lunch, directed the cantata practice and went home.

On Monday, October 16, I expected to hear from Dr. Laura Morris about my pathology report. She did not call.

October 17, 2000. We had a staff retreat at Camp Mack on Tuesday and Wednesday. On Tuesday Verne was at a South Bend hospital with a North Liberty member on his day off. He was home at about 3:00

p.m. when Dr. Morris called. The lump was cancerous. I called Verne at the end of the retreat that day to see if we'd heard. He said we'd talk when I got home and the Doctor would call me tonight at 7 p.m.

When I got home, Verne was talking to our son John on the phone. Verne asked if I wanted to learn the diagnosis while John was on the phone. I allowed Verne to tell John and me together. The diagnosis was lobular cancer. John had called to share the news that the sonogram shows a boy inside of Allison.

At 7:00 p.m., true to her word, Dr. Morris called. She recommends further surgery. More pathology reports will be done to see if this cancer will respond to estrogen blocker.
October 18, 2000. Our son John's 34th birthday. I shared with Becky, the Camp Mack Executive at the time, about my diagnosis. Then during this second day of staff retreat I shared with the entire staff. I told staff that I didn't want to be considered as sick and I did want lots of prayers.

Oct. 19, 2000 – Our good Christian friend, nurse, and person with an enormous amount of knowledge about natural healing remedies, Shirley Fike had arrived in Goshen the day before to visit family. At that time she and her husband lived on the Eastern Shore of Maryland where her husband was pasturing a church.

317

God told her to call me & see when my appointment was. She didn't know I had appointments that day. She called at 7:30 a.m. from her daughter's where she had agreed to babysit a grandson.

My first appointment that day was with Naturopath, Tim Birdsol from Zion, Illinois at 9:00 a.m. Shirley changed her plans, found someone else to watch her grandson and came to the hospital bringing a chi machine that she'd brought on the plane for me.

I listened as Shirley and Dr. Birdsol discussed my treatment. Should I take CoQ10 in dry pill from and eat some oil with it, as the Naturopath's recommended, or take Shaklee's oil based CoQ 10 capsule as Shirley argued. It was agreed I would take ten of Shaklee's 30mg soluble CoQ10 capsules a day. They agreed on my having 20 mg of Melatonin at bedtime. five C's (500 mg each) 4 x day, and five Carotomax 4 x a day. At that time there were only 30 Carotomax (or beta carotene) in a bottle, so we bought it by the case as one bottle lasted me just one and a half days,

Dr Birdsol liked the ingredients in Shaklee's Liver Detox and recommended I increase my intake of those to four a day. He also prescribed 10 cups worth of Yunnan Grade green tea a day.(That was very difficult to find. It was not a brand.) I could cut back on the tea I drank if I took some green tea capsules. (1 capsule = 2 cups tea), I would take optiflora and many, many other supplements. Shirley had brought the Chi machine to the appointment, and left information about it with Dr. Birdsol as the appointment was over an hour long and Shirley had to leave. I thought Verne was just going to put the chi in our car, but he was also taking Shirley over to where her grandchild was being babysat.

While Verne and Shirley were out, Shirley suggested to Verne that I have some cancer markers done – blood tests, perhaps CAT scan and then consider having tissue checked in three months. Shirley would also help me order a FIR (Far infrared) heat machine.

I was with Dr. Birdsol so long that someone went ahead of me to meet with Dr. Morris. Verne was back in time for my meeting with her. I told her I wanted to treat the cancer naturally for three months. Verne asked her if waiting three months was dangerous. Dr. Morris said that the cancer had probably been growing 10-20 years, and that I would be doing things while waiting. She ordered two blood tests to check for cancer in bones and liver.

Next Dr. Morris insisted I see Carl Bell – the counselor there. I didn't think that was necessary. After all, my husband was a pastor. But, Dr. Morris proceeded to introduce me to Counselor Carl Bell. His words that are etched in my memory are: **The two most valuable treatments for cancer are prayer and a positive mental outlook.** Carl Bell was a valuable help to me especially as at later appointments we discussed that fact that "I am not my mother." My mother died of cancer at age 60.

October 19, 2000, continued - It was on to the hospital for the two blood tests that Dr. Morris ordered. After getting the blood tests, "I stopped briefly to see Valerie Reuter who had a foot of intestines removed this week because of Crones disease. She can't eat anything for three days. Verne didn't go in to visit her because of his bad cold.

At 3:00 p.m., I got to work, typed the staff retreat minutes and left at 4:30.

October 24, 2000. The blood test results that I was anxiously awaiting came back. There was no cancer in bones or liver. Praise God.

Action Plan

Now I was in cancer fight mode: I had an unwelcome visitor and it would not be invited to stay. I memorized Psalm 103:1-5 and repeated it often especially while I was using the Chi morning and evening. I also read Psalm 91 often and worked to memorize it as well. Aunt Orpha had recommended these scriptures.

Shirley Fike sent us the information so that we could purchase a Fir (Far Infrared heat machine). I was to use it eight hours a day. That was impossible as I was working full-time. So the alternative was to use it at night in bed. The FIR was like a rounded half circle enclosure over me that was open at the top and bottom. The machine beeped every 15 minutes and beeped longer at the end of an hour at which time it shut off. When Verne heard the long, hourly beep, he would turn the machine on for another hour. I was pretty good at sleeping through the beeps. My husband was very caring. I don't know how he got his sleep.

I strictly adhered to my diet. No sugar, period. I still believe that sugar may grow or feed cancer cells.

I ate a radical diet of organic food so as not to tax my liver that was working to detoxify the cancer. I ate a whole organic lemon every day. We bought them by the case. I ate the entire lemon except for the seeds. The skin is often sweeter than the inside of the lemon. When I was working a banquet at camp, I took my own food, trying to find organic foods that looked similar to the non-organic foods being served at the banquet. I took much of my own food to church, and the church people were very kind to tell me what was organic that I could eat. And, of course I took lots of supplements four times a day. The large amount of Beta Carotene I took turned my skin somewhat yellow. I didn't notice, but Verne's doctor asked once if I was jaundiced. I had to explain that the color was from Beta Carotene.

I broke open a Shaklee Vita E cap each day and rubbed the antioxidant "E" on the site. I may have added a little crushed Vita C to the "E" at times.

I walked over noon hours and practiced and deep breathing. I shared in my North Liberty Story about how a member suggested I read Bernie Siegel's book, *Love, Medicine & Miracles*. Another very helpful book was Andrew Weil's book, *Spontaneous Healing*.

Cancer was visiting me, but I didn't plan to keep it or make it welcome. I was feeling great and felt like the cancer was going away. Some said I didn't need surgery; what should I do?

Here is what I emailed to family and friends on the evening of March 20, 2001.

Hi Friends and Family,

As some of you know, I was walking about three Fridays ago (I often walk over my lunch break) when the Lord told me to call Alma Long. She is a very wonderful, spirit-filled Christian and I was sure she would tell me to have faith and not to have surgery. I only see her once every few years at Annual Conference. What a shock when she told me that she had a breast removed a year and a half ago and that she was doing great and that I should do it while the rest of me was healthy. Her husband came on the phone and encouraged me to have it off, also.

I felt like my lump was getting smaller and I didn't know what to do. I went back and forth through a very hard time. I tried three days to call the 800 number at the Cancer Treatment Center of America (the one then at Goshen, Indiana) to schedule an appointment, but always got an answering machine saying someone was away from their desk. So I said, "Lord, three times should be enough. I guess I am not supposed to have surgery." Then early on a Wednesday morning at 4:00 a.m., I dreamed I was on the way to work. I had turned onto old 15 and was diagonal across from our property when I heard both my husband and my son,

Verne, calling to me to come back home because the hospital was calling. What a dream!

I went to work, went into the conference room and fell on my knees in prayer. Soon the phone rang and it was Dr. Morris' office returning my call to schedule surgery. After I scheduled it, I finally had peace. Then Thursday night, March 15, the night before my surgery, the phone rang and it was Alma Long. The Spirit had been telling her all day to call me. She had no idea that my surgery was the following morning. She prayed with me on the phone. She said to have Verne anoint me. I told her that we had a beautiful anointing service for me the preceding Sunday. Now I was certain that I was to have surgery, but I still hoped that the surgeon would change her mind when she recognized that the lump was disappearing.

I was bathed in prayer on Friday morning. The naturopath, Marcia Prenguber, had given me things to help me heal quickly and to help any stray cells not stick to other cells in my body. Dr. Laura Morris, the surgeon, came in and told me that Marcia wanted to be in the operating room with me – so I had the breast specialist and the naturopath both besides nurses, etc. The surgery went well.

I saw the recovery room clock at 9:45 a.m. and soon left recovery for day surgery. At about 11:30 a.m., I was on my way home much to the amazement of my day surgery nurse. I did not feel bad at all.

Dr. Morris called the following morning to see how I was and I told her I felt great, but was afraid to take off the bandage as per her orders. Finally, Verne's sister Ruth Ann came Sunday night and helped me take it off. Everything inside look great – not as scary as expected. Verne didn't want to help me because he had unknowingly visited a man who might have staff infection. (He found out just as he was leaving him.)

Here's the great news. I went today to get my drainage tube removed (a week before I was originally scheduled). My pathology report was not back, but others were from Friday surgeries. It seems they were doing a micro-something on my tissue.

Anyway, Dr. Morris called me this afternoon and said that the pathology report showed only a milligram of residual cancer. "You are cured," she said. And we talked a long while about prayer and hydroxgen and the fir machine. And then I understood why Tim Birdsol and Marcia Prenguber had come to see me this morning after my tube was removed. The naturopaths may have known that no cancer was being detected in regular tests. They came in exclaiming how great I looked.

Anyway, praise God! I did what I felt I needed to do and God blessed me beyond words.

Even an eighty plus year old man who came to visit me Sunday, two days after surgery, was so amazed that he said, "Maybe I should be on Shaklee."

I believe all my natural helps have been from God and I need to give Him credit. Praise God!

Love,
Phyllis Leininger

Let me share a few words I heard on the day of my mastectomy surgery that linger in my mind. First, when Pastor Jim Davis came to pray with me before surgery and met Dr. Morris, a beautiful, young-looking, lady, he said, "And you're going to let that kid operate on you?"

At an appointment prior to surgery, Dr. Morris had said I could bring a cassette tape (yes, that's what we had then) of music I wanted played during my surgery. If I didn't, she would provide the music. On the morning of surgery I gave her a tape of hymns with nature sounds, I believe. The last words I remember hearing before I was "out" for surgery are, "Do you hear your music?" I heard a phrase or two and I was peacefully asleep.

My Mother

"You are not your mother." Carl Bell, my counselor at the Cancer Treatment Center emphasized this to me. I recalled vividly my mom's death from cancer at age 60. Would that be my life's ending age? In reading my journal entries written during my cancer fighting days, I find thoughts about mother scattered throughout. I have gathered them here. Remember I was 57 years old when these were first written.

"I am Phyllis Leininger. I am not my mother. I have no false teeth. I have not had varicose veins surgeries on both legs. I have not had cataract surgery. I have not had breasts removed. I feel great! I have many healing "resources" and many prayers for my wellness. Dear Jesus, keep my mind fixed on you and thinking positively. My mind is my biggest enemy. Jesus, you healed over and over. You can heal all my diseases. Psalm 103 and 91! Thank you, Lord! Please guard my mind!"

I remember when we had so little money for Christmas that Mom spent hours sewing beautiful new clothes for all our dolls.

I remember Mom loving to have fun. When she found my lost class ring, she wrapped it in aluminum foil and baked it in a cupcake which she made sure was the one I got for dessert. The ring with its black onyx was just fine and so was my laughter and joy!

I remember Mom often playing "The Flower Song" by Lange on the piano – especially while waiting a meal – for people to all arrive.

Mom sewed beautiful clothes for us girls – a blue taffeta dress with an outer shell of blue lace for me when I played for my first wedding, Donna Hluchan's wedding – on a pump organ moved into the Bristolville Church of the Brethren for the occasion. I was 14.

My mother cared for Grandma Mahan about the time we were dating, marrying and having Verne Edward. What a job! Grandma messed the bed and mom didn't have paper diapers - not an automatic washer either,

Then there was the stress of Dad building houses and their moving a couple of times. Then Mom cared for Aunt Jennie, who never married and of course had no children. She had a few more modern conveniences by then, but it was untold work.

Then possibly the last straw – or maybe the one that broke her health, who knows, was. . Dad split the Bristolville church (or at least encouraged it) and the split off group and the pastor held church in my parents' house. The church food pantry was in the basement. Church children roamed freely through my sisters' bedrooms, according to my sisters. I was married and gone. By the time Dad and Mom moved to their last house, dad had given land for the building of a church on his property – actually he deeded it to the church. . . . The church building was a house which dad built. The pastor's family lived in it. Mom didn't live too long in the new house. She died March 11, 1981.

On December 29, 2000 I wrote: I am my mother's daughter.

> I love the Lord, as did Mom.
> I like to sew – so did she.
> I believe in my children – I think they are all great. Mom seemed to make me feel "bigger than human" – I mean she believed in me.
> Mom was a very caring person; I hope I am, too.
> Mom was always a good neighbor – with Everitts and Brookers on either side of us and later with Aunt Lena when the folks moved into their last house near her.
> I hope I can be neighborly.
> Mom came to help when Barb was born. I am able and glad to help with mothers and grandchildren, too.

I few days later I find this about mom's husband, my dad: I am my father's daughter.

> I work hard – as dad did.
> I love the scriptures – so did he.

I have his strong sense of justice – right and
      wrong (which is mellowing somewhat).
I love being with family – as dad did.
I love Christmas. So did dad.
I love music – Dad played in a band in his early
      days – saxophone?
I like flowers and being outside. Dad had lots
      of beautiful flowers.
I like pretty things – like dad's gazebo
I love being involved in church.

I remember how welcoming Mom was to Verne when
      we were dating and how she let him stay all
      night when there was only a davenport or
      studio couch for sleeping options. I remember
      how I looked forward to the letters she wrote to
      me in college and then even after we were
      married. Mom was a beacon of light and love.

Mom left a great legacy. And I hope that I will, as
      well. But, I am not my mother.

Construction

Our family was growing. Squeezing everyone around the table in our small dining area was snug. If someone on the north side of the table needed to use the bathroom, they had to go our the patio door around the house to the front door and come in to get to the needed place. The table even blocked the kitchen door.

My journal entry from July 12, 2002 reads:

> "I have been concerned and wondering in the night how God feels about us putting a room on the house when many in the world have no houses. Our dining room is so small. I want to be able to seat my family or other guests. I will be thankful for all God's blessings and the opportunity to add on to the house and not let it make me sick from lack of sleep. Thank you, God, for caring for me – for caring for my family – for my health – for your love – for my job – for friends and church. Lord, what should we do about the chipmunks that are gobbling up our peas as well as things underground?"

We went to visit Jess and Shirley Beer who owned the land next to us on the east. They agreed to sell us enough land so that we could build and meet the necessary requirements for set back from the boundary. We paid $4000 for a quarter of an acre.

And so we began. We got a building permit and the necessary mortgage. We also had to move a tree on the east side of the house. I don't remember whether the tree survived.

We started adding a 24'x 32' addition that July, but work seemed to go slowly because of sub-contractors. .Right after our new basement was dug, it rained. It looked like we had a big swimming pool. The next day we were amazed that the water was gone. The bottom of the hole was sand. When Thad, the general contractor, worked on our addition, things really moved along. Verne helped with much of the construction. I have pictures of Verne helping to frame the walls. He also did all the painting including the primer and two coats of paint. He spent hours in our pole building garage staining and finishing all the trim and inside doors. Verne enjoyed the learning opportunity, the fellowship with the "guys" and saving money on our project.

Verne and I agreed that we wanted a useful, but not extravagant addition. We picked out our carpet and had it stored while we waited for what seemed a long time for subcontractors to come to do needed plumbing, wiring, heating and cooling. The carpet off-gassed for months in storage and didn't have a strong smell when it was finally laid. We also picked out the sofa and loveseat for the east end of the room and had them held until the room was ready for them, again thankful that they were off-gassing in storage.

We had a big pile of dirt on the east side of the house that had come from digging the basement. Marc Beer worked in landscaping and he and his father asked whether they could have the dirt. We were glad that they wanted to haul it away. They came for the dirt while Verne and I were both at work, Verne at Wawaka and I at Camp. They ran into the new well with their equipment and knocked dirt down into it. Before we even knew this happened, they called a well-drilling company who worked on the problem and fixed the well. We had good friends.

Let me add that in later years when Verne could no longer run our snow blower to clear snow off the driveway, Marc Beer would gladly come with a blade on his truck and plow our snow. He had one stipulation – that we mark the place of the well which was easily covered by snow.

Back to our addition. When family came, the new room sofa opened into a queen-sized bed and Morgan and Leah often slept there while Dylan and Sean slept on the sofa bed in the living room. Verne's family was seldom there overnight because of their many birds and animals that needed care. I remember their family sleeping on air mattresses in the basement on the rare occasion they could stay overnight. There was also a futon in the computer room and a couch in the basement besides the bedroom in the basement and the guest room on the main floor. With the addition, we had quite a bit of sleeping space.

The addition was a blessing. It was built for the big table from Verne's home that we kept in its extended position and easily seated fourteen persons. We had three lights installed over the space where the table would be. Family, church groups, district committees and Camp staff had good times gathered around this table.

Some of the events that the "new room" witnessed include Thanksgiving dinners, Christmas celebrations, an Epiphany Party for Wawaka members, and cousins getting together. On December 14, 2007 we hosted the Camp staff at our house for the annual Christmas party. We set Verne's big table to seat 14, my family table to seat 10, and a card table for 3 persons, all in our big new room. During the summer of 2014, we hosted the farewell party for Rex Miller who was stepping away as Camp Mack's Executive Director.

God seemed to bless the room and to increase our joy through the activities it enabled us to host. By the time we had to say "good-bye" to our Milford home, the new room mortgage had been paid off for some time. The addition was an asset to the property when we sold our real estate at auction shortly after Christmas in 2018.

. Wawaka

Verne's work on construction of our addition was
nearly completed. He had been working on our
addition: plans, financing, and actual construction
since he finished his interim at North Liberty on
January 15, 2002. He was ready to get back into
ministry. His call came from the Wawaka
congregation located between Ligonier and
Kendallville, Indiana, just off U.S. 6. After meeting
with Wawaka's board and the District Executive,
Verne agreed to begin as Wawaka's interim pastor on
April 1, 2003.

Our introduction to Wawaka was during the busy
Lenten season. Cantata practices were underway for
the combined Methodist and Wawaka Brethren choir.
The cantata would be presented at Wawaka Church of
the Brethren during worship on Palm Sunday. The
Methodists had worship earlier and could attend their
service before coming to the Church of the Brethren to
sing or to hear the cantata. Preparations needed made
for Love Feast. Good Friday and Sunrise services,
joint efforts between the two churches at Wawaka,
needed planned. Whose turn was it to preach? Which
church's turn was it to host which service and serve
breakfast? Verne needed to meet the Methodist pastor.
Thankfully, Easter wasn't until April 20th that year.

Verne met Ed Gilmore, Pastor of the Wawaka United Methodist Church. They determined that the Good Friday service would be at the Methodist Church with Verne preaching and the Sunrise Service and breakfast would be at our church with Pastor Ed preaching. Love Feast didn't involve the Methodists. Members shared their memories of who did what last year. So the rotation was clarified and plans established for the services.

On Wednesday, September 3rd I set out on an adventure traveling by myself by United Limo as the support person for my sister Carol during her appointments at the Cancer Center of America at Zion, Illinois. A CTCA owned Limo picked me up at O'Hare in Chicago and took me back to the bus terminal on Friday. We stayed across from the hospital at a lovely Inn. It was a beautiful place and the weather was beautiful for walking whenever Carol and I had a break.

It was an appointment-packed, tiring time. Carol had lots of tests, blood tests, urine tests, brain, lungs and pelvic area CAT scans. Thankfully, all looked good. Carol had a hysterectomy in July for uterine cancer. At Zion, she saw a dietician, a naturopath, a mind body specialist, a spiritual counselor and a case worker. The doctor with the same last name as our maternal grandparents wanted Carol to have six weeks of radiation in case of microscopic cancer cells as no lymph nodes were tested when she had surgery. Carol declined and decided to go the natural route with diet changes and supplementation, a route which she (and I) tries to follow yet today.

A Trip to the Post Office Brings Change

Later that same September in 2003, I went to Milford Post Office for the Camp Mack mail. Becky Doll had carpet remnants on the sidewalk next to the Post Office. I saw a lovely blue 12' by 12' and 10" piece for $40. At home that evening we measured our bedroom, saw that it would fit and called and left a message that I would take that carpet if it wasn't sold. It was left from Grace Village decorating.

But. . . I'd been wanting a new mattress. We'd had the one on our bed since very early in our marriage. On Friday, September 12th, I was off as I worked the next day, Saturday, the day of the Mission Village dedication at camp. We went mattress shopping and picked out a mattress that was supposed to be good on my back. It has a special kind of foam.

Then we came back to Jerry's Carpet at Milford because I wanted the bedroom carpet laid before the new bed was delivered. While there I picked up three carpet samples. The living room carpet in the original section of the house badly needed replaced. We came home and narrowed our choices to two. Then we went back to Jerry's and asked which would wear better.

Jerry said that the bur bur would not mat down in traffic areas like the plush one, so we bought it.

We weren't home long before Jerry called to say that the carpet layer would arrive between 2 and 5 p.m. on Tuesday. So we had to move all the furniture and get up the old carpet. Our friends, the Camp Mack Staff, came at 1:00 p.m. on Monday and helped Verne move furniture.

Verne worked very hard to get up the carpet. Many, many staples were used in the living room pad. The bedroom carpet had a foam backing, I think, that had caked hard as cement. What a job getting ready.

Tuesday the living room and hall carpet was laid. At 7:00 a.m. on Wednesday morning the carpet layer began working in our bedroom and was finished by the time Verne needed to leave for Wawaka later that morning. On Thursday, Camp staff helped move back the furniture.

Friday afternoon the new bed was delivered. But we rushed off to District Conference and I didn't have time to make the bed. We slept in the spare room again that night. On Saturday, my 60th birthday, I stayed home from the business day of conference, made the new bed, played the piano, read, made a pumpkin pie and some lentil stew. Verne came home from conference and we went to Wawaka. We still had not slept in our new bed!

Sunday night came. Verne complained about the new bed. The new bed was much higher than the old one. It's too high to sit on to dress. Verne was afraid he would fall out getting up to go to the bathroom in the night. Finally, he did sleep in it. To his credit, Verne wanted me to choose the mattress that felt best on my back. It was very comfortable. I will note that the bed provided at Wawaka that we slept in on Saturday nights was also quite comfortable and not nearly as high as our "new bed."

Nearly 16 years later I had to have the thirteen inch box springs of that bed removed and replaced with a three inch box spring. Colleen, Verne's occupational therapist at Greencroft Health Care, brought Verne over to our apartment to see what changes would be necessary in his surroundings for him to navigate at home. The bed was lowered and railing added for Verne's safety.

Back to Wawaka. In September of 2004 the Wawaka congregation celebrated its 150th anniversary. Many persons were involved compiling pictures and displays, sending invitations, planning the meal, and lining up special music. Walt Wiltschek, then the editor of our denominational magazine, Messenger, was the guest speaker. A balloon launch completed the afternoon service.

This was our second church anniversary celebration in two months. In August we traveled to Brethren, Michigan where Verne had served as summer pastor the summer we were married. I packed a dress with a red jacket, not realizing that the ladies at Brethren had made black "garb" and bonnets for the church's 100th anniversary. Still, these Brethren seemed very glad we could help them celebrate a century of ministry at Brethren.

My "normal" seats during Wawaka's worship services were the piano bench for gathering music and then the organ bench for the prelude and service music. Once in a while a guest would play a duet with me.

Christmas at Wawaka was a time for lights! I am told that in the year 2000 the church (which is fairly small) decided to decorate with 2000 lights. Those lights were in the boxes of decorations that were used in the following years. Helping to decorate for Christmas was no small undertaking. Lights were threaded through the roping on the railings, through decorations on the piano, around the ceramic piece of Mary on the donkey and Joseph walking beside her on the organ, around the nativity on the altar, on the Christmas tree and through the poinsettia tree.

On the Sunday before the day of decorating, men would set up the heavy wooden frame for the poinsettia tree and bring up the large artificial tree from the basement. During our time at Wawaka, artificial poinsettias were purchased and saved in the parsonage basement instead of purchasing enough potted poinsettia plants each year to cover the entire tiered frame. A skirt was attached to the bottom of the frame.

I usually worked with our children, often recruiting those who didn't regularly attend, to prepare a Christmas program which I wrote to accommodate our situation. One of the favorite Children's programs I created had a loving grandmother sitting in a rocker on stage. Her "grandchildren" come to visit her and she is about to read them the Christmas story when they ask her if they may use her dress up clothes to act out the story. She says she will listen to some Christmas music while they go dress up. The congregation sings a couple of Christmas Carols and the children are back and seated for her story. As Grandmother reads, she instructs children in how to act out their parts and a lovely pageant happens pretty easily.

The last Christmas we were at Wawaka, 2014, I was asked to teach children traditional Christmas Carols. That was a challenge for some of the little ones. So I made poster boards with words and pictures and had the children alternate from being a singing choir (of Christmas carols) and a speaking choir (of Scriptures). I also had some speaking solos. I fastened the poster boards together with rings so they could stay in order and turn like a book. Gwen Leer kept the children focused on the right card while I played the piano. I used a variety of rhythm instruments and we played Silent Night on tone educator bells after singing it at the end. I was happy that Cathy Eberly was willing to sew white capes with big red bows for the children for this program.

When we went to Wawaka, Verne suggested small group get-to-gathers to help us get to know people. At one of our first small group meals at the Shells, couples shared how long they had been married. We had been married only 40 years and the total combined years of marriage for this group of four couples was still over 200 years.

With the congregation having a large number of older persons, it seemed like we were often having funerals. I remember Marilyn and I marveling at the flowers on the tall tulip tree between the church and parsonage one night after prayer meeting. She was found dead with her bicycle along the road. She often rode but that day her heart quit as she biked.

I remember Mary Kay who sewed reversible aprons and sold them in Florida during the winters. She also contributed aprons to our Camp Mack Festival booth. Her husband, Jack, froze fish he caught in Florida and provided them for Wawaka's annual fish fry. On their last trip together to Florida they went walking the morning after they arrived. Mary Kay took the long route and Jack walked the shorter route, planning to meet up when finished. Mary Kay, possibly thinking about the vehicle that she needed to get unpacked so that she could start sewing, stepped out in front of a car, was killed, and never met up with Jack.

I remember two separate instances when we felt called to visit and other church persons also felt the same call. We sang, read scripture and in one case sang the requested song, "I'll Fly Away." In both cases these men died within a few hours after our visits.

The Wawaka ladies went "all out" to serve large funeral meals. Sometimes my assigned part of the menu would be two 9 X 13 dishes of green bean casserole. Sometimes I made a very large bowl of cut up fresh fruit. Besides meats and scalloped potatoes purchased by the women's work, salads, pies and Texas sheet cakes were popular contributions to the menu. The area funeral directors expected to be invited to the meal and complemented the ladies on serving the best funeral dinners around.

Wawaka was a hard working congregation. We hadn't been there too long when they decided it was time to put new carpet in the fellowship hall and entry way. Verne helped more than I did at taking up the old carpet. I think he'd had practice at our house!

Another physically tiring job that parishioners undertook was killing the weeds in the cracks and sealing the black top on the parking lot all the way around the church. Verne worked with them to spread the sealer.

Marvin who refused to let Parkinson's slow him down, loved to work around the church often doing painting and repair jobs. He kept his wonderful wife Carolyn busy worrying about him.

Helping Hurricane Katrina Survivors

The last week in August of 2005, Hurricane Katrina viciously slammed the Gulf Coast destroying homes and causing many to become homeless in New Orleans, Louisiana, Mississippi and Alabama. This category 5 hurricane caused 1833 fatalities. Its highest wind velocity measured was 174 miles per hour. Escaping was difficult with jammed highways and gas stations running out of gas. Twelve survivors arrived safely to our Wawaka area coming to the home of one of their parents. Pastor Verne and Wawaka members had already been ministering to this older couple with physical needs who lived in a small yellow house. Now we had twelve additional needy persons that we cared about.

We collected food. I picked green beans and they canned some. Those who fled were worried about their jobs as well as their homes, but they were a thankful group and very appreciative of whatever the church did to help. They were anxious to go home as soon as their jobs were restored.

Thanksgiving 2005 was at John and Allison's home. Verne and Kathy's family stayed with her sister Brenda and came over Thanksgiving morning. Sarah and I both enjoyed playing John's new digital piano. Sarah and Rob played clarinet duets. I had fun playing a challenging number that John recorded to accompany Barb's choir. I enjoyed telling my choir that I would be accompanying Barb's choir on the Sunday I was supposed to direct the Christmas Cantata at Wawaka. Of course, thanks to John and technology, I could do both! Caleb read the Christmas story and we celebrated Christmas that afternoon before the Virginia family had to leave.

On June 4, 2006 we celebrated with our daughter, Barb, and her family as Barb was licensed to the ministry at Union Bridge Church of the Brethren in Maryland. On that trip we helped Sean with his interesting school project, building a house that dispensed gumballs. Morgan took advantage of our weekend stay to polish Grandma's fingernails, something pretty unusual as I don't normally have polished nails.

On June 10 of that summer we enjoyed hosting the annual get-together of Verne Henry's family. It was too wet for the grandchildren and great nieces and nephews to play outdoors, so it was a challenge to keep them entertained in the basement. I played hide and seek with the children for a while.

The following Saturday we set out very early in a rental truck and went to Verne Henry's childhood home at Stryker, Ohio. When we arrived, Verne and Kathy's family were already there, having traveled all night from Virginia. John and his son, Dylan, soon arrived.

Why the gathering? Well, years before Verne Henry had purchased a large amount of lumber. He painted the ends of the boards and stacked them to dry with slats in between the boards. On one of our early church moves, the lumber was brought to the farm and stacked in the corncrib. To say it had collected dirt and other yuck over the years would be an understatement.

It was a long, laborious day of loading Verne's lumber into the rental truck. But loading was just the beginning. The lumber had to be hauled, unloaded and restacked in the front area of our pole building at Milford. Verne Edward's son, Caleb, did a lot of the work in the granary rafters. Sarah and Kathy worked with the men, too. Grandma Phyllis mostly played ball with Dylan and Micah. We had fun, especially when the ball disappeared into the ground. I think Micah reached it out of a drainage hole. Anyway, there was a white pipe down in the hole.

Verne Henry wanted all the wood in the pole barn that night, but some wood was too long to fit inside so John went to Warsaw for a saw blade and some ice cream. Verne Henry went back out after supper. It was getting late. Everyone was tired; exhausted would be a better word. When we discovered that Verne Henry was not in the house, I went out and found him sawing wood. He insisted that it had to be done that night, so Verne, John and Kathy went to help. Then an overly tired Verne Henry sawed through the saw's cord and went for his hand saw. He insisted that John fix the cord that night. So John did. The wood got sawed and moved inside and some very tired people went to bed.

Verne and Kathy had driven all night the night before to get to the farm. After breakfast the next morning, Verne and Kathy and family left to deliver some show chickens and spend time with Kathy's parents at her Uncle Joe's, prior to going to Camp Mack for niece Joanna Long's wedding. They stopped by our house to pick up Verne Edward's pain medicine for his back. I'm sure that handling lumber the day before didn't help the back pain.

Annual Conference at Des Moine, Iowa was another highlight for me during the summer because Verne Edward and I were both delegates and could sit together during business sessions. He drove to our house and then helped his father drive the car we rented for the trip. What a special time together. While we were there, on July 2, 2006 a big storm downed – uprooted and/or sheared off 50 trees at Camp Mack. The Facility Manager Galen's house sustained damage when a tree went through the roof, taking down deck railings and shattering the large glass in the door to the deck. The straight line winds brought electric lines down at Sarah Major. We saw Camp's massive damage on a computer in the exhibit hall at conference.

Volunteers came to Camp Mack with big equipment all the next week – 85 volunteers on July 4th alone – and cleared the mess. No one was injured. It was the only Sunday of the summer that we had no campers at the site. God is good!

For the record, 2006 was the year I had both the trabecalectomy (glaucoma surgery) and cataract surgery on my right eye on the same day. At the follow-up eye exam for glasses, the pressure in my right eye was 9 and in the left eye which had no glaucoma surgery, it was 14, the lowest pressure I can remember having recorded for the left eye.

In May of 2007 Verne Henry and I spent a week caring for Barb and Rob's children while Barb was at seminary and Rob was working. Verne was the driver all week for ballet practices and dress rehearsals, soccer practices, Frederick Children[s choir and Sean's pottery class. Piano lessons didn't fit into the schedule because of ballet rehearsals.

On Friday we were chaperones for Morgan's 5th grade field trip to Harpers Ferry. It was very hot and humid with the temperature nearly 100 degrees. Verne was wearing a heavy leather back pack with three lunches, six water bottles, sun screen and more. He was nearly wiped out trying to wear his hot, heavy load and keep up with active 5th graders in the heat. When we got back I wondered if he had a heat illness, but he survived.

Sunday afternoon we had a great view of Morgan's ballet, Swan Lake, from the balcony, but it was swelteringly hot up there. Finally, when we could stand the heat no longer, we left at the beginning of Act 3. There were very few left in the balcony by then.

Our 44th Wedding Anniversary

Here's how we happened to celebrate our 44th wedding anniversary on June 22, 2007 at the farm at Stryker watching a bomb squad at work. A couple weeks before our anniversary a man pulled up to the farm house with a trailer and a neighbor, Mike Britenracker, confronted him and he left. But he came back that night and loaded his van and trailer with things out of the house, including Ruth's handmade bookcase/desk from the dining room But Mike had given the sheriff the man's license plate number and the Williams County sheriff notified area law enforcement. The burglar was pickup by a Defiance sheriff .before he got back to where he was staying. The bookcase had a lot of papers inside that identified Verne Ernest Leininger, Verne Henry's father as its owner.

Verne Henry was called and he and Ruth Ann made two trips with my truck to retrieve the stolen items. When Verne and Ruth were talking with the sheriff they shared that things had been missing earlier from the shop, but they didn't know when it was broken into. Verne Henry also shared that his father had kept dynamite in the safe. So the sheriff said he would call the bomb squad to dispose of the dynamite.

We got word the bomb squad would be at the farm Friday morning, June 22. We left for the farm at 7:10 a.m. expecting to have to move all the metal that was piled against the overhead garage door – piled there by a tornado or strong wind last summer that took down a lot of the shed at the end of the barn. We also expected to have to clean out the garage in front of the safe. Besides lunch, I packed first aid supplies. Moving all that metal could be a dangerous job.

When we arrived at 9:00 a.m., the big garage door was open, Brian's Volkswagon was out of the garage, the metal was all pushed out of the way outside and the area in front of the safe was cleared. A big barrel, nearly full of new oil was moved out and the tire changer was unbolted from the floor. Wow!

John and his friend Preston had come the night before, got a room at Defiance, and had begun working at the farm at 7:00 a.m. Preston drove his truck pulling his trailer loaded with his John Deere tractor with a loader. They didn't even break a sweat or get a scratch. We were all in the barn at 9:30 a.m. looking at a planter when I looked out and said, "The Bomb Squad is here."

The sheriff and the bomb squad truck parked near the end of the driveway and were walking in. They talked with John and Verne Henry, looked at the safe (which by the way has never locked) where the dynamite was supposed to be. Then they called for the fire department and the Williams County EMS. They also said they would need a hole about 2 feet deep and 2 feet wide, angling toward the woods.

Neighbors Mike Britenracker, his father and his son were watching the excitement. Most of us went to Mike's where they changed buckets on their Bobcat and then proceeded to dig the requested hole in the bean field.

The emergency personnel got ready. There were three persons from the EMS including a paramedic, a level two person and one other. Firemen stretched out their hoses. Now it was time for one of the bomb squad guys to suit up the other guy.

The bomb squad shared with us that the suit itself weighed 75 pounds and the one wearing it had to literally be dressed by the other. The guy being suited also wore a cooling vest. If he wore an entire cooling suit under the regular suit, that would add an additional 25 lbs. He had a knit cap under the huge helmet. Verne told me there was a fan inside the helmet. Maybe that is how he breathed. I don't know.

So the suited man went to the safe and came back. He didn't find the dynamite. Then he went to look again. Still no dynamite. All he found were caps and fuses. The dynamite was gone.

The bomb squad put the caps and fuses in the hole and we had one big bang and smoke. It was pretty quick.

There were no injuries. But now the sheriff wanted to know where the dynamite is. He planned to question the kids who broke in months ago and stole the chop saw and torches. It could be dangerous for them if they tried to use the old dynamite.

The firemen rolled up their hoses (at least four hoses); the bomb squad searched the refrigerator in the barn looking for the dynamite; the EMS left. and finally the bomb squad and the two sheriffs left.

We ate the lunch I packed and then gathered and loaded some more things from the farm to take home. On the way home we celebrated with our anniversary dinner at Fashion Farm at Ligonier. It was a lovely, peaceful place with delicious food. When we got home I was happy to fit into and be able to zip up my wedding dress. I left it on a little while, but I must admit it was snug around the waist.

We began January, 2008 with the Christmas Cantata that was postponed because of about 17 inches of snow at the time it was to have been presented in December, 2007. That year I directed two Christmas cantatas, presenting *Emmanuel* in December 2008.

In June of that year Verne Henry and I celebrated in Cincinnati, Ohio with our daughter-in-law, Allison Leininger. John, Leah and Dylan completed her onsite cheering team as Allison received her Bachelor's Degree from the University of Phoenix.

That summer we attended another grand celebration during Annual Conference at Richmond, Virginia. We celebrated the 300th anniversary (1708-2008) of the founding of our denomination! Barb's entire family spent a couple of day with us there. I was so surprised and happy when Verne Henry and I entered the exhibit hall on Saturday of conference and saw Verne Edward's family who had come for the day! Their menagerie of animals prevented them from staying overnight, but we enjoyed the evening meal and the evening service together.

At Grand Camp in August I experienced two ah-ha moments. Dylan, age 8, and I made a maiden voyage taking out a row boat – and returned to tell about it. Leah surprised me with her adventuresome spirit as she scooped up mud with a net along the boardwalk and felt for life in the muck!

As I write this, I am surprised to discover and be reminded of the many joys that Verne and I often experienced together. One of the great joys was going to our second National Older Adult Conference. Thoughts of trips to Verne and Kathy's in Virginia evoke warm memories. Like the trip in the fall of 2008. We saw and heard Sarah's Broadway High School band at Madison University as one of twelve competing bands. Broadway received third place. We visited Caleb's elaborate cabin with real windows and a loft that he built in the woods. We observed that 6th grader, Micah, did a fine job of baking a birthday cake for his mother's birthday.

Another highlight of 2008 for me was attending the Outdoor Ministries Association (OMA) conference at Camp Myrtlewood in Oregon. Camp Myrtlewood is in a temperate rain forest. I marveled at how tall the Douglas pines were there. I saw salmon spawning in the river right behind the camp cabins. I saw the Pacific Ocean for my first and only time on this trip and picked up some small driftwood.

I returned home in time to host John's family for Thanksgiving. One tradition their family has that was very helpful to me usually happened the day after Thanksgiving. Leah and Allison, and other family members if they were there, put together and decorated our Christmas tree.

I recruited the ladies at Wawaka to help me surprise Verne with a carry-in Birthday party dinner on his 70th Birthday, April 1st, 2009. During that period of time Verne spent Wednesdays and Wednesday evenings at the Wawaka parsonage. And April 1st that year was on Wednesday. Besides Wawaka members, I invited some friends and Verne's cousins, Gloria and Larry. His sister, Ruth Ann, brought the beautiful birthday cake. Verne's office windows had a better view of the road than the parking lot, so he seemed surprised when Marvin Heller went over and told him he was wanted at church. The current Board Chair, Ron, gave a wonderful speech about Verne's ministry and caring for the folks at Wawaka and Cathy Eberly added her kind thoughts as well.

I was a "proud" mother when I learned that Verne Edward received the Bridgewater College 2009 "Teacher of the Year" award in May. This prestigious award included a check for $5000. I think the award was the result of students voting.

I had an exciting summer in 2009, taking some vacation and some professional growth time off from Camp after summer camps ended. The week before Labor Day, Verne's sister, Ruth Ann, and I went to Beavercreek, Ohio to care for John's children so that Allison could accompany John on his business trip to Hawaii. We got Leah (5th grade) and Dylan (3rd grade) off to school. Each of us helped one of them with homework. We went to soccer practice and even attended "meet their teachers night" at the school.

Verne Henry left church after preaching the day before Labor Day and drove to Beavercreek. He arrived about the same time that John and Allison returned from Hawaii. Then Verne and I started out for the Church of the Brethren National Older Adult

Conference (NOAC) at Lake Junaluska, North Carolina. We visited and ate with lots of old friends, enjoyed fun, music, exhibits (especially the book store) worships, and workshops. We took a field trip to an Indian Village.

After NOAC ended we spent a couple of days with my sister, Carol and her husband Dennis across the border in Tennessee. As we were nearing their home, we saw a sign for Mountain Valley Church of the Brethren. Carol and Dennis usually went out the opposite direction and didn't know that church was near them. The next morning we set out to find this church. If we hadn't been looking for the sign, we never would have found it. It apparently had been hit after we passed it, because now it was lying off at the side of the road. The four of us did find this welcoming country church and Carol and Dennis have been active there ever since. I should say that Carol grew up in the Bristolville Church of the Brethren, but prior to marrying Dennis was a Methodist pastor.

For the last "leg" or our trip, we went back to North Carolina for several days at the Billy Graham School of Evangelism at the Cove. That was the icing on the cake of a series of inspirational events. The Cove was a beautiful retreat center in the mountains. I remember wonderful food, good meal conversations, beautiful piano preludes by George Beverly Shea and inspiring messages. The school of evangelism generated a lot of helpful ministry ideas.

Whenever possible we took an annual October trip to Verne and Kathy's farm in Virginia.. We drove past an apple orchard on the way down the long lane to their farm. As we did for several years during the fall season, we picked apples and took boxes of several kinds of apples back to share with people at Wawaka. Wawaka members would ask us when we were going to get apples, because they really looked forward to us bringing them.

Prayer meeting met weekly at the parsonage. We studied scripture and prayed. Possibly the seed of an idea for Wawaka to have a Vacation Bible School germinated at Prayer Meeting in the winter or early spring of 2010. One problem was that the Wawaka basement walls for all except one room in the basement were crumbling. There were all kinds of things stored and mostly forgotten down there. There was a water problem. It would take a lot of work to revive the basement classrooms.

The congregation accepted the challenge of preparing for a Vacation Bible School. Verne's Brethren reminder shows work nights scheduled beginning that April. Bible School was scheduled for the last full week in June. I did a lot of praying that the rooms would be ready and that no one would be injured working on them.

The Prayer Meeting prayed and God provided. North Liberty Church of the Brethren loaned us – actually delivered to our church – curriculum, large props, music, scripts for skits and some costume supplies, everything we would need for an exciting VBS in 2010.

One of our Prayer Meeting members, Lynn, was the major evangelist who recruited many more children than the rest of us for Vacation Bible School. Even though she had broken her back and had great difficulty getting around, she was a very active VBS recruiter.

Verne helped welcome and sign in the children and keep track of attendance. I worked to get the needed teachers and helpers and also helped with music. The first VBS was from 6:00 to 8:00 p.m. each evening. The following two years VBS was from 6:00 – 8:30 p.m. The last year we had Bible School (2013) we found summer league sports to be happening on so many evenings, that we had Bible School only on Tuesday evenings during the month of July. Still we had competition from sports.

The winter day in 2010 that UPS delivered the score for the Stamitz Concerto to me was a "Praise the Lord Day!" Sarah asked me to accompany her on the

Stamitz Concerto in her audition for a music scholarship at Manchester College. She had ordered the music; but had not received it. She was practicing from a copy her teacher made for her. I called Fort Wayne and South Bend Music stores. I called my musical friends. No one had the music. I needed it immediately. My friend Peggy, my boss's wife, suggested I call a large music store she knew about out East. I did. They had the music. They were under a blizzard warning so they would get the music out right away while they still could. I paid for it to be sent overnight. The next day we saw a UPS truck go by, but it did not stop. Late that afternoon, another UPS truck pulled in and I received the music. The music arrived February 10, ten days before the audition.

The day before the audition, Friday, February 19, 2010, Sarah and her mother visited Manchester. Then they came to our house. After supper Sarah and I practiced the Concerto. We didn't work on it long and then we visited while Sarah worked on some sight reading. The next day the audition went well and Sarah was offered a scholarship and a place in the orchestra (which the guide said no Freshman could receive). She was also offered a music scholarship. Dr. Planer remembered both of her parents and spoke about the honors math thesis that her father wrote. Then another music professor quipped, "I can't remember my students from four years ago. Planer remembers all his students, but he doesn't remember where his car is parked." Planer looked at me and mouthed the words, "I know where I'm parked." It was a good day.

We went to Verne's Alma Mater, Bethany Seminary, which had moved to Richmond, Indiana since Verne graduated, for our daughter, Barb's graduation in May of 2010. Barb had made many long trips to seminary from her home in Frederick, Maryland. She also was able to take a number of classes through Bethany's on line program. Verne and I stayed with Morgan and Sean while Barb and Rob went to a special banquet the night before graduation. We stayed overnight in a Bethany house and were able to host a reception there after the graduation.

Movements of Mozart's Clarinet Concerto were played as the graduation prelude and postlude. I enjoyed the music and determined then that I would purchase that concerto as part of our grandchild Sarah's high school graduation gift. Sarah graduated on Saturday, June 12, 2010. After giving the valedictory address and taking just enough time for a big buffet meal with her family, Sarah was off to play in a community band outdoor performance. Her open house was the next day. Ruth Ann, Verne's sister, and I helped put the meringue on the Lemon meringue pies (Sarah's favorite pie). The chocolate peanut butter pies were delicious. There was an abundance of

367

wonderfully good food, but the pies were really special.

July found us at Pittsburgh, Pennsylvania for the Church of the Brethren Annual Conference. We stopped at Mary Yoder's Amish Kitchen at Middlefield, Ohio on our way home and had a wonderful surprise visit with my youngest sister, Betty, who manages the gift shop at Mary Yoder's. We asked for Betty and found out she goes by her real name, Elizabeth, there.

We were on vacation the Sunday after Annual Conference and went to worship at North Winona Church of the Brethren. When we walked in, I was bombarded with questions about Becker. That's when I learned that our main building at Camp Mack was on fire. Mike Dilling, a member of North Winona, was Camp Board Chair. He had gone to the fire and was sending information back to the church. After worship, we drove through a fast foods place for sandwiches, went home, changed clothes, and hurried to Camp where we became part of an unfolding story. You may read about the Becker Fire in the next chapter, "25 Years at Camp Mack."

There were more leftovers than usual – and there are usually a lot – at Thanksgiving in 2010 as our son John had just had all his wisdom teeth removed the day before they came. Soup and soft foods were his

Thanksgiving menu. John didn't slow down a lot. All of his family along with Verne and I went to see Cinderella at Amish Acres on Friday night. Then on Saturday morning, Leah and Dylan kept their very helpful tradition of putting together and decorating our Christmas tree.

February 25, 2011. A group of Manchester College students including our granddaughter Sarah played 4-square for 30 hours in an attempt to set the Guinness world record for the longest 4-square game. They raised money for the Camp Mack building fund, money especially needed because of the Becker fire. Verne and I provided six different kinds of cheese and 4 large boxes of various kinds of crackers for snacks. We watched the game live on Friday afternoon from about 2:30 to 5:00 p.m. We enjoyed supper at the Golden Coral in Warsaw on the way home.

On Saturday I worked. When I greeted Jason Railton, he told me that the game was on a web cam. I emailed Kathy, Sarah's mother, and she found it on Spartan cam 4. She emailed me back and I got to watch the game on the web cam for a while on Saturday afternoon. Kathy was very happy to be able to see Sarah. I called Barb and she and her family watched some of the game, too.

The year 2011 was the 50th anniversary of my graduation from Bristol High School at Bristolville,

Ohio and Verne Henry's 50th anniversary of graduating from Manchester College. We celebrated both of these milestones together. In May my class met for a chicken dinner at the Bristolville Grange Hall. Truthfully, I barely recognized some of my classmates and there were only about 33 in my graduating class to remember. I had been away for 50 years. I recognized Marilyn (Mahan) Taylor, Ron Mahan (both cousins) and Loretta Lew. Some saw our car with the Indiana license plate and knew who I was immediately. The next night we went to the Alumni Banquet at the school and sat with those from my class who attended, giving me more time to get reacquainted with my classmates.

We spent the first two days of June, on the Manchester College Campus celebrating Verne's 50th anniversary in an overnight – get to sleep in a dorm - event. Sharing on Wednesday was full of laughter and inspiration. Laughter at remembering pranks pulled, like how they rigged the chimes stringing fishing line from the chimes to their dorm so that the chimes could mysteriously play in the night. Inspiration at how they faced health and financial challenges.

A memorial service in Petersime Chapel was a reverent time as the list of Verne's deceased classmates was read. Fifty-eight of the class of 1961 had passed away since graduation. About one in three of the 177 graduates were deceased. Surprising to me, more women than men had died.

At a meeting about how to help your grandchild go to college, I was upset to learn the reason why current students may not use scholarships for room and board as our children were able to do. Room and Board scholarships would now be taxable income.

We chose to take the chime tour. From the third floor of the Administration Building we went up more stairs to the "keyboard," big wooden levers attached to an apparatus that went through the ceiling and pulled the appropriate clapper on a bell. The bells cost $8,700 in 1922. The smallest bell weighs 550 pounds and the largest bell weighs 2600 pounds – over a ton. There is an octave of bells plus three additional bells. They looked so heavy that I was worried they would fall. Each bell has a subject and a scripture on it. For example: Peace (subject) and a peace scripture. Lila McCray, our tour guide, said she found the bell company on the web a few years ago and priced the bells at $145,000 – just the bells. It takes a lot of energy to push the large wooden levers that clank when they return to position.

Having been in the Church of the Brethren all my life as well as in the ministry and working at Camp Mack, I knew a lot more people at Verne's 50th year Brethren school, Manchester College celebration than I knew at my high school gathering. I enjoyed his reunion.

During Sarah's first two years at Manchester, she traveled home for breaks by Amtrak. We would pick her up at college, eat supper, and then help her pack food to take for snacks and breakfast on the train. We always drove as far as Wawaka where we would go to the parsonage and call Amtrak to see whether the train was running on time. When we were at Wawaka we were closer to Waterloo where she got the train sometime around 10 p.m. If the train was running behind schedule, Sarah and I played games, especially an apple word game while we waited. One Friday night in March of 2011 we took Sarah, and two friends, Melissa Bowman and Sotomi (a Japanese exchange student) on our evening ritual trip to the train after enjoying the evening meal together and of course packing their food.

Leah and Dylan Leininger, John and Allison's children, each spent a week at Camp Mack this summer; I saw them at meals briefly while they were there. Dylan was ten years old so this was his last year to be eligible to attend Grand Camp that Verne and I directed in August. Dylan graduated from Grand Camp that summer and so did we. We decided it was time to let someone else direct the camp which we had led for many years.

Sarah let me know sometime in the fall of 2011 that she wanted to come to my house and help me make my annual pumpkin rolls. I usually made five before Thanksgiving each year, put them in the freezer and pulled them out at Thanksgiving and Christmas times. The determined Saturday arrived. We baked together and had so much fun. I got out and measured ingredients and chopped walnuts. We greased the pans, lined them and greased them again. Sarah beat the eggs and mixed in the measured ingredients Each time a pumpkin roll was ready to come out of the oven, we had another one ready to go in. I had never made pumpkin rolls this quickly. Soon they were cool and ready to stuff with cream cheese icing.

Somehow the secret was shared. Sarah had come to help me prepare. She wasn't going home for Thanksgiving. All my children and their families were coming to our house. This was an unusual treat for me. Sarah's family brought Ellie, one small representative of their many animals at home. All of us hiked at Camp Mack and also checked out the new offices, dining rooms, kitchen, restrooms and meeting areas in the new John Kline Welcome Center, completed in less than a year after the Becker fire. John managed to get us all in a picture in front of the fireplace in the new building.

Early in February 2012, we were glad to host Caleb and Kathy, and Caleb's friend, Dakota and his mother

Deb for a couple of nights when they came to see Manchester College. Caleb and Dakota, good friends, chose to room together at Manchester for their freshmen year that fall. During the 2012-13 school year, I would have two grandchildren, Sarah and her brother, fairly close by.

On Saturday, February 18th, we picked Sarah up at Manchester and headed to the Embassy Theater at Fort Wayne for the Philharmonic Concert. Andrew von Oeyen played Brahms Concerto No. 1 in D minor for piano. I wondered how his fingers could move so fast. He played 45 minutes – the entire first half. After intermission, clarinets (including Sarah's teacher, Cindy Greider) had a major role in Tchaikovsky's Symphony #5 in E minor. It was a great concert. Sarah's teacher gave us the tickets. We got to the Wawaka parsonage, our usual Saturday night location, at 11:30 p.m. When I got out of the car I realized that my purse was still hanging in the Embassy Theater's lowest level bathroom. I called and left a message, but of course no one was at the theater at 11:30 that night. I left more messages on Sunday.

I was without credit cards, insurance cards, keys for my truck, the house, camp and church, my driver's license, a gift card and $50 in cash besides miscellaneous small stuff.

Verne took me to work on Monday. After a morning meeting, I called and learned that my purse had been turned in. We went right after work to Fort Wayne, got my purse with all my belongings still inside, drove through a fast foods restaurant for sandwiches and got to Wawaka in time for Bible study and prayer meeting. I praised God for his care.

Pocketbooks and bathrooms were my nemesis. I remember one time when we were on the way to Verne and Kathy's, driving my truck to bring back apples. We stopped to use facilities. The women's bathroom was more spacious than many, but there was no counter for setting my purse, so I put it in the sink. When I got ready to wash my hands, I realized that the water at the sink had come on automatically and filled my pocketbook. I dumped it out and dried my leather pocketbook as best as I could. We continued our trip and I spread out wet money to dry in the truck. When we arrived at Verne and Kathy's, I hung my purse on the clothesline to dry.

March 10, 2012 – Probably a once in a lifetime shopping trip. Sarah was not a dress-wearing young lady. She did have one plain black long dress that she wore for regular Orchestra concerts. It was a dress from her high school days. Sarah needed a long, elegant dress for May 6 when she would play the 1st movement of Concerto No. 1 in F minor for Clarinet by Carl Maria von Weber with the Manchester

Symphony as a finalist in the student concerto contest. We picked up Sarah and her friend, Melissa Bowman, at 9:15 a.m. and headed to Fort Wayne.

First we went to Von Maur. The prom dresses on the first floor were mostly short and youthful looking. We were directed upstairs to the great selection of long, elegant dresses. The atmosphere was surprisingly peaceful upstairs. There was a couch for Verne to sit on and wait. Live piano music was playing. Melissa helped Sarah find the right size dresses to try on. Sarah liked a dark blue and also a dark purple dress. I took pictures of everything that she tried on. We had the two dresses Sarah liked held until the end of the day and went to Macy's.

At Macy's she tried on several dresses, but nothing that she wanted. We ate Chinese at the food court in that mall. Then we went to David's Bridal. That place was crowded. They had lots of dresses on sale. There you picked the style and color you wanted and they ordered the dress for you in your size. Sarah tried on just one dress there and we left.

Next we went to Sweetwater music as we had promised Sarah we would get a music stand for at home. Ours was at church. Sarah needed to purchase some music for her clarinet pupil.

Now it was back to Von Maurs. The girls looked at the pictures in my camera on the way and Sarah decided she would get both dresses. She would need them for her Senior recital and possibly for soloing with the orchestra again. When we got there Sarah saw a pretty, light aqua dress she liked. She tried it on and it fit, too. She liked it a lot. So we bought all three. It seemed wise because with Melissa graduating in the spring, she won't be around to go shopping with Sarah another year. And to find three dresses Sarah liked and was comfortable in was truly amazing!

Thankfully our two grandson graduates that spring didn't graduate on the same days. We were able to attend each of their graduations, Caleb Leininger from Broadway High School in Virginia and Sean Dickason from Walkersville High School at Walkersville, Maryland. We arrived in time to attend Sean's Honors Celebration the Tuesday evening before his June 6, 2012 Wednesday afternoon Commencement at Mount St. Mary's University.

Caleb's Commencement was held at James Madison University on Saturday, June 9. I was impressed by the deep thinking in his valedictory address. I was amazed when a girl – not particularly a girlfriend – asked him for his yellow honors cord and he gave it to her.

After graduation both grandsons headed to Ecuador with David Ratcliff for a ten-day New Community Project learning experience. The girl Caleb met there would draw him back to Ecuador for several more trips, including a year studying abroad in Quito.

In August our daughter, Barb, moved to Lincoln, Nebraska to begin her ministry at the Antelope Park Church of the Brethren. Morgan moved with her while Rob stayed in Maryland to prepare their home for sale. On her way to Nebraska, she dropped Sean off at his Dickason grandparents in Michigan. We and the Dickasons worked together to move Sean into Hope College a few weeks later. Lowey and I found the campus health department on move-in day and went with Sean to get a shot and a TB test that he could now receive as his wait time after returning from Ecuador was about up. It was now just one day before his wait time ended.

Caleb and Dakota fulfilled their plan of rooming together that fall at Manchester. One day at Camp Mack I got a phone call from Verne Henry. Caleb's mother had just received word and called him to share that they were taking Caleb by ambulance to Lutheran Hospital in Fort Wayne. Verne asked, "Do you want to go?" What a question! I left Camp and hurried home and we were off to Lutheran Hospital.

Caleb had had a high fever for a week and he was losing much sight in his right eye. Dakota's mother worried in might be contagious. At the hospital Caleb was receiving many tests for many serious diseases, but none of the tests found his problem. An eye doctor specialist was called and came after he completed his office appointments, arriving shortly after 5:00 p.m. I was surprised to see that one area of the emergency room complex was set up like an eye doctor's office. The eye doctor couldn't tell us much either. Maybe it would get better; maybe it wouldn't. We got back to college in time for the band concert and Caleb went back stage to assure his sister that he was back from the hospital.

Meanwhile, at home in Virginia Kathy was doing research. Could Caleb have Lyme disease? When he came home for fall break in October, she took him to their doctor and insisted that he be tested for Lyme Disease. When Caleb came back from break, we took him to Fort Wayne for his needed appointments. He got a PIC line through which he received antibiotics for 29 days for Lyme disease. After he got the PIC line we took him to the store to find the recommended stretchy brand of plastic wrap to tightly cover the area so that he could keep it clean and take showers. Our time with Caleb was basically spent in the car going to appointments at Fort Wayne. It was different than the way we had related to his sister through music.

God was gracious and worked many miracles. The home health nurse came daily to Manchester to administer the medicine. Caleb insisted that he could care for the PIC line and administer the medicine himself over Thanksgiving vacation. His request was granted. He was not to drive for long periods while the PIC line was in his arm, but Sarah could take turns driving. He took the necessary doses of medicine home on ice and administered it himself. He managed to do well at college in spite of his eye problem.

The sameness of the rhythm of life at Wawaka continued. The same meetings. The same people. We had buried many of the oldest members. Being out in the country, our growth opportunities were limited. The rare visitors were warmly welcomed and did often return. But Wawaka had no online presence to share our existence and the internet at the parsonage didn't work. Communication by internet had to be done from our Milford home. Wawaka needed new life, young life.

And then I made a huge mistake, possibly the biggest of my life as pastor's spouse. It was getting toward the end of our ministry time at Wawaka, possibly sometime in 2013. Verne was moving more slowly; I don't think he had a walker yet. When we went visiting, especially to Fort Wayne, I had to help him watch for traffic.

Anyway, Verne Henry was asleep in bed at our Milford home when the phone rang. It was a sheriff that I didn't recognize and I assumed the caller was trying to raise money. Maybe this was even a scam.

We got lots of calls supposedly from police organizations asking for money. The caller begged to talk to Pastor Verne, I didn't listen; I refused. The next morning we learned that it was the Wolcottville police trying to get Pastor Verne to minister to one of the new couples who had been attending Wawaka. Dave and Karen's daughter had committed suicide. Of course we went right away that day, but it was too late. They had found a Mennonite pastor.

I felt terrible as we later went to visitation and then to the funeral. I shared my regrets with them. Dave and Karen didn't return to Wawaka for worship. But they supported us. They came to Verne's retirement party. They wrote to me when Verne passed away. They have been living examples of God's forgiveness.

In May of 2013 we traveled with Dave and Lois Dickason to Lincoln, Nebraska for Morgan's ballet on Saturday evening and our daughter, Barb's ordination the following day, Mother's Day. Lois, a retired physical therapist, shared with me on the trip that she wondered if Verne had Parkinson's.

The morning worship and ordination service was moving and didn't feel to me as long as it was. Barb was glowing. I observed that after the service she greeted each person with such caring, looking deeply into their eyes. The Antelope Park Church of the Brethren had a luncheon for Barb after the service with lots of unhurried fellowship. What a special congregation to have a two-hour worship service and a lunch on Mother's Day!

June 22, 2013 was a Saturday, the same day of the week as when we were married in 1963. Our son John's family came in time for Friday evening supper. John mixed up a large egg casserole for breakfast. Allison worked on pictures for the celebration that all of our children were planning at Camp Mack. Verne and Barb's families came home during the night or early in the morning of our 50th wedding anniversary.. Sarah was doing a summer internship at Texas A & M University and was the only grandchild who could not come. On our anniversary morning, Kathy woke Caleb early – well before breakfast – and went shopping for a car load of vegetables, fruits and cheese cubes. I think Caleb had finished working on a picture show in the wee hours of the morning.

What a lot of work our children did! After a good breakfast of egg casserole, fruit, juice, toast and Cherios, Kathy put persons to work cutting up peppers, celery, cauliflower, broccoli and more. John cut up watermelon and cantelope. They even had blue berries as well as strawberries. They put all cleaned produce in ice cream buckets to transport.

Kids used the air compressor in the garage to blow up many gold balloons. Allison had a number of balloons blown up with helium. For lunch we all ate at 11:30 a.m. at the Golden Corral at Warsaw.

I heard that the camp chef, Tony, pointed to his table decorations and said to use whatever they wanted. Barb went to a florist and got beautiful white carnations and used camp vases to put a flower on each table. She also had some larger bouquets with white roses on the table for cards. The picture show was quite extensive and wonderful. I wonder what happened to it. It must have been saved somewhere. There was a big pile of gold balloons that never got made into an arch, but there were plenty of decorations. The large Happy 50th Anniversary banner with our picture on it was beautiful. It hung for a long time afterwards over the arch between the kitchen and new room at home.

Ruth Ann baked a delicious lemon cake and sprayed the icing gold. She put an angel food cross on top for me. The children served ice cream with the cake.

A memorable moment was when Allison gave the keys to her Prius to Micah and sent him and Leah out to put up signs. When Kathy found out, she sent Caleb after them. Micah did not have a driver's license yet. Micah and Leah were already coming back when Caleb got to them.

Seeing my sisters, the twins Sharon and Karen, from northeastern Ohio was a happy surprise. Karen's

husband, Joe, drove and brought them. Becky and
Paris Ball-Miller also surprised us by coming. There
were a good number of Wawaka members who came
as well as many other friends.

When we went out after the party, our car was
wrapped all the way around with gold ribbon. About
four #10 flattened tin cans were tied on behind the car.
A sign on the trunk said, "Just married, 50 years ago!"

Soon after our party, Morgan left for Joffrey Ballet
School in New York City. She had been accepted to
take part in the summer ballet program at this well-
known school. She spent the rest of June and all of
July apart from family in the "Big Apple." Morgan had
two ending recitals on Friday and Saturday, July 26
and 27. Rob and Sean, who had been working with his
father that summer, went by bus to New York City for
the Saturday performance. Morgan went back with
them on the bus, and they took her to the airport at
Baltimore where she flew to Grand Rapids where
Dave and Loey picked her up. Morgan liked New
York City better than her "country grandmother" does.
Morgan turned seventeen shortly after her summer
classes ended. I was glad she had a safe summer.

My journal relates my dream of inviting all the young
couples in any way related to the Wawaka church for a
party/supper at the parsonage on September 20, 2013.
I wouldn't have shared the reason I wanted the party.

It was personal and probably selfish. I really wanted a 70th birthday party. I had no party, except a pitty party. It was District Conference weekend. No one wished me Happy Birthday until I called about 5:50 p.m. to wish Allison and John (he wasn't home) a Happy Anniversary and Allison wished me Happy Birthday.

I was working at Camp during District Conference, selling meal tickets, assigning lodging and greeting non conference guest groups. I prayed often for people in Syria to keep my mind off myself. When ladies working at the District Conference registration table sang Happy Birthday to me, I broke down crying. Verne hadn't even told me Happy Birthday. He thought it was the next day. I am sure Verne's mind was beginning to deteriorate because he had trouble remembering my birthdays for the rest of our lives together. He used to take me out to eat and get me something special for my birthday. When we got home from the evening conference session, Verne gave me the red roses that he had bought when I was at work in preparation for the next day he thought was my birthday. He was still caring; he just couldn't remember dates.

Because birthdays meant so much – maybe too much – to me, I especially tried that year to make other family members' birthdays special. I had so much fun calling the Bridgewater Bookstore and ordering a

Bridgewater T shirt in Crimson and Gold. On his birthday, the bookstore staff humored me and notified Verne Edward that he had a gift to pick up at the bookstore.

We sent Sean a box of assorted goodies including large packages of both double A and triple A batteries for his calculator, mouse and other needs. He also found Shaklee meal bars and healthy candies. healthy lollipops, and sour gummy worms in his box..

Sarah asked for a stainless steel turner for her birthday like we had given her mother with a couple of cookie sheets. We were at an Orchestra concert on Sunday before her birthday and she may have wondered why we didn't bring her a birthday gift. She also may have wondered why we didn't take her out to eat to celebrate her birthday that night after the concert. We had taken her out to eat to celebrate birthdays in the past.

We had a surprise party planned for Tuesday evening, her 22nd birthday. Her housemates were in on the surprise and knew that we would be bring supper at 5:30. Sarah was baffled about why they were cleaning house that Tuesday. Miriam was the "on site coordinator," She invited Dr Planer and his wife, Walt Wiltschek and Angela, the other clarinet student. Walt brought an extra table. Enough chairs were gathered. We waited a bit for the last guests. Sarah didn't know at first that we were waiting for Dr. Planer and Dr. Traxler. I think Sarah was surprised. With Verne and me, there were fourteen of us all together.

Beside the hors'd oeurves of deviled eggs, cheese and crackers, I set out notecards for persons to write memories of Sarah. I read them during supper and persons guessed who wrote them. The meal was barbequed goat (Kathy had told me how to fix it), sandwich buns, broccoli casserole, Green bean casserole, corn, tossed salad, milk, cider, ice water. After gifts, Sarah's housemates were great at helping me serve desserts: Angel food cake, strawberries, raspberries, Lemon meringue pie, and vanilla ice cream. They also helped clean up afterwards and packaged leftovers to keep. There was only about a pint of goat left. Of yes, we did give Sarah the small stainless steel turner she requested and also a larger one.

Barb turned 40 years old that November, another milestone. She was way out in Nebraska. I wouldn't be with her on her birthday, but I wanted it to be special. So I purchased 40 small gifts: a rubber scraper, pencils, pens, paper clips, Shaklee PM treatment, Shaklee AM treatment, Carrot cake mix, frosting in a can, birthday plates, birthday napkins, sticky flags, dish scratcher, dried apples, dried pears, balloons, music mold, number candles 40, small flash light, ceramic cross, key chain, playing cards, scrub brush, note cards, a notebook, scotch tape, 6 envelopes of pomegranate tea. I wrapped each of the 40 gifts separately and instructed her to open one each day. I think there was a card with her main gift to be opened on November 15.

Barb said she was so happy and loud when she opened her box that she thought everyone in the adjoining apartments could hear her yell, "I love my mommy."

On December 1st I was the focus of another wonderful celebration at Camp Mack. Camp gave me a beautiful retirement celebration that Sunday afternoon. Tony went all out with a great variety of foods along with a beautiful cake and ice cream. My friends, people I'd met at Camp from churches and groups throughout the state of Indiana, came and celebrated with me. Rex ordered beautiful roses and staff put together a picture show. There were speeches and sharing of memories. My official retirement date was December 31, 2013. I had worked in the office at Camp Mack for 25 years and four months.

January 1, 2014. My plan for the beginning of my retirement or my New Year's resolution, if you want to call it that, was to prepare to be the accompanist for my granddaughter Sarah's Senior Clarinet recital at Manchester College. It was a resolution I adamantly stuck with, practicing the piano at least four hours a day, usually two hours in the morning and two a hours each afternoon, every day except Sundays. On Sundays, I only played for church worship services. Sarah's music was challenging. She was not allowed to play for this recital anything that she had played for previous recitals. Everything was new.

Sarah had a lighter schedule during January term at Manchester and she planned to spend January weekends with us so that we could practice for her senior recital. We didn't know that the January 2014 weather would often be too bad for travel. An excerpt from my journal written January 5: "Lots of snow! Then tonight actual temperature is to be -8 degrees with wind chills at -30 degrees Fahrenheit or lower. It is windy. Our wind chimes are busy. Sarah has no class tomorrow. MU is closed.

Sean is stranded at Union Station in Chicago. Barb called and we gave her phone numbers for cousins Brian and Kevin and also for Aunt Ruth. The train to Hope, Michigan (Sean attends Hope College) is not running today and Barb says it's full for tomorrow's trip. Dear Jesus, Sean needs your help and your care." The train ran on January 7 and Sean arrived two days later than expected. I think he spent his wait time with a kind family of a girl on the train from the Chicago area who was also trying to get to Hope.

The weather was not good, but Sarah came to our house and we practiced January 10th and 11th. We practiced for the second Friday evening and Saturday on January 17 and 18· It snowed more on Saturday and we were concerned about Sarah driving back to North Manchester. Just as we were finishing supper, about 5:40 p.m. the lights went out. Sarah left in bad weather about 6:00 p.m. We stayed home and didn't pack up to go to Wawaka until the lights came on at 9:30 p.m. We arrived at Wawaka at 10:30 p.m. Verne ran bulletins early Sunday morning. We did have church that day.

We ate a quick lunch and Verne Henry blew out the area in front of the garage door that was drifted in. We had just got out on the road in front of the parsonage when we got stuck. Verne was able to go back and forth and get going. Then we turned onto 300 W, the county road leading to US 6 and really got stuck. Several guys appeared – probably from the blue house on the corner- and pushed us backwards until we were free enough to go forward. We came to one accident on the way home, but the wrecker was already there and we didn't wait long. When we got home, we carried our suitcase, briefcase, music and food in from the garage – quite a long, strenuous trek through the snow.

Weather prevented many churches from having services in January. Wawaka cancelled church two Sundays that month because of the weather. One Sunday they had worship, probably because we made it there on Saturday evening. But the roads were so bad that Ron Leer, our Board Chair, insisted on driving us the 25 or so miles to our Milford home with his wife, Gwen, following in their SUV.

Another Sunday that winter the sidewalk from the church to the parsonage was icy and difficult to keep clear. Ron thought I should have help walking to the parsonage. So I took his arm and we inched along. Verne was closing and locking up the church. I was safely home when Verne came in and told me that Ron had fallen on his return to the parking lot. He had injured his shoulder and would need rotator cuff surgery. I felt bad. Ron needed strong arms in his job as a chiropractor. I was glad when Ron's shoulder was healed and he was back at work.

I was retired but I was also wrapping up loose ends on some projects that needed completed. I was completing my research and writings about John Kline, Manly Deeter and Kate Warstler and finding pictures to go with the writings. Again, in our togetherness style, Verne took me to Michaels when we chose frames and had the writings and pictures mounted. John Kline's plaque hangs inside the main doors of the John Kline Welcome Center. Manly Deeter's plaque hangs in the Manly Deeter Office Complex and Kate Warstler's is in the Kate Warstler Dining area. These may not have been completed before the May 6th recital.

With the May 6th Senior recital looming, Sarah had two lessons a week whenever she and her teacher could find the extra time. An email from Sarah on March 4 already shares that there will be two lessons that week. Verne did a lot of driving, making trips to Manchester for lessons, for juries (playing in front of all music professors for grades), semester recitals, as well as band and orchestra concerts and even a mini recital for perspective students, held on Saturday, March 1st.

Sarah was with us over Easter weekend as she would spend nearly the entire weekend traveling if she went home to Virginia. I recorded these thanks in my journal, "Thank you, God, for Sarah being here this weekend. – for helping us play Weber's 2nd movement for the sunrise service and the 1st movement for the main service – both as preludes. – for Sarah playing all hymns for both services with me on her clarinet – for a very warm and beautiful day today, after a long winter." It was good to test our nerves and get used to playing a bit of the recital in front of people. Interestingly, Easter was April 20, the same day of the month it had been when we went to Wawaka in 2003.

Saturday, April 26 was the fiftieth anniversary of Verne Henry's ordination at his home church, Poplar Ridge near Defiance, Ohio in 1964. On Sunday the

Wawaka congregation recognized Verne's fifty years in ministry and gave him a beautiful dahlia plant and a gift certificate to Applebees.

Monday, May 5th was the "dress rehearsal," a time to go through the entire recital, without actually wearing our formal attire. I remember needing to be softer when Sarah played in the low range. Besides driving to Manchester, Verne was busy that day also doing all the shopping for fresh fruits and vegetables and cheeses for the reception after the recital. He also got some goat cheese because Sarah raises registered boar goats. We had already purchased all the paper plates, cups, napkins, crackers and anything we could get ahead of time. . Sarah and some of her friends were making cookies.

Early Tuesday morning Verne Henry picked up Sarah's father, Verne Edward at the Waterloo train station and thoughtfully took him out to breakfast so that I could stay home and practice. Sarah's parents took turns coming to her major events. Her mother came when she soloed with the orchestra. Someone always had to stay home to do the many hours worth of chores.

I put two kinds of soups in slow cookers and we also had cold ham and turkey sandwiches for lunch. On the way home after breakfast, the Vernes stopped at the Milford florist and picked up the flowers I'd ordered for the table centerpiece on the refreshment table. They were yellow roses, black treble clef sign, black ribbon and baby's breath.

One of my camp friends, Jessie Kreider, came that morning and cleaned all the veggies and fruits and cut the cheeses for the refreshment table. She stayed for our soup and sandwich lunch. Ruth Ann, Verne's sister came and brought a friend. The two of them helped me get punch and ice rings in 2 gallon containers/coolers.

We got to the recital in plenty of time for finding a table and getting it set up with a table cloth, plates, cups and any non-food item that could be put out ahead of time. The punch bowl was placed ready to receive the punch. When we sat the bouquet of flowers on the center of the table, Sarah's friend, Miriam, asked why the bow was black. Sarah reminded her that Manchester colors are black and gold.

Sarah's other grandparents, Bill and Alice Martin arrived in time for Alice to offer Sarah and me some calming lavender essential oil. I accepted, putting some on my wrists. Sarah did not.

The concert opened with Henri Rabaud's Solo de concours, the shortest of the selections . The Grand Duo Concertante by Carl Maria von Weber was certainly a duo between clarinet and piano and at times was very energetic. We had played some of this for Easter services.

Following the intermission, Leonard Bernstein's sonata for clarinet and piano that one famous clarinetist told Bernstein was too difficult to play had a contemporary, somewhat dissonant sound that took a while for me to fall in love with. The concert ended with the Premiere Rhapsody by Claude Debussy,

Sarah's Senior Recital went very well. I remember a time that spring .after a band or orchestra concert when someone told Sarah and me how special it was to have grandmother playing for her granddaughter, and then said something like, even if Grandma couldn't play it all as well as Sarah might like. Well, that was a challenge. I practiced. I prayed. I know the Wawaka prayer group prayed. I had a small list of five scriptures that encouraged me. The first was: "For God did not give us a spirit of fear, but rather a spirit of power and of love and of self-discipline." 2nd Timothy 1:7. The concert was a great success by any measure. The music professors current and retired were "gushing over it." Thank you, God!

Life went on. Our home needed a new roof. We lived on what was known as the windy corner. The wind break of trees planted across State Route 15 from us that served as a wind barrier for years had become broken down from many high winds. The trees were removed and not replaced. Verne couldn't keep climbing up to fasten down shingles after every windy storm. Two days after Sarah's recital, we closed on a home equity loan for a new metal roof.

It was getting more difficult for Verne Henry to prepare sermons each week. The Wawaka congregation loved Verne and was unanimously supportive with their vote to get him help A group of usually four ministers, mostly retired or between churches, met monthly and decided who would preach on each Sunday and what their theme for the following month would be. Verne continued to do the visitation, the bulletins and the monthly newsletter, but he only needed to prepare one sermon a month.

We celebrated two graduations, one week apart that May. Sarah's Manchester University graduation was May 18th. She headed up a big noon feast for her housemates families after baccalaureate. Kathy stayed with Sarah the night before and helped with packing and cooking preparations. Verne Edward and Micah came and ate with us and stayed all night. Sarah graduated with highest honors and three majors: music, math, and bio-chemistry. Sarah and family packed up and left soon after graduation. Kathy couldn't get out of teaching on Monday. She had taken time to go to Ecuador over Easter to see Caleb, even though Easter break was used to make up some snow days. So her time off was used.

Morgan's graduated at Lincoln, Nebraska with an international diploma on May 25. Barb and Rob who had been living in an apartment, closed on their house on May 20th. Their apartment was still available to house some family members. Leah stayed with Morgan at the apartment. John had reserved a lovely place for us to stay with our own bedroom and bath. There was a kitchenette – living area with a hide-a-bed where Aunt Ruth, Verne's sister, who was also traveling with us, stayed. Dylan was able to be with us because his soccer game was cancelled.

Saturday our family and Rob's parents all helped fix graduation food in the big church kitchen. Ruth decorated the cake Barb had baked. Most of us cleaned veggies and fruits. I fixed venison and noodles for the thirteen of us for lunch.

Morgan's open house was from 5 p.m. until people finally left. Lots of church persons may have wanted to see the home their pastor just purchased four days before as well as congratulate Morgan. Supper was Thai food. Many friends, and new neighbors, as well as church folks came. I seem to remember that Morgan had gone door to door on her block to meet and invite her new neighbors, and some of them came.

Barb preached a wonderful Memorial Day sermon Sunday morning, beginning with a Heintz Catsup story. Then we ate party leftovers for lunch and headed to Morgan's graduation. Verne and I had been in the graduation site auditorium years before for Annual Conference.

Sunday evening was relaxing, family time for adults. Morgan was off to friends' openhouses. Rob grilled various kinds of brauts. Monday morning we ate at the Comfort Inn before leaving for home.

I was still emotionally connected to the wonderful place where I had spent my last 25 working years, Camp Mack. Galen Jay called me on a Monday soon after the camp staff received the news from Board members of Rex's retirement. During that call Galen, now the acting Executive Director, asked me to present the Camp Scholarships at the Milford school award assemblies for elementary and middle school as I had done for years as a staff member. I agreed. Galen and I decided to meet on Thursday to plan for a party at our house in Rex's honor.

This September District Conference was at Goshen City Church. I was there as a member of the District Conference Program and Arrangements Committee. Verne was focused on Conference and forgot my birthday for the second year in a row. I had to keep tears from coming.

I wrote in my journal, "It did feel like a horrible day. Yet, I should be happy. Our Nigerian Brethren are fleeing for their lives; their houses and churches are being burned. Their girls are kidnapped. In Syria and Iraq there is much terrorism – and also in Palestine and Israel and Russia and Ukraine. Lord, forgive me for worrying about Verne forgetting my birthday. Please help Christians to be peacemakers. Help me to be thankful, positive and loving."

We got in a big storm on the way to Wawaka between 5:00 and 6:00 p.m. Saturday evening after District Conference. A piece of tire retread flew through the air and hit the car. Then Verne braked for a flying five gallon bucket. Torrential rain! We pulled off a couple of times. We were thankful to make it safely to Wawaka.

On October 11, 2014, I was glad to be playing for Sarah's (and my) friends' wedding. Miriam Zielinski and Todd Easter were getting married at a beautiful park in the South Bend area. I carefully timed my prelude of 30 minutes. But as I have often experienced, weddings don't always begin on time. The father of the bride was late and I repeated some of the music.

It was a beautiful outdoor wedding. I played on an electric keyboard. Sarah was the Maid of Honor. Caleb was an usher. Puzzles on the reception tables in the pavilion challenged and entertained guests..

The bridal party ladies all went to have their hair done the morning of the wedding. Sarah drove. When they were done, Sarah's car would not start. So Saturday night after the wedding, Verne Henry, Sarah, Caleb and I all went to see about getting Sarah's car going. Finally Sarah had it towed to Prices near us at Milford.

We got home about 10 p.m. and I put out sandwich fixings, veggies, grapes and blue corn chips. Sarah and Caleb ate a little standing up and then Sarah drove Caleb's car and took him grocery shopping and then home to North Manchester where he is a junior. Sarah had to drive Caleb's car as he can't see to drive at night. I heard Sarah return shortly after midnight. Sunday morning we left at 8 a.m. for Wawaka and Sarah left for Penn State shortly thereafter.

I directed choir practice for the Christmas Cantata after worship and it was late when we got home to Wawaka. Verne's sister arrived shortly after we got home and as soon as we were packed up, she and I left for Virginia. I took a big watermelon that I had raised and a little cheddar cheese. We got to Leesburg and realized we'd forgotten the crates and boxes that we wanted to take to bring back apples. Verne wasn't going on the fall apple trip this year. It was a "ladies trip." We went back home, got our boxes and finally got on the way in my truck between 5:00 and 5:30 p.m. Ruth was our driver.

Later that night when we stopped for gas, there was a subway there and we had subs for a late supper. We stopped near Bolivar Dam for the night. I think that was near where Camp Zion used to be.

The colored fall leaves were awesome and the truck drove well. At first Ruth didn't know how to start it. So I'd start it and then run around to the passenger's side and hop in. After not many times, she figured it out.

We got to Verne and Kathy's on Monday afternoon about 4:00 p.m. It was Kathy's birthday, October 13, 2014. It was also 4-H night and Kathy and Micah had to go. Micah came home from cross country practice with a terrible headache. He didn't feel like eating supper. Ruth and I made rice krispie treats for one of their 4-H snacks. It was their turn to furnish refreshments. Verne Edward had made Kathy an angel food cake, but there was no time to eat it that evening.

Tuesday Verne Edward took us on a driving tour of Bridgewater College where he teaches. It was too rainy for a walking tour, but we did go into his building and see his office. He took a bird and a small animal (hedgehog?) to his office and made a space for them.

Then we went to the book fair. I was looking for the book on melatonin that I loaned and never got back. The book told about the studies on melatonin that showed its ability to fight cancer. I had purchased it there several years ago, but they no longer had it.

Tuesday evening we had time to visit. After a ham steak meal we had the watermelon I grew and probably birthday cake, too.

Wednesday, while Kathy and Verne were teaching, I did their laundry. It was October 15, 2014. I missed the bottom step going to the basement but continued carefully carrying laundry up and down. Wednesday evening we went to church for pancakes, bacon and applesauce. Men cooked. Verne Edward flipped pancakes. Kathy, Ruth and I sayed and helped wash the dishes. It was dark when we got back. We picked apples by the light of Kathy's vehicle. We hurried. I was afraid of the bear. My back was hurting from my fall when I missed the step. We loaded my truck later that night.

Thursday morning we left at 7:30 a.m. Verne Edward stayed to see us off. I was afraid he'd be late to Bridgewater, but he'd arranged not to arrive until 9:00 a.m. We took along a gift from Verne to Ruth's son, Brian – young quail in an aquarium with some food and water and a quart waterer.

We found Lehmans in Kidron, Ohio at about 3:00 p.m. and stayed until they closed at 6:00 p.m. There were so many interesting things to see there. I purchased four stainless steel tumblers, a goat cookie cutter (so that Sarah would have a spare), and a set of sleigh bells for Dylan's Christmas present.

We ate a leisurely evening meal at an Amish restaurant and then drove until 11:30 p.m. to a motel at Napoleon, Ohio. First we fed and watered the quail in the back of the truck on the parking lot. I had hoped, actually my back was "wishing" that we would have stopped much earlier. But Ruth felt "good to go." It was much too late at midnight, I thought, to call Verne, although he was expecting me to call that night. I didn't realize how worried he was when he didn't hear from me.

The next morning Ruth called Brian to tell him we'd be there soon with the quail. The first and last words from Brian to Ruth were "Have Phyllis call Verne." Verne had worried all night. He had called Brian early that morning to see whether Brian had heard from us. Of course at that time, Brian had not. When I called Verne, he was about ready to call the highway patrol to see if we'd been in an accident.

Soon it was Thanksgiving. With my cracked vertebrae, I was glad for all the help hoisting the heavy 23 pound turkey in and out of the oven. Everyone was very helpful. I had exercises to do from my physical therapy visits. Our chiropractor friend gave me some kind of treatments (laser?) to help me heal. I would heal.

Barb scheduled surgery with my breast surgeon, Dr. Laura Morris for December 10. She had a small lump in one breast and a suspicious spot which was marked with a wire after an MRI in the other breast. Barb came through surgery well. She, too, appreciated Dr. Laura's care. After her morning surgery we arrived home at about 1:30 and the soup in the slow cooker was fine. Barb just preferred to eat hummus and crackers. Barb's friend, Pastor Bev Weaver spent the morning with us at the hospital and came to visit Barb the day following surgery. Barb and I both try to eat a cancer preventing diet. She may do a better job of it than I do, but I am usually careful.

Again the church looked amazing with its many lights and Christmas decorations. Christmas program practices were underway. I was glad for twelve children in Wawaka's children's Christmas program on December 21. The many phone calls I made inviting those who didn't regularly attend to be in the program were worth it. I only wished they could come more often. Usually there were only three children at worship. I directed the adult choir cantata at the 7:30 p.m. Christmas Eve service using the accompaniment CD. Now it was Christmas. I enjoyed long conversations with all my children and grandchildren on Christmas day.

I seldom saw my brother and my sisters. We were at church on weekends and I was at Camp Mack during the week. None of my siblings lived close enough to just "drop in on for a visit." I learned that my sister

Karen was having a cornea transplant on Tuesday, January 13, 2015 at Cleveland Clinic. She came through the surgery very well. Her loving husband, Joe, had to drive her to her school teaching job for quite a while after that surgery. Her twin sister, Sharon, was going through a traumatic divorce.

Verne and I were excited to have Micah coming by train for a Manchester University visit on February 12. The train was scheduled to arrive at 6:36 a.m. so we stayed overnight at Wawaka to be closer to Waterloo where Micah would get off. The train didn't arrive until 9:30 a.m. and Micah's appointment was at 11:00 a.m., a long way from Waterloo. We dashed through the parsonage, grabbed breakfast for Micah to eat on the way and called his brother Caleb to have him relay the message that Micah would be late. We arrived about 11:20 and met with a physics professor.

After lunch we attended a physics class taught by another physics professor. Micah worked problems with the class and the enjoyed the class. On our campus tour I learned that ballet is a physical education course, that students can take their papers to the Success Center and an English major will help them correct them and that students can get free note cards there. When we met with the admissions counselor, he gave Micah a coupon for a free T shirt. After he picked up the shirt, we took Caleb and Micah to Caleb's house

Saturday, February 14, 2015 was Valentine's Day and the Wawaka Church had paid for Verne and me to go to the Valentine's dinner at Camp Mack. There were white out conditions that cancelled the dinner.

Meanwhile, we were planning to celebrate Micah's 18th birthday at noon. He had stayed with Caleb overnight. They were on their way to our house and were between Leesburg and our road when they couldn't see anything. They hit the ball hitch of the truck ahead of them. That truck had run into something ahead of it. Caleb's license plate was folded up and some grill work was damaged cosmetically. Both boys were physically fine. Another accident or traffic delay kept them sitting in another location. Finally, they arrived.

We ate and celebrated Micah's birthday. Before I had dishes done, two ladies knocked on the door. They were stranded at the funeral home parking lot and needed to use a bathroom. They said there were others stranded there, too. We told them to tell others to come over where it was warm. A number of persons came over. Two were in the area visiting from Kansas over this Presidents Day holiday. Our guests sat around our big table, visiting and playing games. I went about making my big kettle full of chicken soup. I baked a couple "sticks" of washboard cookie dough. I had cut a big pineapple that morning and also had the big, untouched salad from lunch and leftover potato rolls.

We were willing to keep our guests overnight, but they left after the wind died down. A police escort had led persons who chose to remain at the funeral home to the Milford Community Center. There was no church on Sunday morning. Caleb left mid morning. When it became obvious that Micah couldn't go home on the train Saturday night as planned, Kathy changed his ticket to Sunday night. We went to Wawaka Sunday afternoon and Micah and I played games, and ate leftovers. His train arrived about 11 p.m.

Our granddaughter, Morgan, spent her week of Spring break from Butler University with us in March. We cooked together, we baked together, we went grocery shopping together and Morgan insisted that we take time to relax together. Our relaxation was watching movies on videos. Morgan seems to know how to balance work and play.

During our more than 30 years living at Milford, Verne's sister, Ruth Ann, often stopped in to visit us. Sometimes she was on her way to see her son, Brian's family at Stryker, Ohio. Sometimes, she came and stayed overnight with us when she had a morning meeting in our area with some of her Manchester College girl friends. Both Verne and I loved seeing Ruth Ann when she arrived from her home at Gary,

Indiana. Verne Henry had been close to his sister ever since he was a child who didn't want to start school and leave her at home.

Ruth's end of life and celebration of life stories deserve a separate chapter. Here let me share that while we were visiting Ruth on Verne's Birthday, April 1, 2015, the transitions specialist, Lori, came in the afternoon. Ruth was just drinking, unable to get even a deviled egg to go and stay down. On Friday, April 3rd, Ruth Ann decided to do what her brother had encouraged her to do – she decided to go with Hospice. Events leading up to and following her April 15th passing are shared in the next chapter.

Losing his sister was a difficult time in Verne's life. It wasn't easy for me either. Just six months earlier as we returned from our trip to Virginia, I couldn't get my energetic sister-in-law, Ruth Ann, to stop driving for the night until nearly midnight.

About May 26th, Verne asked me if I wanted to plant sweet potatoes. He dug the holes for me to plant over 100 sweet potatoes that I had started. On May 27th I planted about 40 broccoli plants and then took my leftover plants to Caleb to take home when we celebrated his May 28th birthday. We went to Maria's at North Webster and I took Angel food cake and organic raspberries for dessert after our meal. Caleb recognized where our waitress was from by the dialect of Spanish she spoke. Spanish was one of Caleb's three college majors.

Barb's family came in the wee hours of June 4th. After breakfast and Barb's appointment with cancer surgeon, Dr. Laura Morris, we left for John's house. I had things out so that each person could pack their own lunch. We left about noon and ate in Barb's van. All four of Barb's family plus their two friends and Verne and I were all fit squeezing together.

We left John 's in our caravan about 4:30. Verne and I rode with John that evening. After a very long break for an evening meal at a Thai and Chinese restaurant, we found the chalet that John had rented between 3:00 and 3:30 a.m. Verne and I stayed there that night so we didn't wake up Verne and Kathy. Friday morning we had pumpkins muffins that I had made and then we went to Verne and Kathy's. Verne Henry and I stayed with Verne Edward and Kathy Friday, Saturday and Sunday nights.

Micah's high school graduation was held at James Madison University on Saturday, June 6, 2015. After a meal of ham, potatoes and beans, a number of us helped fix the veggie tray, cheese and crackers and cookie trays and cut the watermelon for the back yard reception.

Later Saturday evening, we had a bonfire. Micah burned his unwanted school papers. Guests enjoyed making Micah's papers into paper airplanes and trying to fly them over the fire. We enjoyed hotdogs and s'mores. Then Micah and Caleb celebrated by setting off a lot of beautiful fireworks. Some were loud and received noisy, scolding reactions from the peacocks. The sheep headed to the back of the field.

Kathy's parents and sister's family said their good-byes that night and headed home Sunday morning. Verne and I went to Sunday School with Verne Edward and Kathy. There was no Sunday School at their Linville Creek Church for children in the summer. The rest of our family came to Linville Creek for the morning worship.

Micah ran home from church, seven miles. Kathy had a roast in the oven for lunch. While we were waiting for Micah, I cut Verne Edward's hair. It was quite long. I rarely see him, but when I do, it is usually hair cut time.

Caleb and Micah left about 8:00 a.m. Monday morning for Manchester University. Caleb had a summer internship and Micah had orientation. We left with John shortly after that. We stopped at John's for a while and then we got scrunched into Barb's van and headed home. We arrived about 10:30 p.m. and went to bed.

I fixed bacon, gluten free pancakes and fruit for breakfast. When I realized that Barb and Rob weren't getting up, I began fixing lunch. The family and Ben and Joslyn left at about 1:00 p.m. to take Joslyn home and then head on to Lincoln, Nebraska.

It was July 2, 2015. Yes, I was retired, but I still had a job to complete. Verne took me to Michaels and I chose matting and frames for the pieces I wrote and the pictures for with them. Information for each of the following would hang in the areas named for them. John Kline's information and picture would hang inside to the right of the main door as you enter the John Kline Welcome Center. Manly Deeter's information and picture hangs in the Manly Deeter Office Complex. Kate Warstler's picture and information hangs in the Kate Warstler Dining Room area.

That year Camp Mack celebrated its 90th anniversary. Camp Staff requested that I put together a timeline of happenings in programming and construction throughout those 90 years. And so, I made a long timeline which hung for months across one end of the dining room until it was decided to preserve it by getting it laminated.

Verne and I enjoyed the evening of July 22, 2015 when Caleb brought his friend Amanda Basham to our home for supper. We were glad to get to meet Amanda. She is trying to catch and test blood from Chickadees for a college project on genetics. She is "doing Manchester" in three years and will graduate with Caleb in 2016. We served Caleb's request of bison burgers with mushroom gravy plus corn on the cob, mashed potatoes, salad, raspberries, strawberries, Angel food cake and ice cream. Great night!

Verne Henry drove us to New Philadelphia, Ohio for my sister Karen's son Buck's wedding in August. We got to spend time with Sharon and her daughter, Holly, as well as Karen and Joe's children and grandchildren, many of whom we had not previously seen. Verne drove the trip in sections. We stayed in Wooster, Ohio the first night and then arrived at Hampton Inn at New Philadelphia on Friday. It was not easy to find the Hampton Inn which sits "way back" off the highway. But praise God for a safe trip, even though it wasn't easy. I repeatedly told Verne Hampton Inn and he turned in at Knight's Inn. I praise God for the things he can do and that he was willing to make this trip. He said he could drive to the wedding because he didn't have to be on really busy highways.

Verne was looking forward to visiting Lehman's Amish Store where Ruth and I had been the previous October. We enjoyed the huge store with an incredible variety of Amish and other merchandise. Verne bought a file for sharpening our garden hoes.. (Now five years later I wish I had that file to sharpen my hoes for using in my Greencroft garden.) I bought a cooling rack, a stainless steel sieve or strainer. As I write this, I have both of these items.

Lindsay's father walked beside her as the bride rode her motorized scooter to the altar. The pastor's very good message was on becoming one through loving and forgiving. At the reception Buck helped support Lindsay as they danced.

The DJ called all married couples to the dance floor. He called number of years married. If you were married less than the number he called, you sat down. Verne Henry really surprised me and took me to the dance floor. We had never "danced" before. I do remember "dancing" with our son John at his wedding – or at least pretending to dance. Well, we sat down at 52 years. The winning couple was married 57 years. That couple had to give their advice – the lady had to give advice to Lindsay and the man had to give advice to Buck, each one over the microphone. Verne and I were somewhat glad we didn't win.

Table seating was assigned for the reception. We were seated at the table with Joe and Karen, parents of the groom, Sharon and Holly, and Jack and Mason Keller, whose parents, Tina and Dan Keller were both in the wedding party at the head table. Guests had to look at the posted table listings to see where to sit.

On Monday, August 24, Sean and Morgan started out from Lincoln on the way to their respective colleges.

They stayed overnight with friends at Springfield, Illinois Sean did all the driving as Morgan had just had all four wisdom teeth pulled on Friday and was on medicine that didn't allow her to drive.

On Tuesday they left before the sun was up and drove to Butler University at Indianapolis where they unloaded Morgan's things. Then Sean started out for our house. He was just about nine miles directly west of us when he ran into a large, four-door white pick up truck. I was on the phone talking with his mother, Barb, about how far along he might be when she got another call and had to go. She said if it was Sean, she's call me right back.

It was Sean. Our car was in the driveway – we didn't have to walk over to the garage. We got to Sean long before the police. Sean was driving the Toyota Sierra Minivan. When he ran into the ball hitch of the pick up, the van became attached to the truck. The truck couldn't leave until the van was raised on the wrecker bed and persons worked to get them apart. The fire department came and cleaned up the fluids on the road applying what looked like kitty litter before they swept it up. The EMS took the older gentleman who was driving to be checked out for seat belt damage as he had had a quadruple heart bypass and also back problems. Sean and the truck driver's young passenger were checked on site and their vitals were fine.

Joslyn Haldeman, Sean's friend, came on Wednesday. They picked rose hips, helped shell lima beans and picked early pears. On Thursday they headed to Hope College.

Ruth Ann's children scheduled the burial of her ashes for Labor Day weekend. Her ashes would be beside her husband's at Altoona, Pennsylvania. Our son, John, came on Thursday, September 3rd. He wanted to leave by noon, but Verne Henry thought we needed to wait until Kozon came to look at our air conditioning that wasn't cooling right. The serviceman came and found the only problem was that the filter needed changed. He changed it and we were on the road at 12:30 p.m. after I paid $153 for something we could have/should have done ourselves. We learned a lesson. Dirty filters don't allow air to circulate.

John's children, Leah and Dylan, did not have cross country practice that day because of the heat. But surprisingly, soccer games were still on for that evening. Dylan was the sole referee (center referee only) for a game for boys about nine years old. After John parked, it was a long walking distance to the field for this game. I enjoyed seeing it. Verne Henry was glad he stayed at John's house. It would have been too much walking for him.

When the children got home from school, Dylan, John, Verne Henry and I started out for Altoona. We got into such heavy rain on the interstate that cars were pulled off on the berm. Those moving had flashers on; that is the only way they could be seen. We stopped at a Wendy's for some supper. We arrived safely at the Altoona Marriott about 10:30 p.m.

Saturday morning in the Marriot while I was having a most delicious smoothie of spinach, pineapple and avocado, Sarah arrived from Penn State. Soon her mother, Kathy, arrived. We all enjoyed sharing family updates in the breakfast area.

The family gathered at Alto Rest Cemetery at 11:30 a.m. Verne led the service at noon. He did a good job. He invited sharing. Then he had Bob read the 23rd Psalm. He had taken his minister's manual and I had taken my small travel Bible, so Verne Henry had everything he needed although he didn't know ahead of time that he would be leading the service. I thought he did a good job. Maybe it was good that he didn't worry about his responsibilities ahead of time.

After a family gathering at Hoss Restaurant and some outdoor play for the children with Dylan entertaining Kevin's children by tossing a football in the parking lot, John asked us where we would like to go on the way home. I thought about my siblings who lived in northeastern Ohio. Should I choose to visit Karen, Sharon, Betty, or Fred? I had seen Karen and Sharon recently at Buck's wedding. Verne and I had seen

Betty a year or so before. So I said I wanted to see my brother Fred. I said that with fear and trembling. I hadn't seen him – at least on good terms- for 16 years - at Dad's funeral. I might have seen him at a distance in court after Dad's death. So, John took us to Fred's.

Nanci and her daughter, Kimmie, were sitting at a table on their patio in front of their house. Nanci came and greeted us warmly as we got out of John's Volva. Fred was at the cemetery where he often mows and decorates granddaughter Kayla's grave. He soon came, slowed to turn in and went on past to Mikie's - the next place on his side of the road toward Warren.

Before long, Nanci sent someone to tell Fred we were here and he came right over. He had gone on by because he thought Jehovah Witnesses were at his house. He looked good. He said his cholesterol had been really high so he started running and jogging eight miles a day and got it down. He looks trim and healthy. There was a can of raisins on the patio table. He snacks on them instead of sweets.

Nanci shared that she had lymphoma cancer last year and lost all her hair, even her eye lashes. But she is well now.

Fred and Nanci's children all live near them. Kim's family has always lived with them. Mike's family lives next door. There were lots of young relatives at Fred's to entertain Dylan. Kimmie's daughter, Kyra, is Dylan's age and took him for a four-wheeler ride. Then a group of young people (they may not like to be called children) shot baskets with the basketball.

Fred loved retelling stories of chasing me with chickens and rigging cans of water at the outhouse door and in trees to dump on unsuspecting sisters. He said that once when our parents were gone and I was in charge, he opened the back kitchen door and chased as many chickens as he could into the house.

We stayed until almost 10:30 – past our bedtime, but it was a very good visit. Then we drove to Akron and stayed at Marriott Suites. Before we left, Fred gave us his email and phone numbers. I have a brother again.

The Marriott accommodations were wonderful. We arrived at 11:30 p.m. I popped the microwave corn in our suite and washed some apples that Kathy had given us.

In the night I had a bad leg cramp and got up to work it out and to use the bathroom. I couldn't find the toilet and fell over backwards hitting my head hard on a low corner porcelain shelf in the corner of the shower. I had stumbled around with my leg cramp and fell over the low lip of the handicapped shower. I had put my traveling ice pack in the refrigerator freezer. Verne got it and I sat it on the back of my head in bed. I stayed awake a long time intentionally.

We ate breakfast at the hotel and stopped for lunch on the way home. Since Kathy had sent apples, canned peaches and snacks for Caleb and Micah, I called them on the way home and invited them and Amanda to come for supper at 6:00. I really had to hustle to get everything ready especially with a bad head. Dylan scrubbed the potatoes. We ate at 6:00 as I had promised: bison burgers in mushroom gravy, a grandchildren favorite, corn, green beans, cantaloupe from our garden, fresh carrots, peppers, tomatoes.

After my birthday experiences in 2013 and 2014, I thought that Verne Henry would never again remember my birthday. And then came Sunday, September 20, 2015. Verne told me "Happy Birthday" before we were even out of bed. He brought me a hand written birthday card when he came to breakfast. When I went to Sunday School, there was a card at my place from two of the class members. During the worship service, the congregation sang "Happy Birthday" to me a'capella.

When we got home mid-afternoon, the phone started ringing. Wow! Thank you, God. I am usually so depressed on my birthday because no one – even Verne Henry – remembers it. Quoting from my journal:

> "God, thank you for this very special birthday. I write with tears in my eyes.

First Sean called
Then: Micah
      Morgan
      Sister Carol
      Kathy
      Sarah
      Caleb
      John (I had tried to call John & Allison between calls and left a message wishing them Happy Anniversary. He called on cell phone and I talked to the entire family.
On Monday, September 21, my sister Sharon called. On Tuesday, Barb wished me a Happy Birthday. Joy continues!"

On Wednesday morning, September 23, Verne Henry met with Torin Eikler, our Northern Indiana Church of the Brethren District Executive and Verne decided to announce his retirement sometime after Christmas and before Easter. I think he needed to give six months notice. He didn't set an exact retirement date at this time.

On Thursday afternoon, October 22nd, Barb called from Nebraska to say she and Rob were coming our way. They were getting ready to leave for Hope College as we were leaving for Manchester University where I needed to play for a clarinet student, Angela's, lesson at 11:00 a.m. We were packed for Defiance

420

College homecoming and my 50th Anniversary Celebration and would head to Defiance via Shecklers Pickle factory and store near Butler, Indiana.

At the Comfort Inn at Defiance we changed into dressy clothes and drove to the banquet location at the college. We skipped the hors'deurves and cash bar. The meal was interesting– no one knew what was in the crust on the chicken. I thought the tastiest part of the meal was one of the two desserts on our dessert plate, the "no flour" dark chocolate square that tasted like very rich cake. The program honored seven different graduates who had done or were doing treat things. There was a slide show presentation before each award was presented. We didn't stay for the dance.

We went back to the hotel and called Barb. They were going to Hope because Sean hadn't been going to classes. They were considering taking him home. Sean didn't know his parents were coming or that they had talked to the administration. It was decided he would drop down to six hours and work to catch up in those couple classes.

Saturday morning we ate at the Comfort Inn because we thought our President's breakfast wasn't until 10:00 a.m. We got there at 9:30 a.m. and it had already begun. Different information listed different times, I guess. Anyway, we were seated by a young couple, Josh and Jaime. Josh graduated in 1998. It was an interesting breakfast. The plated breakfast was Canadian bacon pieces and chunks of hard-boiled egg on three biscuits with gravy over. In a dessert bowl was something like a baked banana on French toast with syrup.

I shared at breakfast that I spent a lot of time studying in the stacks at a secluded desk in the old library. I wondered if the new library had individual study carrels.

Verne and I walked to the new library after breakfast, but it was closed on Saturday. It seemed to me that Homecoming guests would want to see it. Or what if a student wanted to study here on Saturday? Just as we discovered the library was closed, Josh and Jaime whom we had met at breakfast appeared, opened the library door and invited us in. I worried that alarms would go off. Josh gave all three of us a wonderful tour. Downstairs in the stacks were the study desks.

After the grand library tour the four of us went to the building where I used to have convocations and where my senior recital was. The seats sloped down to the stage. The stage was dark, but there was a grand piano there. I didn't see the bench. It was probably somewhere on stage in the dark. I played a little of Rustling of Spring standing up.

Josh and Jaime and another couple were in the auditorium talking. Verne and I shared that Manchester University often used golf carts to transport persons from parking lots. Immediately Josh called the head of Alumni affairs and asked for a golf cart. It arrived and he took us to our car so we could take it nearer to the stadium.

But it was still a long way to walk from parking to the tailgating tent, so after we parked, Jaime and I walked and Verne rode with Josh to the tailgating tent outside the stadium where our lunch was served prior to the football game. Our young new friends were so helpful. Our class had special seating for the game and Verne was able to manage it.

That evening my class, the class of 1965, and our spouses went to the Defiance College President's home for a lovely dinner. It was interesting talking about experiences at college 50 years ago.

We went back to the Comfort Inn and stayed Saturday night so that we could attend Verne's home church, Poplar Ridge, the following morning. Poplar Ridge is where Verne and I met on a Sunday when he was home for a weekend in the fall of his first seminary year. The visit to Poplar Ridge was extended as they were having a carry-in at noon and invited us to stay. That gave us more opportunity to see and talk with people there.

Barb's daughter, Morgan was with us Thanksgiving week. On Tuesday before Thanksgiving Morgan had two appointments. In unbelievably dense fog – fog so dense we couldn't see stop lights until we were passing under them – Verne drove to Wakarusa for Morgan's very specialized blood test to check her allergies – a long ordeal. Thankfully, Verne knew the roads and knew about where the stop signs were that we could barely see.

After we ate our packed lunches, we traveled to Morgan's afternoon appointment with a nurse practitioner who works for a gynecologist to see about the pain in Morgan's abdomen. She ordered an ultrasound which Morgan got at Goshen Hospital Friday after Thanksgiving.

Christmas programs meant that 2015 was drawing to a close. After a terrible rehearsal for the children's program on Saturday, the children looked and sounded fantastic and played instruments well on Sunday, December 13. On December 20, the adult cantata was "The Love of God at Christmas," presented with nine singers. On Christmas Eve it felt like we should be in church. But Ministry Team thought too many would be out of town to have the service. We are planning to have an Epiphany party at our home in January.

We got a Christmas card from Fred's family this year! What a wonderful surprise!

Meanwhile, I finished 46 pages of family information. I sent this to my children and all my siblings. As persons grow up and others age, move, or die, the information seems to keep changing. This is a work that will often need updating.

On December 23rd Gloria and Larry Taylor came and brought us a gallon of frozen cider from apples they picked off our Jonathan tree. They think it is the best cider they ever had. That evening, Steve, Savannah and Caleb, our Amish neighbors stopped in on their way to an Amish School program and brought us a delicious loaf of whole wheat bread and some jelly. Julia stayed in the buggy. She is expecting a baby on January 4.

December 25, 2015 was another Christmas with no company. I am thankful for phones. Barb and Rob left at 6:30 a.m. for Florida and Christmas with Rob's folks. Verne Henry and I planned our Epiphany party and prepared items for it. I walked outside. It was 46 degrees – no snow. We talked with Verne Edward. Caleb plans to fly back from Amanda's tomorrow night. Caleb seems to be in charge of Christmas trees at their house. He's not there – they put up a branch.

John, Leah and Dylan came on Sunday night, December 27. We made personal pan pizzas and then opened gifts that night. I got everyone a "Jesus Calling" devotional book. It is a good thing they didn't wait to come on Monday morning. We were iced in and the wind was howling and brought down some pine branches. Leah and I cooked Swedish meatballs and coconut washboard cookies. John, Dylan and I played a lot of Tri-ominoes. I really enjoyed being together and having persons to play games with me.

On the last day of this year, Dylan would turn fifteen years old. He would be home for his birthday.

Micah's Manchester January term final was the morning of January 22, 2016. We picked him up at noon but did not take him to the train station. He wasn't going home to Virginia for term break because a blizzard in the east made that impossible. I was glad to have Micah at our house. I loved playing table games with any grandchild who was game. Micah usually won whatever game he and grandma played – chess, or checkers, or bogus or connect four. He was always thinking several moves ahead.

On Monday Verne Henry and I took Micah to the Amish store called Rentown. We bought him some of his favorite nuts, black walnuts, cheddar cheese and M & M candies. I got him a Newton's Cradle and wrapped it for his February birthday. With one of his majors being Physics, he knew more about Newton's Cradle that I did. After lunch we took Micah back to Manchester.

On the last Thursday of 2016 we received a phone call from Amish Acres. That was surprising because Amish Acres where we often attended musicals was closed in January and February. It was even more surprising when the person on the phone said that Verne and I had won the drawing for the quilt that had been displayed during the recent program season. I wondered how that could be. I certainly didn't stuff the entry box. The caller shared that season ticket holders – which we had been for years - were automatically entered in the drawing.

The next day we went to Nappanee and posed for the newspaper with the quilt and Amish Acres officials. The colorful quilt is hand quilted by Amish quilters in various designs. Those who know I am afraid of roosters laughed when they saw the big appliquéd rooster on the center of the quilt. When we were in Nappanee we picked up a form at the Bureau of Motor Vehicles for our doctor to sign so that we could get a handicapped person insignia for our car.

I waited until February 1st to start my sweet potatoes. When I started them in January, they really got gangly before the end of May when I usually plant them After placing six orange and six yellow sweet potatoes each in a quart jar of water and each held up by nails at intervals near the bottoms, Verne and I went to Warsaw.

At the Warsaw Pillbox, Verne looked at walkers. He chose one with brakes, a seat and wheels large enough to move easily outdoors.

March 11th was the Camp Mack Annual dinner which Verne and I had supported for years. Micah, Caleb and Amanda were at our table. After the dinner I gave them a window box of yellow sweet potato starts and a window box of orange sweet potato starts to take home on Spring break. The sweet potatoes started February 1st were growing well. There would be plenty more for me to plant.

John came on Thursday night, April 14. John had taken off work on Friday. John hooked our trailer to my truck and he and his dad went to New Paris to purchase 2 yards of cedar mulch. John and I spent the day weeding and mulching. That night Allison and the children came after work and school.

On Saturday Allison and I planted the garden behind the house and John and Dylan built a fence around it to protect the plants from rabbits. After completing the fence, John built a fabulous gate. I wouldn't have to step over the chicken wire and Verne could get in as well.

On Sunday I was the pianist for the Northern Indiana District Worship service held at Camp Mack. Worshippers provided snacks that were enjoyed after the worship. I didn't realize how much pain Verne

Henry was in during the service. Finally I was able to get my dish from the refreshment table and we went home, leaving the car in the driveway as Verne didn't feel like walking across the yard from the garage. Here is what I later wrote about this evening.

Pulled Over

Whee, whee, whee. A siren and flashing lights behind me. I was being pulled over – the first time ever in my 72 year life. I don't know how, but I managed to pull to the berm and stop. I turned off the ignition. Then I couldn't put down the window or open the door. I was scared!

It is May 1st, 2016, after 9 p.m. With drizzly rain coming down, it really seems dark. I'm somewhere around New Paris, maybe eight or so miles from my home at Milford, Indiana.

My passenger got his door open. An Elkhart County Sheriff Deputy at the open door looked inside and said that I'd been called in for driving slow and all over the road. I leaned over and blurted out, "I usually do not drive this car and especially not at night. I'm trying to get my husband to the hospital emergency room. He's in a lot of pain." Without hesitation, the policeman said, "Get in the back seat of the car and I'll drive you there."

On the way to the hospital the sheriff deputy told us his name was Casey. He looked to be in his thirties, and was training a younger cop who was riding with him. They were on their way to check out an accident where a deer was hit. They said that could wait.

Casey drove us to the Goshen Hospital Emergency Room door and went in and got a wheelchair for my husband, Verne. The trainee had followed in the police car. After we got inside, Casey parked our car. He had never asked to see my driver's license or our car registration.

I thought, "I wish we had gone earlier before it got dark and rainy? But how?" It had been a busy Sunday for both Verne and me. Teaching Sunday School, I had an autistic child I don't usually have, so I was on my toes and things went well. Then during worship Verne, Pastor at our church, wasn't feeling well in the pulpit. Busy at the church organ, I didn't realize his distress. He left the sanctuary when our preacher for the day took over at about 11 a.m. He was sweaty and in a lot of pain. He had a hernia that he couldn't get to go back into place. After trying for a long while in the bathroom, he came back into the sanctuary and sat at the back.

Verne kept going. With no mention of his pain, we stayed for the congregation's carry-in meal. Then we made trips across the church parking lot to the parsonage (our week-end home) carrying our leftover food, Sunday School materials, music bag, autoharp, rhythm instruments, and Bibles.

Finally away from important responsibilities, Verne admitted his pain and lay down at the parsonage while I packed up to go home. I read a few minutes to let him rest. At 3:00 I began getting him up to leave as I had to be at Camp Mack to play the piano accompanying congregational singing for the 5 p.m. District Worship Celebration. After our forty-five minute trip home, we unloaded our weekend items, suitcase, music, brief case and ice chest, got ready and left for Camp. I thought I should go by myself, but Verne wanted to go. It was a long service with many kinds of special music, lasting until at least 7 p.m. with refreshments after that. When it seemed that most were done eating, I got my dish and we left for home. It was around 8 p.m. Verne was really hurting.

He got ready for bed but couldn't get comfortable. I asked a couple times about taking him to the emergency room, but he wanted to try to wait until morning and see his family doctor. Finally, he realized he wouldn't get any sleep and so he got up and dressed and we left. I prayed that I would be able to get him to the hospital safely.

The Emergency Room Doctor said he'd done the right thing in coming to the hospital. A strangulated hernia could be life threatening. The doctor raised the bed, lowered the head end and with the help of gravity, gently put the bulge back in place. Then he leveled the bed, and the nurse covered Verne with warm blankets and let him rest.

While he was resting, the nurse came in and said, " Verne, you have two visitors. May I bring them back?" I thought, "Who even knows we are here?" Well, the police were back. Casey needed my keys to retrieve his flashlight he had left in our car. When the officers came back to give me our keys, they shared that they had investigated another deer hit since they'd brought us to the hospital. Casey said the deer were really running in tonight's rain. I'll never know if being pulled over kept us from experiencing an encounter with one of God's four-legged creatures.

As the officers were leaving, Casey took out a business card and put his personal cell phone number on it. Handing the card to me, he said, "If you don't have a ride home when Verne is released, call me and I'll make sure you get home. " (We don't even live in his county.) He added, "It is really storming now outside. "

Verne was released with instructions to call a surgeon in the morning. Since he was now "back together," Verne was able to drive home in the pouring rain.

Casey never saw the motorist who called about my driving. Did one, two or three angels care for and protect us that night?

Who would have thought that being pulled over would be God's answer to my prayer?

Our Time at Wawaka Nears Conclusion

Verne really wanted to see Caleb and Amanda graduate from Manchester University on Saturday, May 14. His doctor allowed him to wait until after graduation to have his hernia surgery. He was able to have a handicapped seat at graduation. We both also enjoyed the reception at the house at Caleb's rental house.

At Verne's appointment on May 2nd, the day following his trip to the Goshen Hospital Emergency Room, Surgeon Dr. Daniel Diener had explained what he had in mind for Verne's hernia repair. He said, "My father is also a doctor and when he needed hernia surgery, he said he didn't think persons his age should be put totally under with anesthesia unless absolutely necessary. He had his surgery with just something to put him in a twilight zone. The operating surgeon used numbing stuff at the incision and the area stayed numb for three days. At the end of the week after his surgery my father went to the celebration of his mother's 99th birthday."

"So," Dr. Diener continued, "This is how I want to do your surgery. You will be breathing on your own. You won't need a chest X-ray or stress test. You should have very little pain. I cannot do laparoscopic surgery this way, so I will be opening you up like you were opened for your last three hernia surgeries."

On the evening before surgery, John arrived and then took us to the hospital for our 8:00 a.m. arrival time on May 17. An IV was started and then the doctor came in and put his initials on the spot to be repaired. Verne was taken from the room at about 9:30.

At 10:20 John and I were allowed to go to the room where Verne had started out. There he was; wide awake. On his bedside tray were 2 cheese sticks and 3 packs of soda crackers. He also had water. Neither John nor I had ever seen anyone come out of surgery this alert and pain free. After Verne ate these, the doctor came in. He had just repaired the area of Verne's first surgery done in 1966, that lasted 50 years without mesh, and was intrigued at how it was done – he hadn't seen anything quite like it in his textbooks. He teased that at least his repair only had to last 30 years. He gave Verne a prescription for pain medicine, but didn't think he would need it. Then Verne got dressed and we came home, after stopping at the Dollar General in Milford where I purchased two small bottles with 24 each of Ibuprofen at regular 200 strength. I warmed up home-made vegetable soup for lunch and Verne ate at the table with us.

On Sunday following the Tuesday morning surgery, Verne counted the number of Ibuprofen remaining in the first and only bottle we opened. There were 15 of the 24 pills left. He used only nine. The pain medicine prescription remains unfilled. This was the least painful of his four hernia surgeries.

Yes, Verne was black, brown, red and yellow in a large area that is getting progressively lighter. And his incision has a long ways to go to become just a scar. But never in his past three hernia repairs did Verne have such relatively comfortable experience. Praise God for His wonderful care.

Sometime during our early years at Wawaka, Verne had accepted the call to be Wawaka's part time pastor instead of being an interim. He had served for years with the strength God provided. Verne was now serving Wawaka using his walker to help him keep his balance. In the spring he had submitted his letter giving six months notice of his retirement plans. His service to Wawaka would end on September 30th, 2016. We were grateful for the love and care of the Wawaka members as they continued to provide help for him to continue with them in ministry.

It was his turn to preach and so Verne preached on May 29, just twelve days after his hernia surgery. We knew that our first grandchild, Amelia Grace, was born to Joslyn and Sean Dickason on May 25th. Amelia never visited Wawaka. In fact, we did not meet Amelia in person until Christmas Day, the day she turned seven months old.

Caleb and Amanda stopped in on Monday to get some meal bars to take on their trip to Ecuador, the place where Caleb had spent much time studying abroad. The next day Barb and Rob were here from Nebraska when we woke up. They helped a lot - painting around the picture window and weeding the garden.

In August Micah's Grandpa Bill and Grandma Alice brought him to our house. After lunch Micah brought his stored items up from our basement and put them in my green Ford Ranger to go to Manchester University. He was on the third floor of East Hall in the same room he had last year. Verne Henry drove us to Manchester but did not climb the stairs to help us carry up Micah's things as he had the year before. It was a blessing that Micah travels light.

September 20, 2016. Another birthday. I am 73 years old. No celebration. A disappointing day. But it was a good evening. I had a number of phone calls wishing me a "Happy Birthday." Verne mowed and ran out of gas. He went to Leesburg but couldn't get gas because he couldn't remember our zipcode. He came home upset so I went with him even though I was very dirty from weeding the garden and also from digging mountains of grass from off and under the mower. He finished mowing after we got gas.

Again I read my journal. "I get depressed being home. It's getting hard to share feelings with Verne. He

439

doesn't play games or joke around anymore. He takes my jokes as serious so I can't joke much either. He doesn't understand how important birthdays are to me. I'd love to do something special. (We used to.) I'd love him to tell me Happy Birthday. He doesn't want me to remember or notice his birthday, or so he says. Rejoice always! Stop feeling sorry for yourself. God is good!"

Wawaka members planned a wonderful retirement party for Verne on Saturday evening, September 24th Vases of flowers graced each table. Children eyed the four helium filled retirement balloons. The cake showed our picture on the top left and the church's picture on the bottom right. Our granddaughter, Morgan, came from Indianapolis. The other family members present were Verne's cousin Gloria and Larry Taylor. The Wawaka cooks lived up to their reputation with lots of good food. Homemade ice cream was served with the cake. The church gave Verne a lovely clock that may be set to play a range of six hymns or six Christmas carols.

The next day, September 25, 2016 was our last Sunday at Wawaka, Doug Archer preached and Verne led worship. We had our last membership class that morning during Sunday School. Alexander Eberly had been baptized the Sunday before with Verne giving the vows and Jeff Copp doing the baptizing. We enjoyed the fellowship of our last carry-in meal at Wawaka that day at noon.

That week church members helped us move our belongings from the Wawaka parsonage where we had spent weekends for over thirteen years to our Milford home. Saying "Good bye" was not easy.

25 Years at Camp Mack

A New "Job"

At the end of the 1987-1988 school year, I was out of a job. The Christian Church at Milford did not get a 75% needed vote to keep their school open for the students in grades 1-4 and the kindergarten children taught by another teacher in another room. The microscope and equipment that was purchased for my class along with textbooks went to an Indian reservation out west. It had been a fun year. We wrote poetry. We did the musical,"100% Chance of Rain." John Rouch judged some pretty neat science fair projects presented by each of my 12 students. We even had our own little yearbook.

Having experience from teaching in Ohio and Maryland public schools, I was too expensive to hire in our Indiana area. At least once an administrator frankly admitted that my years of experience kept me from being considered.

Verne was active in camping in whatever district he was currently serving. He served as Camp Board Chair in Northern Ohio, Southern Ohio and West Marva Districts. We were both leaders at the first national Junior High Camp at Carter Caves State Park in West Virginia. He had attended national camping events and knew camping leadership.

So it was that one day in August, 1988, Verne stopped in to visit Arden Ball, currently the Camp Mack

Executive. He came home and said that Arden was offering me a job in the Camp Office. I went to talk to Arden and we both decided I would give it a try. I remember thinking it would be like a year in BVS (Brethren Volunteer Service) for me and I would soon be back teaching in a classroom. I had loved church camp so much as a child and youth. God was giving me this great opportunity, but I didn't recognize God's hand in this for a long time.

Verne and I counseled a Junior High Camp the summer of 1988 – before I began working as a Camp staff - under the leadership of Jean Updike. We immediately realized that this was not our favorite style of camping. Beginning in 1989 and for years thereafter, Verne directed the Mildly Wild Camp for those completing 5th and 6th grades, where campers stayed in the northeast cabins but prepared all their own meals. I usually helped him in the evenings, especially by leading singing at evening activities. Verne planned all the menus prior to camp. Then for each meal he picked up food at the kitchen and pushed the garden-way cart up the hill and around to each camp family group to deliver their food for that meal.

Often Verne would drop me off at Camp on his way to Bethel Church in Milford. My first "space" was pretty much straight inside the south Ulrich House Door and just before the Ulrich House kitchen. Becky had a section of that large room also, while Arden's office was the room with the private door to the outside as well as a door to Becky and my offices.

My major job was helping to write curriculum, which at that time Camp Mack did "in house." We had a three-year manual and each year I worked on supplements for the year's theme – a supplement for each age group with Bible studies, games, worship suggestions, etc.

Becker Renovations

I was not there long before the Becker renovations began. The open, barn-like space in upstairs Becker was divided into eleven sleeping rooms, each with private bath.. The sloping theater like area on Becker's main floor was leveled and turned into a beautiful dining room with a sparkling ceiling. The main summer camp dining room was right below it. A handicapped lift was added and a dumb waiter. The outside steps facing west were enclosed and a gift shop was designed on the lower level near those steps. The large lower room that had served as the guest group dining area became the lower program room. One of my jobs during this renovation was to write and send out volunteer newsletters every two weeks noting the progress of the renovation, the names of all who had volunteered since the last newsletter, and projects (like dry walling or plumbing) needing workers.

The Youth Campers' service project during their 1990 Camp was moving the Camp Office from Ulrich House to Becker. I remember that a youth leader (It seems like it was Julia Stout) was typing the Youth Camp Waubee Waves on a typewriter. The youth moved the typewriter stand and typewriter from Ulrich House to the Becker office. The leader followed the typewriter and immediately sat back down and continued typing.

The Becker renovations were far from completed when the office moved. We had space heaters in the offices. Janice Shipe had to clean saw dust and/or drywall dust off the serving line whenever she wanted to set out a meal for the main floor dining room. That fall's seasoned citizens camp often ate in chilly temperatures or brought their food into the offices where we had some heat. I remember when the patio and decks were poured. We staff watched from the upper Becker Dining Room as cement was pumped up to the deck.

During one of the cold winters working on Becker renovation, Mike Kauffman, who at that time was working in facility, got a critically bad case of pneumonia and was hospitalized. Prayers went up for him from all over the state. When it was learned that Camp did not provide insurance for employees and that Mike had none, donations for his medical bills poured in. The result was that the Indiana Camp Board decreed that every year-round staff employee at

445

Camp Mack had to have insurance either provided by Camp or through a spouse's employment.

In the early 1990's, Susie Weybright worked at camp for a year registering and greeting guest groups. I enjoyed working with Susie in Becker. We did get in trouble once. The lights went out and it was dark in the office. We hunted and hunted and found a candle. We lit it and enjoyed its light until Arden appeared and demanded in no uncertain terms that we blow out the candle. He considered all the wood in Becker to be highly combustible. Arden was concerned about what a fire would do to Becker, and did not allow any candles to be lit. What a prophesy for an event about 20 years later that destroyed the entire Becker!

A Vivid Dream

Arden retired December 31, 1993 and Becky became the Executive Director on January 1, 1994. I went home for Christmas vacation at the end of 1993 knowing that Becky was about to choose between Sara Haldeman-Scarr and me for the next Program Director. Susie was no longer at Camp. As part of the job, I would be required to move into the staff house where Becky and Paris had lived (and where Galen and Carleta live at the time of this writing) and answer the phone, "Hello, this is Phyllis at Camp Mack." Becky moved to Arden's former home on Lake Waubee.

Arden purchased an RV and traveled, spending a lot of time in Alabama, and then buying a home at Gulf Shores, Alabama.

Verne, Pastor of Bethel Church of the Brethren at Milford, did not want me to take the new job. He didn't want his church calls answered by Camp Mack. One night during vacation I dreamed of a large, wide, beautiful pink bird. It hovered right over me. I could almost reach it. And then in my dream Verne took a long stick, sharpened it to a point on one end and stabbed my beautiful bird. I woke up very upset with Verne, knowing exactly what the dream meant. I was not to take the Program Director's job. I went to work after vacation and Becky told me that she was hiring Sara as Program Director. I already knew.

Mission Village

I remember the building of Mission Village. Camp tried yurts from at least two different companies. They were built just to the west of the Camp's main entrance. It was decided that the wooden yurt was more satisfactory for our needs than the canvas one. So we ordered five more like the "sample" wooden one and also a larger wooden yurt as a program area yurt and a smaller yurt for housing camp directors. Finally a round bathroom facility was built. That was a unique challenge. All the yurts were named for

447

Church of the Brethren missionaries and were connected by a board walk up a distance from the ground. It was exciting seeing the wooden yurt from near camp's entrance creeping very slowly to its new location in Mission Village.

Grand Camp

By 2005, if not before, Verne and I were directing a Grand Camp each summer for grandparents and grandchildren ages 4-10. We set up a program area with puzzles, play doh, Lego, Lincoln Logs, Story books, art projects and various fun things that grandparents and their grandchildren could enjoy in spare moments and especially if an activity was rained out. This was usually set up in Crumpacker, the program yurt.

We also streamlined Grand Camp registration/check in, which was important as Grand Camps grew to about 100 participants. We gave each Grand family a packet with all their information inside: their room assignment, their schedule, completed name tags and lanyard for each of their family members, a map of the grounds and any other needed information. All they had to do was check their addresses and get their packets. We had contacted specific grand families prior to their arrival at camp, shared daily topics, and asked them to be in charge of either the morning worship or the camp fire worship on a given day. Their advanced preparation led to some great worship experiences geared to the children's ages. We also instituted a short graduation service for 10 year olds at our Camp closings. I have a Grand Camp Waubee Waves from 2009 and we were still the leaders. I think that 2011 was our last year at Grand Camp, as our youngest grandchild, Dylan, would turn 11 on December 31 of that year.

The First Camp Mack Festival

In about 1997 our family attended a Camp Festival at Woodland Altars, our Church of the Brethren Camp at Peebles, Ohio in the Southern Ohio District. I thought, "Why couldn't we do something like this at Camp Mack?" And so I approached Becky Ball-Miller with my idea. She told me that if I could get persons to work on it, I could do it.

My original idea was to have a Brethren Heritage style festival. And so I asked Brethren historian Bill Eberly, and his wife, Eloise to be on the planning committee. I knew that Jeff and Laurie Fackler had been to Camp festivals in Pennsylvania. So I invited them. Don Myer, (Jim and Jeannie's father) was also on the original committee. Of course I was a part of it. I don't recall of anyone else at the beginning.

There was much to decide. What would we call the festival? What is the best date for it? What kind of subcommittees did we need? We needed to write a constitution and job descriptions for all involved. We worked on finding persons for parking, demonstrations and displays, entertainment, children's activities, foods and crafts, banking, publicity, auction, facility, hospitality and first aid. I was so excited at all the work getting done. I hoped we could have the first Festival in 1998. And then Bill Eberly made a profound statement. He said that we needed to make sure that our first festival was so good that persons would want to come back the next year. Therefore, he said, we aren't ready enough yet. And thus our first Alexander Mack Festival (that is what it was called in the beginning) was held in 1999 and has been held every year since then on the first Saturday of October.

In the early days of the Festival, there were always a couple of mural tours scheduled. When Medford Neher had a problem getting beards painted to suit him, my Father-in-Law, Verne Ernest Leininger, grew a beard for Medford to use as a model. He was scheduled to tell his beard story at the first festival on October 2, 1999 but died on September 28th. As I related in a previous chapter, the family held his body until after the festival. We had visitation on Sunday and the funeral on Monday.

Often Alexander Mack, portrayed by Casey Drudge roamed the camp and spoke at a given time. The Rupel sisters had displays of Brethren clothing in the basement of Becker Lodge. One year Amy Gall-Ritchie created a display of Brethren bonnets and coverings in Ulrich House. Communion Bread was also baked in Ulrich House at least one year. Jim and Norma Cross from South/Central Indiana, the White Branch Church, I believe, brought their horses and beautiful white buggy to Camp the night before the Festival and were there to give horse-drawn carriage rides for as many years as they were able. The Greene Township Lions Club Train was also popular at the Festival for years. I asked for donations from both our local Lions and our local Kiwanis to pay for it. The Children's activities have always been popular and always located in Sarah Major. Our first Children's Activities Sub-Committee leaders were from Pleasant Chapel: Tim and Cathy Wells. The children's activities have annually been very popular at the Festival with a succession of great leaders making sure that children have a wonderful time. For several years, Columbia City youth presented "The Cornfield that Grows People" as a puppet show. Then another church offered a different puppet show on alternate years with Columbia City. Eventually the puppeteers stopped bringing shows to the Festival. The food booths were located on the ball court before the new sewage system made it impossible to drive on that field. Churches brought their own tents or canopies. The ball field pavilion was also used. The entertainment was originally on a low boy located at the north end of the ball field My original dream was that someday the Festival would cover the entire camp.

Prior to the first Festival, I spoke at every Camp Mack event that would give me time. I shared the Festival information with every guest group that I could. Our publicity chair, from Syracuse would come each month and prepare bulletin inserts for churches. Then the big day came. We had the auction in Quinter Miller. Quilts hung around the edges below the murals. We had a lot of hand quilted, beautiful quilts. But the Brethren were not about to pay what they were worth. Our auctioneer bought a number of them, I think. We had a lot of auction items. Before it became dark, we went outside where four old cabins in the center of camp were to be auctioned. Then back inside to more auction items. Money raised at this 1999 Festival was designated to fund the creation of a new "mural" depicting Church of the Brethren happenings from 1950 to 2000. Margie Petry was chosen to research and paint it.

The Festival has changed dramatically over its 21 year history. There are no mural tours or Camp Mack postcard displays. The name was changed to the Camp Mack Festival to be more inclusive of our non-Brethren groups that use Camp Mack, who might not know who Alexander Mack was. When the new septic system ruled out using the Ball Field for food booths, food booths moved to the West side of Camp. Then after a few nasty weather festivals, the foods moved inside Quinter-Miller where the major entertainment had already began to perform on stage. The auction moved to Becker and then to the John Kline Welcome Center. Changes happen, but the Festival continues. Upon Rex's arrival as Director, he determined that at least half of the moneys earned at the Festival would fund Camper Scholarships.

Staff Trips

In the Spring of 1999, Becky took the year-round staff on a week-long tour of Church of the Brethren Camps in the East. Eight of us – I counted those in my pictures – went in two vehicles. We took group pictures at the Camp Entrance Signs for each camp we visited: Brethren Woods, Camp Eder, Camp Swatara, Camp Blue Diamond, Camp Harmony, Camp Bethel and Shepherd's Spring. At the end of the week we visited Hershey's Chocolate World. When we got back to Camp Mack we kept the tradition alive and took our picture at the Camp Alexander Mack sign. It was a beautiful and fun week.

Throughout my time at Camp I had opportunities to travel to Christian Camp Conferences in San Antonio,

Texas, Orlando, Florida, New Orleans, and Colorado, opportunities I would never have experienced were I teaching school. Verne sometimes also went to CCI conference. After the conference in Florida, Becky took us to see the Christmas show at Disneyland. I got apart from Verne and was panicked for a while at that show. Once the staff went to Gulf Shores, Alabama and celebrated Thanksgiving with Arden and Charmaine after a CCI Conference. Verne and I stayed in Arden and Charmaine's RV. They had a house by that time. I saw the Pacific Ocean when I went to the Church of the Brethren Outdoor Ministries Conference at Camp Myrtlewood in Oregon. These are great memories.

With Andrew Young on Camp's 75th Anniversary

In the year 2000, Camp Mack celebrated its 75th Anniversary by planning a special event for each month. Some of those events included a Sweetheart Banquet in February, a Wellness Retreat, in March or April, our Grand Celebration Event on May 20, 2000, a performance by Christian Comedians Ted & Lee, "The Creation Chronicles" on June 25, A Family Carnival Event on July 8, A staff reunion weekend from August 12-13, a Golf Outing on September 24, Alexander Mack Festival on October 7, Volunteer

Honors Banquet on November 19 and a Caribbean Cruise from December 2-9.

Camp was blessed to have Andrew Young speak at the 75th Anniversary Grand Celebration in Quinter-Miller. According to Frank Ramirez in *Brethren Brush with Greatness,* Young said, "I got here and lived in one of these cabins." Referring to the children's book, *Cornfields That Will Grow People* (Probably talking about my book, *The Cornfield that Grows People – the story of Camp Alexander Mack),* he remembered, "I was one of those people grown in this cornfield. That was forty-nine years ago. I don't remember much here besides the corn."

My special memory of Camp's 75th Anniversary Grand Celebration is sitting at a table beside Andrew Young in the back of Quinter-Miller Auditorium where we were each signing our books. I do not remember which of his books he was signing: *A Way Out of No Way* or *An Easy Burden.* I was signing *The Cornfield that Grows People – the Story of Camp Alexander Mack.* I had written this on a whim at home on vacation. I showed it to Becky who read it to residents at Timhercrest when she went there to lead worship. They liked it, so she decided Camp would have it published.

Rose Window Restoration

I recall how for years Miriam Cable had kept asking Camp to restore the large rose window in Quinter-Miller Auditorium, and the answer always had to do with the fact that we couldn't afford to do that. The window had been covered over for years. We had to hire a stained glass specialist to carefully assess damage and determine the needed replacement pieces. Then it needed a sturdy new wood frame with all the correct curves, angles and shapes to put the glass pieces into. This was a long 2004 summer job taken on by Ben Brubaker, a high-school shop teacher. Anyway, with his computer he was able to calculate and recreate the design of the intricate wood frame, truly a work of art. Watching him work was quite amazing. Frick Lumber supplied the beautiful lumber. On May 1, 2005 Camp Mack celebrated its 80th Anniversary with a special service and the dedication of the restored Rose Window in Quinter-Miller Auditorium.

Nature Study: Wind and More

The buyer who purchased one of our cabins in 1999 was moving and asked whether Camp would have a use for the cabin if they returned it. At first I believe that cabin was used to store lumber. And then. . . the returned cabin got a face lift and became the Nature Center in 2006. A grant from Outdoor Ministries

456

Association and other grant monies helped to purchase the windmill that. along with solar power, keeps the Nature Cabin off the grid. It was an awesome time for me as I watched the windmill go up in May of 2007.

An easy stone's throw away from the Nature Cabin, a 280 foot board walk over the wetlands was constructed in July of 2008 that allows for a wide variety of nature study as campers dip nets into the wetlands and study their "catch." It stopped at a ditch or stream. When ChoreTime Brock bought the Golf Course property in Milford, I tried unsuccessfully to convince the company to sell Camp Mack the iron bridge that is on that golf course property so that we might extend our board walk. They would not give it or sell it. The Board Walk was not extended.

One year during Annual Conference a straight line wind went through the camp. Broken off trees covered much of camp. We could scarcely believe what we saw when we brought up Camp Mack on line at conference. Whatever day this was, the miracle was that we had no campers at Camp that day. Many disaster workers came to help cut and clear the fallen trees and limbs. This happened during Rex Miller's tenure so it was 2002 or later.

Hosting staff at Our House

Reading one of my journals I found this fun Camp event noted on December 15, 2007. "Last night (12/14) we hosted Camp staff at our house for the annual Christmas party" (Let me add that the addition to our house was nearing completion at this time.) "We set Verne's big table to seat 14, my family table to seat 10, and a card table for 3 persons, all in our big new room. I expected 27 persons; 26 came. . . . . We used china and corelle ware. After the meal we each shared our Christmas plans. We gave Rex birthday (December 7) and Christmas gifts. Persons washed dishes at both sinks. Then we crowded into the living room to sing carols. After that, persons played pool and table games. The last persons left at 10 p.m. "

The next time we would host the entire staff at our house would be in the summer of 2014. Galen called me. What should he do? Galen, Acting Executive, couldn't have a farewell party for Rex at Camp Mack. That would likely be unacceptable or at least uncomfortable. Rex had to leave Camp under not too pleasant circumstances. The staff celebrated Rex's time at my house. It was a good celebration for something many of us had difficulty accepting.

The Becker Fire

July 11, 2010. Verne and I were home from the July 3-7Annual Conference at Pittsburgh, Pennsylvania. Verne had the Sunday off, so we decided to worship at North Winona Church of the Brethren that day. When we walked into the church we immediately learned that Camp Mack's main building, Becker Lodge, was on fire. Mike Dilling, the Indiana Camp Board Chair and a member of North Winona, was at Camp sending back information. We left immediately after worship, picked up sandwiches at McDonald's (maybe the only Sunday to ever do that), and headed home to change clothes and hurry to Camp. In the brief time I was home, I received two phone calls. One was from the Beavercreek Church of the Brethren in Ohio that had already heard about the fire. The other was from the media. I told this caller that our Executive Director was the only one who could give them information.

Verne and I hurried to Camp. I grabbed a stenographer's pad and a manila envelope from home to take which would come in handy as I collected bills and took notes. As we passed the public beach there was a Fire Tanker Truck loading with water from the lake. Because of the fire the trucks didn't have access to the lake at Camp. Soon Management Team – Galen Jay, Mike Kauffman, Rex Miller, Curt Rowland, Tony Keck and I met in the west lakeside corner of Sarah Major main floor to make plans and divide up tasks. Since I owned a truck, my job was to go to Lowe's and purchase large water coolers and ice chests – at least five of each, I think. Verne went with me.

The summer staff lived in upstairs Becker and so they lost most of their clothes and belongings. One of the Morphew boys was missing when staff were accounted for at the volleyball court. The firemen brought him out a window and down a ladder and there were no injuries. The Lance's Supermarket provided all the food at no charge for Sunday noon's meal for counselors preparing for the upcoming week of camp and for staff. Camp registration went on that afternoon. The food service staff and volunteers set up the big grill out and prepared meats (hot dogs?) for the evening meal. They also purchased all the necessary trimmings for that evening meal.

Volunteers from one South/Central church arrived with a van and money to take staff shopping for shoes, clothes or whatever essentials they needed. With Rex's permission, I talked Food Service Director, Tony, into letting his supper staff go shopping and allowing volunteers to fill their places.

By early evening, the Wampler Retreat Center kitchen and meeting area looked like a well-organized Goodwill store. Piles of shorts, jeans, t-shirts, soaps, and toiletries were sorted and stacked neatly. Summer staff slept that night in Wampler and in the Staff residence. I don't remember which location was for the ladies and which was for the men. Then during the coming days, counselors were brought to camp to help staff, usually in groups, deal with this trauma and loss.

Immediately a large 120 by 80 foot tent was ordered to serve as the dining hall. I think it was set up by sometime on Monday. Summer campers liked eating in the tent with throw-away dishes and silverware. They didn't have to do any dishes. The Amish community brought in a complete mobile kitchen. It was narrow and got hot in there, but staff could cook and summer camps could continue. Camp also rented a portable cooler from a Borkholder, another Amish, to hold our refrigerated food. Troyer Foods of Goshen brought a 'reefer' trailer late Sunday afternoon or early evening to store our frozen foods. Although the building was still burning in places, staff lined up and passed food from person to person from the Camp's freezer to the Troyer truck.

Monday morning my job was to set up office spaces in Ulrich House. I am sure that health care must have felt pretty crowded. I went in the side door where Arden's office had been years earlier. I had volunteers carry out mattresses that were lying on the floor and help me set up tables. Rex and I shared one 8 foot table. Mike had a spot right inside the door. Lana was on the opposite side of the room from Mike. To get to my "desk" I had to squeeze between the window and the table. When I needed to sort my bills, I took them to

461

the main program room in Ulrich House if it wasn't being used. The front room was used by Galen, Tony, probably Curt and healthcare.

Volunteers worked for days to clean and salvage anything they could from Becker. Each staff person had to turn in a list of what personal items they had lost for insurance purposes. Losses had to be submitted to one's personal insurance before submitting them to the camp insurance. I did not submit my losses. I lost a clock that Verne had made, some ankle or wrist weights and a hand-held small tape recorder for recording stories for a book I never wrote. What saddens me more is losing all the pictures, newspaper clippings, programs and records from the first 10 years of Camp Mack Festivals. On the other hand, I used to sometimes worry about how I would ever go through all of my years of accumulations in numerous file drawers when I got ready to retire. Well, the fire was indiscriminate. It got rid of things I wanted as well as things I didn't need. July 11, 2010 was a new start.

Rex asked the firemen to save his computer. They went into burning Becker and assumed the computer at the back of the office complex was his and brought it out. It turned out that the only computer saved was the one on which I paid bills and payroll. So Monday morning, I had the only computer. Rex would come in the wee hours of the morning to use "my" computer before I arrived at 7:30. Sometimes Mike would use it after I left at 4:00. Mapletronics worked fast to get us set up with a new network of computers in the next week or two.

Camp had to list everything we lost in the fire. That was a seemingly endless job. Also, we needed a document from the Fire Department to submit to insurance. On Wednesday Rex asked me to call the Fire Department to see about getting it. When I looked out my window, I saw a fire truck and learned that they found some hot spots still smoldering that day.

Back to dining and doing dishes. The health department worked with us at Camp as we set up a dishwashing station basically for pots and pans enclosed with plastic or tarps. Churches signed up to provide cookies for various weeks during the summer. Many cookies were baked and sometimes other food preparation was done at Bethany Church of the Brethren. Late in the summer, we were able to exchange the huge tent for a somewhat smaller one to serve our fall guests. But we needed indoor dining for winter.

A group of volunteers from Pennsylvania, possibly Phil Bohanon's congregation, were the angels who created a kitchen and an indoor dining space in the basement of Ulrich House. They spent at least a week enclosing the patio behind Ulrich House and wiring and plumbing the enclosed deck to create a kitchen suitable for preparing meals for fall and winter guest groups. The lower program room in Ulrich House became the dining room for the winter of 2010-2011.

Meanwhile, plans were drawn and permits were applied for to build John Kline to replace the dining, kitchen and office space lost when Becker burned. Plans did not include sleeping quarters. Many hoped, especially at the beginning, that sleeping quarters would be in a new Becker Lodge. As I recall, Rex made many calls and trips to Indianapolis to expedite the approval of plans and permits. He would receive a permit to pour the footer. Then he would go after the permit for pouring the floor. He was always only to get the very next permit needed or approval of the next phase. The entire John Kline building was completed as we received our final permit.

I remember working with Rex as he chose Gathering Room furniture, looked at chair designs and tables for the dining room, and considered carpet samples spread out in the Ulrich House meeting room. Management team members had to design the layout of their offices and determine what furniture they wanted. We had a lot of good, donated office furniture from the Mennonites (MMA?) who moved to a new location. So we could each choose what we liked.

In late May our new offices were set up. By June 2011, less than eleven months after the July 11, 2010 fire, Camp Mack was operating out of the beautiful new John Kline Welcome Center.

Always Something New

The Camp Mack Festival and dealing with Becker's loss and the choice of décor for John Kline are two major events that involved much of my time when I wasn't paying bills, doing payroll, writing newsletters, thank you letters, grant requests, Management Team minutes or other Camp business. But during my 25 years at Camp many other changes, building projects and improvements happened. When I arrived in August of 1988 the shop building was being constructed. In 1991 the Living Cross was discovered. I cannot tell you how many times I hiked to it over lunch breaks. The Camp Entrance pillars were replaced in 1992, the year before Arden retired. I remember seeing the stones going into place for the arch. Was it Kenny West or Lynn Bollinger who worked rebuilding the arch? Both of these men spent hours doing stone work at Camp.

During Becky's first year, 1994, the Observation Tower was built. Verne and I often took Mildly Wild Campers there to look out over the lake. The first zip line was constructed in 1994, not far from the Living

Cross. It did not have the multiple safety features that the current zip line located in the Wilderness area has. Thus, a few years later, it was taken down.

In 1994 or 1995 the sawdust floor was removed from Quinter-Miller auditorium revealing a number of old coins buried in its allergy producing moldy sawdust. The floor was covered with gravel. Camp found some affordable carpet and covered the gravel during the months that the building was used for activities. It was a very large area to sweep. The carpet had to me rolled up before the building could be used for winter storage. I have enjoyed going into Quinter-Miller since my retirement and walking on the beautiful cement floor.

In March of 1996 there was Open House for Phyllis Carter's dream of a Quiet Place for personal and small group meditation. The Quiet place opened at the old Camp Farmhouse location. It was beautifully decorated in inspiring oak furnishings. Stained glass windows donated or loaned by Phil Dowty were placed in front of the windows at the top of the stairs and beautiful colors poured through them. The Quiet Place at this location was broken into possibly more than once and the lovely new towels, linens and other items were stolen.

In1997 when the large staff residence with four apartments was dedicated, I accompanied Ellen

Swihart who sang, "Bless This House." I remember the Dedication Ceremony was outdoors prior to the open house. I must have accompanied Ellen on a keyboard, as there would have been no piano there.

While I was getting ready for the first Alexander Mack Festival, in 1998 and 1999 the Arky Parky and large wooden animals were being constructed. The small composite or plastic animals for young children were given in memory of Verne Ernest Leininger who died right before the first Festival at the end of September, 1999.

The original 12 panels of the Mural History of the Church of the Brethren were each 5 ft 6 inches tall and 15 feet wide, a set of six spanning 90 feet on each side of the auditorium. Margie Petry's new painting was 17 feet wide and nearly 6 feet high. It sat on the Quinter-Miller stage for a time as persons debated about where to hang it. Leonardo Neher, Medford's son, did not want it placed in a continuum with his father's work. Leonardo thought it didn't match his father's style. After much thought, some of us staff thought we recognized the major difference. Medford Neher's mural told the story of the Brethren from their beginning in 1708 to 1949, the year Medford Neher completed his work. Margie Petry's painting was, some thought, more like a collage of many things that had happened in the 50 year period from 1950 to 2000.

It was finally decided to hang it just inside Quinter-Miller's north entrance.

Rachel Pearson was about 14 years old when she rolled a mower over onto herself and was killed in 2000. She was a beloved camper. My memory recalls that she may have had a twin sister. The family wanted a memorial to Rachel to be built at Camp Mack. And thus the Gazebo was built as a memorial to Rachel in 2001, shortly before Becky Ball-Miller's resignation as Executive Director at the end of that year.

Rex Miller became Camp's Executive Director on March 1, 2002   I've already written about Mission Village. Mission Village was dedicated in 2003. Inside each yurt is a write up about the missionary couple for whom that yurt is named. These were researched and written by Peggy Reiff Miller, Rex's wife.

In December of 2002, the Quiet Place moved to Becky and Paris' former residence on Lake Waubee. Here it continued in ministry for the rest of my time at Camp. The therapy sessions for staff after the fire were held here. I usually took a day at the Quiet Place during Lent and a day during Advent to focus on the meaning of those seasons. When Curt Rowland joined the staff in about 2003, he and Karen moved into the farmhouse

During this time period the West Pavilion was built in 2003 and the West Cabins were improved with added ceilings and heat. Over 2004 and 2005 the Climbing tower was constructed in the wilderness and the Center Campfire Circle was created.

The boulder wall, a small version of a climbing tower, was constructed in 2006 at the playground area. In 2008, a large, colorful swing set with bench seats was constructed. This was used by both young and old.

Some improvements at camp were made because people asked for them. One such improvement was the railing at Vesper Hill. Older persons especially were challenged by the large cement steps. The railing was an answer to many requests.

I remember an old boat storage building at Becker Beach. It must have been "built on sand" because a storm with high winds could blow it into the stream/ditch behind it. I remember that one day volunteer Ray Swihart got the tractor and pulled the boat shed out of the ditch. He left it where it was supposed to be located. The next day I told Ray, "Ray, the boat house is back in the ditch." He didn't believe me at first. But he believed me when he pulled it out for the second day in a row.

In 2005 the North and South swim beaches were established and Becker beach became a dedicated boating beach. In 2012 a sturdy new boat house was constructed at Becker Beach. I am not sure what was being used when Becker beach became the boating beach in 2005

Many Non Brethren Call Camp Mack Their Camp

Brethren are not the only ones who love Camp Mack and consider it their Camp – although it is a ministry of the Church of the Brethren. Here is an example: One group Camp has worked with for years is the Church of God. First John Railton was in charge of their camp and then years later, Jason Railton, his son took charge. Church of God persons have had work days at Camp. They painted the 4-square outside of Becker Lodge when it needed painting. They have donated equipment for sound and lighting and many other items. When they come to set up their camp, they come with a large trailer load of equipment. In 2011 Church of God leadership approached Camp Mack about building a storage shed. Each group would share the cost and each group would share the space. The last I knew, we still have the shared storage building that both groups use.

More Program Additions

2012 saw the Aqua slide added at one of the swim beaches. The Gaga Pit was new for the summer of

2012 and a new 4-square was established behind John Kline Welcome Center. New lighting brightened things considerably in Quinter-Miller when it was completed in 2012. Archery bases were constructed in the wilderness area during my last summer at camp in 2013. I wondered at the time why we were doing archery, but I have discovered there are campers who love archery and come because of it. I guess there are many ways to reach campers for the Lord. The Laundry room was being remodeled as I was nearing retirement.

Time to Retire

My retirement date was December 31, 2013. I had worked at Camp Mack for 25 years, four months and a few days. Camp threw a great retirement party inviting persons from both districts. There were beautiful flowers. Tony went "all out" with refreshments. Mike, Rex, and others shared memories. It was a memorable occasion – a great ending to a wonderful 25 years!

Good bye for now, Sister Ruth

On Wednesday, April 1, 2015 Verne and I went to
visit Ruth Ann, Verne Henry's sister, at her home at
Gary, Indiana. It was Verne's 76th birthday. Susan,
her son Brian's wife, was there that day. We visited.
Ruth lay back in her recliner and added a few words on
occasion. Ruth was pondering whether or not she
should accept Hospice care. Verne Henry, who had
always been close to Ruth Ann, his only sibling,
encouraged her and shared some positive aspects of
Hospice that he had learned over the years working
with that aspect of health care. She accepted the
Hospice offer of care that day. Before we left Ruth
Ann worked to sit up at the edge of the recliner to get
her picture taken with her brother, Verne Henry.

On Monday, April 13, 2015 John took us to spend the
day with Ruth. He came on Sunday evening. When
we got to Ruth's, Brian and his 9-year old son Mattias
were there as well as the oldest son, Bob. Mattias
played quietly on the floor near his grandmother's bed.
Every so often he got up, held Grandma Ruth's hand,
and said, "I love you, grandma."

Ruth lay in a hospital bed and never opened her eyes
the entire time we were there, which was from late
morning until evening. She had a catheter, but was
taking no liquids or nourishment except for the little

water in the eye dropper that washed the morphine down. There was a nearly constant stream of people coming to see Ruth all day. Sometimes she seemed to know they were there, grunting a little once in a while – but never talking. People from the church, her former students, and neighbors were in and out. Once when three or four ladies came from the church, I got the group to sing all the verses of Amazing Grace. Meanwhile John used his knowledge of technology to make it possible for Barb to visit with Ruth and the family via Skype for a long time that day. Sean and Morgan connected with Barb and then came with her some way via technology to see Ruth and the family. When the family gathered for prayer around Ruth's bed, Verne was too choked up to pray, so I did the verbal prayer.

Ruth's son, Kevin, and family came after Kevin got off work. Emma had written a very lovely poem for her grandma. I don't remember for sure whether Emma read it or Allison read it for her. Toward evening the pastor and family came. Pastor Sean read scripture and had a prayer.

The next night, on Tuesday, April 14, 2015, we called Bob's cell phone and he put it up to Ruth's ear. Verne told her that it was O.K. for her to go and he didn't want her to be in pain any longer.

On Wednesday morning, April 15, 2015, shortly after 9 a.m. Ruth's spirit left this earth.

Sunday, April 19, 2015

Ruth's visitation was at Kuiper Funeral Home near Highland, Indiana from 3-8 p.m. Central Daylight Savings Time (4-9 p.m. our time).

Ruth looked lovely in a lavender dress with jacket. This was not the red, black and white outfit that she had intended to be buried in. That outfit was inadvertently taken to Good Will with other clothes that were cleared out by the church ladies helping Ruth's boys to make room for the hospital bed. It was a peaceful looking outfit. Madison had insisted they pick some of Grandma's magnolia blossoms to have in the casket with her. So fitting! Ruth was also holding a long stemmed rose.

I met so many of Ruth's good friends:

Carol – with whom she taught the Nursery School at the church. Celeste – whom she took grocery shopping regularly and then they ate out together afterwards.

Melita – who loved Ruth so much – they could share anything or just sit quietly without the need to talk. Melita showed me pictures of sunsets that she and

Ruth watched together at the dunes. They did this a number of times.

Mary – who came with Ruth to Sarah's Senior recital. She asked about what Sarah is doing now.

Kay – Who worked with Ruth in the church kitchen and has now taken Ruth's responsibilities in that area.

There were teachers she'd worked with in Special Ed. The one who replaced her when she retired was there.

Josh, whom Ruth had taken in, was there. Kevin had gone to get him from the University of Northern Iowa. Josh said he'd grown an inch from 6' 10" to 6' 11" since he went to college. My, is he tall!

Verne Edward arrived about 4:30 our time, I think. That would be only about half an hour after the visitation started. Kathy wished she could be with us, but stayed in Virginia to do between five and six hours of chores each evening. After a long time, when I realized that Verne Edward had a lot of papers to grade, I suggested that he go and get them. He did and worked on making a key. He was still there seeing people.

The Fairfield Inn and Suites had a great breakfast ready on Monday morning. Then we had a caravan – a five vehicle parade – going to the Ross Reformed Church for the Celebration of Life. John led in the

Volvo, followed by Allison in the Honda Accord hybrid, then came Verne Edward in his truck, Barb in their car and Sean driving their van. It was a <u>very</u> windy morning!

Most of Ruth's cousins were at the Celebration of Life service. We saw Larry and Gloria Taylor, who arrived about the time we did. They didn't come the night before. Their daughter, Kimberly, took off school and was there, also. Janet Moden was there. Anna and Emile Cerda had stayed overnight in a local motel – not the one we were in. (Ida Mae was not well enough to come.) Marie and Paul Sprankle had stayed overnight in a different motel. Many church people and friends were in attendance.

The sunset picture on the screen at the service was a picture of the sunset taken her final night on earth. A singer sang all the verses of "Beyond the Sunset" very beautifully. Ruth had told the pastor she wanted that song.

Pastor Sean shared how Ruth Ann and another lady took him, the new pastor and his wife out for ice cream – and paid for it. Then she invited them to see her gardens. He has raspberry plants and flowers growing at the parsonage from starts Ruth gave them. When she saw there was no Sunday School class for the toddlers, Ruth offered to provide one. She taught the pastor's children both in Sunday School and in

Nursery School. Ruth Ann was at the church every Wednesday night cooking the community meals and was in charge of cooking for many special occasions, banquets, funerals, etc. She was the one who led crafts at Vacation Bible School.

She made visits and took meals around and drove persons to doctor's appointments and grocery shopping. She loved serving others in the name of God. God had blessed her and she wanted to serve others. That's how she lived. She was living her faith. Her car was rarely in her driveway. She had to serve others because of God's amazing grace in her life.

1st Cor. 13: 12 Now we see dimly; then we shall see clearly. We see like through a clouded mirror. We'll see God face to face. Ruth was ready to see God face to face. Many wonder why Ruth didn't fight to live. "It was because she was ready to go," the pastor said, "and I can't argue with that!"

Even though you die you will live. Ruth Ann's memory lives on in the raspberries and flowers she gave the pastor and wife. Her memory lives in us, but she lives on in heaven. Jesus says, "I am the resurrection and the life. . ."

Let me share just a few of the memories of Ruth spoken after Sean's sermon. Her son Kevin's words stay with me. He said, "Our whole life is like a plant and we see them rise anew. Everything in life grows out of what one does. One thing mother (Ruth) loved was shopping. I (Kevin) was the youngest member of the Marigold Society and mom took us on a long trip to the meeting. in California. I have a cousin, Barb, five days older than I, so when we were growing up we were the same size. On that long trip and other times, when Mom saw a pretty sun dress or something she thought would look good on Barb, she would have me try it on."

God has a sense of humor! As mom was drawing her last breath, we kept hearing sounds like a helicopter and thought it was coming to get her. It kept going and going. Finally we realized we were hearing the washing machine!

Mattias Cheeseman: Grandma always made our birthday cakes. She made me a dragon and she said that she wouldn't make another dragon because it was too hard.

Susan Cheeseman: Ruth could turn problems into successes. She stored a special cake in the oven and forgot it and turned the oven on. The frosting crystallized – and was still good!

Another lady: When I was taking a group of students to Costa Rica I convinced Ruth Ann to go along. Half the beach was in their shower!

Everyone was invited to stay for lunch in the fellowship hall. It took a while just to find chairs to seat everyone. The gluten free chocolate chip cookies I had along for Morgan Dickason were popular with others as well.

When I realized that Verne Edward was going to lose an hour going back to Virginia and that he had to be back to teach an 8:00 a.m. class – the class he had graded papers for – I suggested that I leave and go home with him so that he could pick up the extraordinarily large (fishers?) ice chest that was left at our house when Caleb moved into his house at North Manchester last fall. Verne had bad traffic on I 75 because of an accident and finally stopped for a couple hours of sleep before going directly to Bridgewater to teach on Tuesday morning.

Barb and Rob left their van for Sean to drive back to Hope. Then he could use it to move his things out of Hope and Morgan's out of Butler at the end of the month when finals were over.

Barb and Rob offered to take Josh back to the University of Northern Iowa on their way home to Nebraska and Allison Cheeseman, who had planned to take him, was very grateful.

Allison Leininger took Morgan back to Butler and Dylan and Leah were with her as they had school the next day.

John and Verne Henry arrived at home about 15 minutes after Verne Edward had taken off. He had changed clothes, loaded the ice chest and got some veggies I fixed for him to take – or maybe it was a large pepper cut up and grapes.

John stayed all night with us and headed home Tuesday morning.

Ruth Ann was a joyous person whom we look forward to seeing again. Good bye for now, Sister Ruth.

"Just Like Everybody Else"

One of our special Church of the Brethren ordinances and part of our heritage is the Love Feast. Simply stated, this service includes a period of examination, feet washing, a meal and the bread and cup communion.

Whenever we would go to a new congregation, Verne would ask the deacons or those in charge of the love feast, "How does your congregation do love feast?" And the answer usually was, "just like everybody else." Well, experience had taught us that every church had its own way of doing love feast.

My first Love Feast was at my home church, the Bristolville congregation in northeastern Ohio. I remember that a ceramic bowl of broken bread topped with cooked beef and covered with a napkin was at each place at the table. When it was time for the meal, the pitchers of hot broth were passed and each person added broth to the contents of their bowl. So far, so good. The meal was eaten in silence and I was one of the slower eaters. Problem: That meant the sound of my spoon clanging in the ceramic bowl was loud enough to embarrass me.

The next place I remember having Love Feast was at Camp Zion. (Yes, here comes another Camp story!) I was chosen to be a deaconess for the youth camp Love Feast. Deacons and deaconesses set up the tables, the foot washing tubs and prepared everything needed with the help of adult counselors. I remember picking wild flowers for table decorations. After this solemn service, campers took their candles and walked to their cabins in silence, blowing them out and going to bed without talking. I stayed to silently help clean up after the service, and then took my candle and left without talking.

During my college days, I had already transferred my membership to Verne's congregation, Poplar Ridge. Love Feast weekend there was long Love Feast. There was preaching on Saturday morning, a noon meal, and more preaching in the afternoon. Then persons went home to do chores or prepare for returning to Love Feast in the evening. The next day, Mission Sunday began with breakfast, perhaps left over sop, pickles, and probably pies, and then there was a missionary or guest speaker with a mission emphasis. Verne's parents were deacons. Esther invited me, and I attended the deaconess meeting and helped make communion bread.

Usually communion bread, made by the church deacons' wives, was placed on the table in pieces just big enough to share with the person across the table from where you sat.. Two persons would hold the bread together across the table as we all said the statement of faith regarding the bread. At the County Line Love Feast there was no communion bread on the tables. I remember the deacons seating persons, indicating the end of table spots for deacons or deaconesses, depending upon whether you were at the men's side or women's side. When it came time for communion, the deacons came around with long sticks of communion bread Deacons broke off and handed a piece to each participant.

Prices Creek took their Love Feast preparations very seriously. All the tables were moved in the basement so that the floor could be scrubbed. When it was time to put the tables back, there was a special measuring stick to indicate how far apart the tables should be placed for Love Feast. Another stick helped the deaconess ladies know how to score the bread and a special fork was used to prick the holes representing Jesus' wounds. Prices Creek had long Love Feast with preaching before and after the noon meal. The noon meal was chicken and homemade noodles, probably red beets and pie. I knew who made homemade noodles and had them for sale. I bought my noodles to contribute. I can make noodles, but there are only so many hours in a day.

Prices Creek had a row of high cupboards in the kitchen each with multiple shelves. Each shelf was the size for holding a pie. There would be pie for lunch and pie for breakfast – lots of pie! Right after lunch the deacons would put the Love Feast meal meat on to cook in a huge kettle on the large gas stove. After the evening Love Feast, the deacons returned late that night and started over, cooking a new set of meat for the Mission Sunday breakfast. While the meat cooked, the deacons checked out what kinds of pies were available for their in-the-night snacks. They had usually hidden some favorites that they really wanted to eat. Once in the middle of the night, they had visitors. Police on patrol noticed lights on in the church basement and went in to see what mischief was going on. The deacons offered their guests pie and all was well.

Oak Park at Oakland, Maryland, was a fairly new congregation celebrating their 25th anniversary while we were there. Oak Park was the opposite of Prices Creek. Whereas Prices Creek had many traditions, Oak Park had almost none. When I asked the Oak Park deaconesses how I should set the tables, they said, "Any way you want to." The person who had made the communion bread was out of town and the communion bread was in her freezer. We didn't know that in time to make more. Verne was afraid he would be blamed for instituting crackers at our first Love Feast there when the communion bread was not accessible.

At our first Love Feast at Oak Park, I had a strong feeling of missing Linda Smith, my good friend from Prices Creek. That feeling persisted the next day and the day after that. Finally I had to call Linda. She shared that she was so upset that we had left that she couldn't go to Love Feast that weekend at Prices Creek. God surely does communicate.

Churches we served had Love Feasts twice a year, once on Maundy Thursday and once around World Wide Communion Sunday. The meal at the Maundy Thursday Love Feast at Bethel was usually traditional sop – bread, meat and broth. The October Love Feasts at Bethel sometimes had sandwich style or other less traditional meals. By this time, Love Feasts were less silent and talking at meals was allowed.

Love Feasts at North Winona (where we attended between pastorates), Columbia City and North Liberty did not leave me with long lasting memories, perhaps because we were there such short times.

At Wawaka, where we served for 13 years after going just to be an interim, I remember candle light Love Feasts with scripture readers often going to a lectern where there was light to read. I remember helping to set up. In an effort to have the sop hot when we ate, at Wawaka, Deaconessess tried fixing the sop in serving bowls, covering the bowls, and setting them in a warm oven to stay warm until after the examination and feet washing parts of the service. Most who attended at this small congregation helped clean up, put things away and do dishes.

And then came October 3, 2015, our first Love Feast at Bethany, the congregation we chose to attend after Verne's retirement from Wawaka on September 30, 2015. The men sat on one side of the sanctuary and the women on the other side for the examination service. Then we processed to the fellowship hall where candles were lit and the tables – one section for women, and one set for men, were set with old granite ware. Even the serving bowls were granite. Something else different was the passing of attendance pads to sign that you were there. After the service, persons brought out dishpans of soapy water and of rinse water. I helped do dishes at the table and then tables were reset for breakfast the next morning.

It was a new experience, not having anything to do to prepare for the Love Feast at Bethany and not having Verne in charge of the service. Life was changing. And then Tuesday at home at Milford, I was doing dishes and I started to cry. I thought, here I am joining a new church and I don't even know if they have a kitchen. Well, the next Sunday, two youth gave me a tour of Bethany's building. They have a marvelous kitchen and many other wonderful rooms as well. At recent Love Feasts, Bethany has set a table where families may choose to sit together at Love Feast. As young people say, "It's all good!"

Together in Retirement

Through our years together, Verne Henry did most of the driving. During our years in our country home across from the funeral home at Milford, Indiana, I drove mainly to Camp Mack and to Milford. I remember driving to Wawaka when Verne was recovering from surgery. I thought I had plenty of time, but when I arrived the choir, which practiced before service at that time, was waiting for me. That drive made me "a nervous wreck." I had to pull myself together and direct choir.

Now we were both retired. Wherever one went, we usually both went - together. October 1, 2016 was Verne's first official day of retirement. We spent a long day at the Camp Mack Festival; enjoying the many festival foods, displays, demonstrations, and seeing many friends. The festival auction ended about 5 p.m. and we hurried home to get ready to attend Love Feast at Bethany Church of the Brethren. Because many years earlier while serving Bethel Verne had been the pastor of some of the current Bethany members, Verne had spoken with Bethany's pastor and received his blessing to bring our memberships to Bethany.

This was our first time to attend Bethany as soon-to-be-members. Love Feast sop was served in granite bowls. We ate on granite dishes and drank from granite mug shaped cups. After the service ladies came with dishpans of water for washing and rinsing dishes. I helped wash and dry these granite utensils at the tables and then persons reset the tables for breakfast the next morning.

On our first Sunday at Bethany we were warmly welcomed at breakfast, worship and Sunday School. Still this was very different than going to a new church as pastor where we would be shown all areas of a facility and would hear about the congregation's programs.   I was feeling good about our weekend experiences until I was doing dishes in my Milford kitchen on Tuesday. I started crying. I thought: we have decided to move our membership to Bethany and I don't even know if the church has a kitchen. They wash dishes at tables.

On our second Sunday at Bethany, I shared my desire for a church tour with Bethany's Pastor Tim. He asked two youth, Kaitlyn and Cassie to show us around. Later that morning the girls showed me all the nooks and crannies of Bethany. Verne took the main floor tour. I discovered that the kitchen is large and well-equipped with a room behind the kitchen for the dishwasher and storage.   I saw the classrooms that were added with the help of money from the sale of Bethel's building. I saw the baptistery and storage rooms off the chancel area. I went upstairs and saw the youth room, decorations room, and game room. After the tour I felt more a part of my new church community. I was ready to commit to serving the Lord at Bethany when we officially joined the congregation as members later that fall on November 13.

In late summer or early fall, after the Elkhart County Fair was over, the Goshen Home Medical had scooters on sale that had been demonstrators at the fair. We decided a scooter would help Verne get from our house to the garage, a long trek across our yard. So, even though we couldn't take it up the stairs into the main part of the house, he could bring it into the back entryway. While we were at Goshen Home Medical we saw a display of a handicapped bathroom set up by Bail Home Services. Verne needed a safe bathroom with railings and a walk-in shower with a seat.

We met with representatives from Bail. It was decided our entire main bathroom would be torn out, except for the ceiling light. The "tearing out" began on December 8. Randy, the Bail worker who did most of our bathroom tear- down and building, covered our floor from the bathroom to the kitchen door with plastic. When he removed the old tub/shower stall, there were mountains of Styrofoam peanuts underneath. Randy filled his tall trash container with peanuts and wheeled it to the door planning to dump the peanuts into his trash collection unit outside. It was a very cold and windy December day. As soon as the worker opened the door, the peanuts started blowing. He tried to chase them down and pick them up. I saw that it was a futile effort, and I told him not to worry about them. He got many picked up, but I was still picking them off of the lawn and flowers the following summer. Our beautiful new bathroom was finished before Christmas.

Meanwhile we needed to get Micah home to Virginia for Christmas and we no longer had the use of the Wawaka parsonage for a stopping off place. It was decided that Micah would take the train from Elkhart instead of Waterloo. We were in the midst of some of the coldest weather ever recorded for December. Verne was not sure about finding the Elkhart train station and didn't feel up to driving in the bad wintry weather. My friend, Karen Rowland who lives at North Manchester, picked up Micah and brought him to our house. I went with another friend, Herb Reuter, who drove Micah to the Elkhart train station. Unlike Waterloo that had no train station building at the time, Elkhart train station had a building with a restroom and a person on duty. So we waited for the train inside.

The bad weather cancelled one of my favorite Christmas activities, Christmas Caroling. It was cancelled on the 11th because of snow and on the 18th because of cold and ice. I was scheduled to play the piano for the Christmas Eve service at Bethany, but Verne didn't go because the weather was too treacherous. Pastor Tim and Beth Sollenberger Morphew came and got me so that I could play for the service.

On Christmas Day 2016 we met our great granddaughter, Amelia Grace Dickason. Amelia was exactly seven months old on December 25th and this was the first time we saw her. I was amazed at how Amelia was already pulling herself up holding on to cupboard door handles. All of Barb and John's families were with us that day and it was fun to see our grandchildren playing with baby Amelia.

On January 24, 2017 the weather was better than it had been in December. Verne drove and we picked up Micah after his January term final at Manchester. We enjoyed having Micah with us during his January term break. Micah helped Verne change all three water filters under the kitchen sink. He helped me start six yellow and six orange sweet potatoes. Micah and I played games each evening during his break. I was so glad for someone who enjoyed playing games. Of course I lost most of the games we played - chess, checkers, Triominoes, Blockus and Rummikub – but I had lots of fun.

In February I gave the children's sermon for the first time at Bethany. It was near Valentine's Day and I had prepared 36 valentines, finding out ahead of time the names of children who attend and personalizing the cards. The five leftover cards meant that thirty-one young children came forward to hear the story. This was much different than the three children I usually had for children's story at Wawaka.

We purchased a table for seven for Camp Mack's Annual Dinner on St. Patrick's Day. There was a big crowd and I enjoyed talking with our guests at our table and many others I knew. Our two invited couples were both from North Manchester and brought Micah with them to the dinner. Verne and I completed the seven at our table. We left rather abruptly to rush off to the train station. Micah was going home for Spring break. I thanked God for lifting the fog and taking us safely to Elkhart and back. The train was late and left Elkhart at 10 p.m.

When we got home from the train station I was really tired. I had a snack before I went to bed at midnight. The next morning Verne got up, laid out the vitamins and let me sleep. Finally I got up in my nightgown at 11:00 a.m. when there was a knock at the door. Julia and her children, Savannah, Caleb and little Rachel, our Amish neighbors, were at the door. I invited them in, got out some toys, and went to get dressed. Verne

493

had gone to dress when he heard me get up. We had a great visit with our neighbors until about noon. I don't remember any other time I was in bed so late when I wasn't sick.

We celebrated two big events the last weekend in May: Leah's High School graduation on Saturday and Leah and Dylan's baptisms and John and Allison's reception by letter on Sunday at Prince of Peace Church of the Brethren at Kettering, Ohio. Barb and Rob arrived from Nebraska early Friday morning. After they slept a little while, we ate lunch and then we went with Barb and Rob to John's house. Morgan and Ben and a number of Allison's relatives were already there.

I had secured a room at the Springhill Suites motel for two nights and planned to share it with Barb and Rob. But the room Morgan had in the same facility was larger so Barb and Rob stayed with Morgan and Ben. I called Kathy and let her know that we had room for Verne Edward on Saturday night. She contacted him and he cancelled his reservation and stayed with us.

Verne Edward drove up during the night and arrived about 8:00 a.m. at Nutter Auditorium at Wright State University where the Beavercreek High School graduation was being held. Graduation was at 9:00 a.m. Some of Leah's 625 class members chose to graduate at the career center. When 580 graduates

494

processed in at Nutter Center, there was one too few rows of chairs to seat them all. There was some scurrying to get chairs for graduates. We had excellent seats along the side with no steps.

Graduation was well done and moved right along with good music and three good valedictorian speeches. Most amazing to me was the speed with which the diplomas were awarded. Two persons were on each side of the stage, one to call a name and one to hand out the diploma. The sides took turns in pretty rapid succession. Each graduate knew which side to approach for their diploma.

The rest of the day was a big party with lots of food and fun at John's house. Leah's graduation cake was served under a big tent.

Sometime Saturday afternoon the "Family Singers" practiced the song, "Rain Down," that we planned to do for special music at John and Allison's church the next morning. Dylan played drums, Ben, Morgan's friend, played electric guitar and I played piano. Singers were Verne, John, Barb, Leah, Allison, Morgan and Rob.

By about 8 p.m. Verne Henry and I were ready to go to Springhill Suites. Verne Edward had been up many hours having driven all night. I wondered if he would be too tired to get a haircut. But he wanted to get his hair cut and I had scissors along, so it was a quick cut.

After a special music practice, worship, baptism and a reception for the new members, we ate at Red Lobster and headed home. Saturday had been family party day. Sunday afternoon and evening the party at Leah's home was for her friends, neighbors, and church members.

I was getting supper on July 22, 2017 when I decided I wanted to try some of the sweet cherries we had frozen for dessert. That was unnecessary. I had a couple other kinds of fresh fruit in the refrigerator, but I was hungry for cherries. I went to the basement and got a container of sweet cherries out of the freezer. We had a board on cement blocks in front of the freezer to help us reach into the freezer which was also raised in case we would get water in the basement. I stepped off that board wrong and landed on the cement floor on my back. I was not sure I could get up. Verne called the EMS.

Two Bethany members, Joe and Lavonne, were on their way to eat out in Warsaw and driving by our road when they saw the EMS turn into our driveway and thought something must have happened to Verne. They pulled into our driveway right behind the EMS. They watched while the EMS loaded me into the ambulance and then Joe and Lavonne drove Verne to the Goshen Hospital. They said they would eat in Goshen and gave Verne their number to call when we were ready to return home.

I had some very painful days and nights with difficulty getting up and lying down. Lavonne came and weeded my garden. Members brought us meals. God certainly provided the care we needed.

I was much better by Thanksgiving, but still not lifting the heavy turkey. John and Barb's families were there and helped with cooking. Morgan tried to help, too, but she wasn't feeling well and had to lie down at times.

Back at Butler University Morgan got really sick after Thanksgiving. One morning she couldn't lift her head or sit up. When her heart stopped racing, she tried to walk. Walking made her out of breath. Butler Health Center gave her an EKG and said she had an irregular heart rhythm. She went to the heart hospital where they found nothing but told her if this happened again to go to the Emergency Room. The ER thought Morgan had pleurisy. Nothing helped. There was no follow-up. Her symptoms continued.

Meanwhile, Barb, Morgan's mother asked her members in Nebraska and especially a former nurse what specialists might be able to help Morgan and she set up appointments. Barb drove to Butler University at Indianapolis, and took Morgan home. The homeopathic doctor was especially helpful. His diagnosis was that Morgan had infection all through her body possibly that had been spreading ever since she had a hone fracture. He prescribed a number of natural remedies – Golden Seal echinacia three times a day, minerals, oil of oregano, but no antibiotics. She was off sugar and simple carbohydrates for a month and then was to add back fruits.

The cardiologist that Morgan saw didn't believe she had pleurisy. There was some thought that she had pericarditis. The cardiologist ordered tests. Morgan collapsed during the stress test. When Morgan had taken her homeopathic prescriptions for a couple days, she passed a large amount of what appeared to be infection and she felt better. At her follow-up Cardiologist appointment on her third day home, she felt surprisingly well. The Cardiologist okayed her to fly. Her mother got her a plane ticket to Indianapolis and Morgan flew to Butler in time to take her semester final exams.

Friends, neighbors and even a stranger helped Verne and I survive during the winter months of 2018. Travis Hartman stopped on his way to work at Camp Mack each morning after a snowfall and shoveled our steps, walk and back entry cement. Marc Beer plowed our driveways and cleared snow from in front of our garage whenever needed without my having to call every time. On January 11 Verne drove us to Warsaw and we cashed a check at Teachers Credit Union before going to Walmart. At Walmart we got a call over the intercom and went to the Customer Service desk to see why. A Christian lady had found our checkbook and TCU envelope of money on the ground by the driver's door of our car. She turned it in to Customer Service before we even knew it was missing.

The wonderful young Amish family that had visited us the Saturday morning that I slept so late lived about a mile from us around the corner on Old 15. I was delivering some Shaklee laundry products to them one day in March and went inside to visit with the mother, Julia, and see the children. I left my truck door open after getting out the second heavy parcel. After a longer visit than I planned, I went out to find that my truck wouldn't start. I was going to walk home. But Julia said we could charge the battery. She got out a big charger they used to charge lights for their buggy. She set it for my kind of battery; we charged the battery, put the charger away, and I was good to go! I never would have thought that a young Amish lady could charge my truck battery.

On April 4th neither of us was feeling well and Herb Reuter took us to see a doctor at Anglemyer Clinic who was not the regular doctor for either of us. Verne got cough syrup to help him sleep and I got amoxicillin to help me over a sinus infection. My journal praises God for his healing power, that neither of us is in the hospital, and for my heart rhythm returning to normal at the doctor's.

It was important for us to be as well as possible. Our grandson, Sean Dickason and Joslyn Haldeman's wedding was just days away on April 21. Sean's sister, Morgan, and her friend David Besel came from Indianapolis and took Verne and me to the celebration. We borrowed a wheelchair for Verne Henry from our church. David was so good to stop whenever Verne needed a break and push him to the bathroom.

Originally scheduled to be outdoors at the lovely Prairie Landing Golf Club west of Chicago, the wedding was moved inside the Golf Club as the weather was "iffy." I took a bag of little toys, coloring book and crayons and enjoyed spending a little time with Amelia, my great granddaughter when she wasn't needed to practice her flower girl walk at the rehearsal on Friday afternoon. Amelia would turn two years old toward the end of May.

Joslyn's parents had a delicious rehearsal dinner catered at their Batavia, Illinois home. Verne Edward flew from Virginia to Chicago, rented a car and arrived in time for the rehearsal dinner. After the meal we relaxed at the Pheasant Run Resort Hotel where we were staying. The young guys went to Sean's bachelor's party. Verne Henry relaxed propped up on the bed and was a part of the conversations happening as our room became headquarters for our family visits. Barb and Amanda (Caleb's girl friend) sat on the floor spinning wool and discussing various kinds of spinning instruments.

After eating out with some of the family for Saturday lunch, we got ready for the wedding. Persons sat at assigned tables for the wedding and the hors d'oeuvres and dinner that followed. Barb gave Micah Leininger the seating chart and Micah did a great job and getting many strangers to their proper tables. We were seated at Barb and Rob's table along with a young "preacher to be" and his friend. Joslyn was beautiful in her wedding gown and Sean looked sharp in his white tuxedo. The ceremony flowed smoothly with no apparent glitches and then brothers Rob and John Dickason entertained us with saxophone duets. Our John and his daughter, Leah, were in charge of the dance music.

Sunday morning I arranged for our family and the Dickason family, about twenty of us, to have brunch in a reserved dining room. I could do this as I had some discretionary money from an annuity's required distribution. Persons could have their meat of choice carved to order. Brunch choices seemed endless. If you wanted an omelet, you could choose its ingredients. There were all kinds of fresh fruits and vegetables. It gave me great pleasure to host a meal where each person could eat whatever they liked. I didn't have to cook or serve. I just enjoyed the family togetherness. I had a wonderful time that gave me long-lasting good memories. My journal calls those memories "lingering joy."

A phone call from our granddaughter, Morgan, would change our lives radically. Morgan called to say that she had set up an appointment with Nina, a marketing person at Greencroft Retirement Community at Goshen, Indiana. She and David would come from Indianapolis and take us to see Greencroft. She shared that they would be willing on another day to take us to our Church of the Brethren Retirement community, Timbercrest, at North Manchester, Indiana, where I sometimes thought we might live eventually.

The summer day of our Greencroft tour was beautiful. Roses were blooming along sidewalks. In Nina's office we saw some living options. I didn't want a house or even a duplex. I wanted to live close to people. I liked Manor IV with four wings and many apartments. We had been at our Milford country home for over thirty years. After the funeral home apartment no longer housed people but became a break area, we had no really close "next door" neighbors.

Nina showed us through Manor IV and we saw a couple of layouts of apartments. We saw the specialty rooms in this Manor: a family/game room; a rendezvous and exercise area, a quilting room and a library. The dining room was in the center. David liked the looks of the posted menus. When we toured the Community Center, I wasn't sure that we were going to get David out of the exercise room.

We were impressed and took an application. Getting into Manor IV would depend upon our financial ability. That meant I had to compile all our sources of income, pensions, annuities and life insurance policies. I worked hard and fast, calling institutions when I needed up-to-date financial information. Greencroft accepted our financial information on August 3rd and we were in line for an apartment. We were told it could take up to a year to get one, but Nina would get us an apartment as quickly as she could.

On August 22nd we got a call that there was an apartment opening up if we wanted it. It had two bathrooms, but no den. Nina, our marketing specialist realized how difficult it was for Verne to walk even with his walker. She thought the apartment in the 400 wing with the two bathrooms was too far off-center for Verne. She had another opening. We looked at apartment 213 and decided to take it. Once an apartment is sold (we put a down payment on it) the apartment has to be renovated. I had to choose the linoleum for our bathroom. The apartment didn't need new carpet or kitchen flooring unless I wanted it changed because the previous owner had not been there long, maybe up to two years, I think. I was so grateful not to have the strong fumes of a new carpet. Low VOC paint was used, so I was pleased.

Greencroft was and is one mile from our Goshen Hospital. There is a grocery store just across from Greencroft and lots of medical specialties are nearby. The natural foods coop where we are members was just a short distance away. And Bethany Church is within a drivable distance for me. We never went to look at Timbercrest. Greencroft met our needs. After our first meeting with Nina, we knew we would be moving to Greencroft as soon as we could.

The family must have realized our urgency, too. The last Saturday in July Verne Edward, Caleb and John came and spent the weekend helping us start to get ready to move. They trimmed trees and shrubs, burned the brush pile, and got books down from high shelves for me to pack. One big job was bringing everything down from the garage attic and stacking it all on one side of the garage to be auctioned. Caleb did a lot of the trips up and down while the others sorted and stacked. We had cast iron cook ware, a glass churn, flower pots, toys and all sorts of other things. What was the bulky wooden object with a lid that opened? a dough warmer? We didn't know.

Another very big job that day and one inherently dangerous was getting the very old and heavy safe up from the basement. We have a four-drawer fireproof filing cabinet which is heavy, but nothing like the weight of the heavy old safe. I cleared our belongings out of the safe and the guys engineered a plan creating a ramp and using ropes to help pull the safe up the stairs and into Verne Edward's truck. John and Caleb steadied the safe and Verne slowly inched the truck forward. I breathed a sigh of relief when the safe was on the bed of Verne's truck.

Sorting and packing, boxes and boxes of books from three sets of floor to ceiling bookcases and a number of other free standing bookcases, all that Verne Henry had made over the years, was a huge job. When her children were in school, our friend Dora came at least once a week in the fall to help pack. We were filling much of the basement floor space with packed and stacked boxes, many of them full of heavy books. Dean, Dora's husband brought his enclosed trailer to our driveway and helped load boxes of books into it.

It could be pulled over to the garage auction area shortly before the auction.

I asked our granddaughter Morgan who started us on this adventure if she could find us a good auctioneer. Her research found a couple from Warsaw, Indiana who owned Biddle Auction Company. We didn't know how long it would take to renovate our apartment, didn't have a move in date, and still needed to get on the auction schedule. All the Saturday auction dates for fall were filled. We were offered a Sunday auction date. Verne and I would not consider doing an auction on a Sunday. Meeting with Niki and Mike Biddle on October 31, we scheduled the auction for the Friday after Christmas, December 28. The personal property would sell first, beginning at noon, followed by the absolute auction of the real estate at 4:00 p.m. The next morning, November 1st we received a phone call from Nina at Greencroft sharing that we could receive the keys to our apartment on December 20. We had booked the auction in faith. My journal simply says, "Thank you, God!"

We walked through the house and garage with Niki and Mike considering what of our huge amount of stuff we would sell. We agreed on the advertising budget and the auctioneer's fees.

Deciding what to sell and what to keep was not easy. I had a large collection of Beanie Baby Bears that I really liked. I had Princess Diana, Soccer Bear, holiday bears and many other special bears. To me they were valuable and would sell well. I thought I wouldn't have any place to put them at Greencroft. The auctioneers divided them into four boxes and sold them for $1.00 per box, which brought me $.75 for each box of bears, a total of $3.00 for all of my collection. After we moved I discovered there was plenty of area above the kitchen cabinets that could have displayed my Beanie Bears.

I contacted Chupp's Pianos on State Route 15 near New Paris and hired them to move my piano to Greencroft on December 20, soon after the time we would receive our keys at Greencroft. That Thursday morning I put a large venison shoulder in my largest kettle to cook. Dora came to continue packing and to make soup when the venison was done. We still had freezers full of food. I told her to put whatever she wanted into the soup. She was at our house when the piano movers arrived to transport my piano.

The Bethany Church men arrived at our Milford home on Saturday morning, December 22, 2018, and loaded their trailers with our belongings. The furniture company where we had purchased a love seat and recliner delivered the items that morning to

Greencroft. An appliance company delivered the upright freezer we had purchased and set it next to my piano. After Bethany men unloaded at Greencroft, I served the delicious soup that Dora had made and had fixings for persons to make ham, turkey and cheese sandwiches. The men were crowded together wherever they could find seats.

John and Verne Edward came to Milford on Christmas night. On December 26 they came over to Greencroft and helped unpack and get ready for our Internet set up at 3 p.m. that afternoon. Verne Edward unpacked the Shaklee inventory. They both enjoyed going through more containers of old money we'd found. Enjoying the money sorting, they got a late start on building shelves to put in the pantry to hold my canned goods. Verne Henry went to bed and was bothered by their noise, but no neighbors complained. The beautiful and spacious shelves were finished at about 9:15 p.m. and then Verne Edward and John unpacked and organized the canned goods on the shelves.

Six days until the auction. We were moved to Greencroft, but we still had to empty our three freezers. By this time we had cleaned the freezers and may have consolidated everything into two large chest freezers. Rolland's Meat Processing had locker space available to rent. I kept a variety of food that I thought I could get into our new upright freezer and the freezer compartment of our refrigerator. We took all the rest of the food to our rented locker on the day before the auction. That was a cold job. John helped us.

Somewhere in this week was Christmas, but I don't remember much about that. December 28 was a big day. Our Bethany ladies set up a food court in our kitchen. The auctioneers and helpers were busy setting auction items outside the garage and setting up the paying station in our living room.

Persons were coming through to look at the house. Verne, John and Allison were helping to show persons around. The Hollar who built the original part of the house and his daughter who was home for the holidays came to see their former home.

Two grandchildren were at the auction. Dylan was present although he had all four of his wisdom teeth out the day after Christmas and was on medicine and a very soft diet. Sean came and brought Amelia. It was a damp, cold and blustery day. Allison offered a pair of gloves to keep Amelia's hands warm. The gloves were big for Amelia and didn't stay on long.

Verne Henry spent sale day in the garage until he came in for the auction of the property at 4:00 p.m. Household items were auctioned in the basement. Were there two auctioneers working simultaneously? I don't remember. Verne was able to sit on his motorized cart in the garage and also to drive it up to the house when he came inside.

The living room hide-a-bed couch and loveseat didn't sell. Neither did the bed in "Barb's room." John, Allison, Dylan, Sean and Amelia found places to sleep and stayed all night at the Milford house.. We went home to Greencroft.

Before Sean left on Saturday we went to Rolland's Meat Processing. It was cold and windy outside and even colder in the locker. We gave Sean as much food as he thought he would have room for at home in Indianapolis. Then John took the rest, planning to get it to Sean later. I turned in the locker key.

Sunday was a day of worship and rest. On Monday, New Year's Eve, we returned to Milford to begin cleaning up the auction mess. I didn't realize an auction could make so much mess. Verne was going through some papers in a drawer in the "new room." I knew he didn't feel well when he asked me to call his doctor. But I also knew that no doctor would be in on New Year's Eve. The doctor's answering machine said to go to the Emergency Room. So we gave up on the cleaning and sorting and Verne drove us to Goshen Hospital. That was the last time Verne Henry ever drove.

Verne greeted 2019 in Goshen Hospital. The Biddles came and filled the dumpster that I had ordered. It didn't hold half of the items in the mess. I ordered another dumpster, bigger than the first one. After a couple of days Verne was released from the hospital. I think he had gotten dehydrated from being in the garage during the set up and auction a couple days before. His bowels were also blocked.

On Saturday John, Dylan and Micah worked all day to clean up. John sorted and the younger guys carried refuse to the dumpster that was out by the garage. At John's suggestion I invited the Caleb and Rebecca Helmuth, the young couple who purchased our home, to go to the house at 11:00 a.m. and let the guys know what items they wanted saved. They kept the living room couch, the pool table and even the Britannica Encyclopedias. John and Dylan came to Greencroft and shared their day's adventures over the evening meal. Micah didn't come to supper, but headed back to Manchester University.

I survived day by day with God's strength in 2019. Reading my journal entries about Verne Henry's final months on this earth reminds me again of how greatly he suffered, physically, mentally and emotionally. Often he could barely move. Many times he didn't feel like eating. If he tried to dress himself, he might get two legs in one Depends hole or button his shirt unevenly. He was in the Goshen Hospital four times that year counting the time over New Year's Day as the first time. The first time he was discharged to come home to our apartment. After that he was usually discharged to rehabilitation; the third and last time he went to health care he had little hope of returning to our home.

I reluctantly took over all driving. I needed confidence. That was hard to gain when Verne would complain about my driving, probably wishing he could drive again. One thing neither of us wished for was to be back in our Milford home dealing with the frigid temperatures of minus 20 and a wind chill of minus 45 on January 30 and 31. We didn't have to worry about the geothermal heat or about walking outside to the mailbox. Everything we needed here was inside.

Music always brings me joy. Here at Greencroft I continued to teach my two piano students, Emily and Kendra. My friend Margaret and I played piano duets for an hour most Wednesday mornings.

One day Verne Henry asked me why I was making so many Swedish meatballs. I told him I was making and freezing them to be prepared if we got company. I didn't tell him that I was planning an 80th Birthday

Party for him on Saturday April 6, five days after his April 1st Birthday. I wondered how I could secretly prepare everything for the party until daughter Barb gave me the answer. Have the food catered.

Verne went to rehabilitation on the Greencroft Shuttle three times a week. He would ride his motorized cart to the main entrance and visit with passersby while waiting for the shuttle. I made trips to Martins to purchase or check on catered food for the party and pick out a birthday cake while Verne was at rehabilitation.

Verne Henry was really surprised on April 6th when he saw family members arriving. All but two of our immediate family members were at the party. Leah was playing women's Lacross for High Point University in North Carolina and Kathy was caring for the farm and selling chickens at their home at Timberville, Virginia. The family picture taken that day was the last one to have Verne Henry in it. Sean and Joslyn announced that they were expecting in October. There was a little one present "under cover."

I had reserved the family game room. We had space. We had a kitchenette. We had a pool table. We had a counter for food and outlets for the slow cooker of meatballs. I had ordered chicken, mashed potatoes, mashed cauliflower, gravy, a large platter of fresh vegetables and also one of fresh fruits. There was cake and ice cream. I think I fixed corn and green beans. I chose a red tuberous begonia and a birthday balloon for decorations. Verne Edward brought a large bouquet of daffodils.

Because we moved to Greencroft in late December and because the winter was exceptionally cold, and Verne wasn't too well, we had never explored the Greencroft campus. A number of us set out after we ate lunch to explore. Verne Henry was with us for a while until he was concerned that his cart would run out of power.

On Wednesday, April 10, Verne was vomiting and not feeling well. He also had persistent hiccoughs. I got an appointment and drove him to the Anglemyer Clinic at Nappanee. I went in and brought out a beautiful, folded new looking padded wheelchair and two sisters nearby helped me get it open by Verne's car door. Verne received a shot to help with his hiccoughs. I had taken a pan for vomiting and Verne didn't need it until we were ready to leave the doctor's office and head to the pharmacy. A kind nurse emptied and cleaned the pan.

Probably because it is a fairly long trip to the doctor at Nappanee and the Bureau of Motor Vehicles was nearby, we decided to stop there before we went home. I don't remember why we went there unless it was to register to vote or change our addresses. Anyway, going there was not such a good idea. Verne was so weak that a man on the parking lot insisted on making sure that Verne Henry got into the BMV from the parking lot without falling. A very patient BMV worker cared for us working with Verne who was barely moving.

I drove us home to Greencroft and Verne made it up the sidewalk and down the hall to our apartment. He headed to the bathroom. He had so little energy that the walker kept going in front of him and his body stretched out like a bridge before he slid down the wall to the floor near the bathroom. Firemen were called to come and pick him up as our staff are not allowed to do that. Verne was so limp that a firemen had me dial the doctor's office and he asked the nurse what shot Verne had been given. He told them never to give that drug to Verne again. Our resident director, Evelyn, brought a wheel chair for Verne to use, but I had difficulty getting him into it.

The next day, Thursday, Verne couldn't get up. I was doing some laundry and talked to our building staff about Verne. Our facility manager, Anita, said she would get my laundry; I needed to call 911. The EMTs who came to care for and transport Verne saw how dehydrated he was and started an IV even for the short, one-mile trip to Goshen Hospital.

515

On Friday we decided that when Verne left the hospital he would go to rehabilitation at the Greencroft Gables. On Saturday, one week after his birthday celebration he was able to get up, brush his teeth and shave with the Occupational Therapist at the hospital. Sunday afternoon Verne was transported from the hospital to the Gables.

Verne had regular physical and occupational therapies. His occupational therapist, Colleen, brought Verne home one day to see what changes would need to be made for him to live at home. First the bed had to be lowered. I called and ordered a three inch box spring to replace the thirteen inch one. This lowered the bed considerably. Then I had to find and purchase a bed railing that would fit the new height. The closest size I found was about one inch too tall to fit.

 It was May 13, the day I had signed up to go on the greenhouse shopping trip to purchase vegetable and flower plants. Colleen knew I would be gone that day. I gave permission for her to pick up my package with the bed railing if it arrived as promised that day. She did. She had taken her husband's Sawsall to work and had one of the physical therapists saw an inch off each leg for her.

By the time I got home from the trip, Colleen was ready for Verne to try the new bed height and railing. Verne came home to our apartment on Wednesday, May 15, just a couple days before David Besel and Morgan picked us up on Friday to go to Ohio for our last grandchild, Dylan's, high school graduation on Saturday morning, May 18th.

I had reservations at the Springhill Suites where we had stayed when Leah graduated. David and Morgan got us situated there and then John came to our room bringing us a chicken dinner with the chicken right off his grill. We enjoyed seeing children who stopped by to visit.

Dylan's graduation was at 9:00 a.m. on May 18, 2019 in the Wright State University Nutter Center. We sat in front of the bottom row of bleachers. The crowd noise and then the loud band bothered Barb's head as she was still recovering from her concussion injury. She had to leave before the end. As was done at his sister, Leah's ceremony, a pair of persons on each side of the stage took turns calling out names and passing out diplomas.

The party of relatives followed the ceremony with lots of food, thankfully preordered and ready for John to pick up. Some ate inside, some on the deck and some under the big tent. It was good to see some of

517

Allison's relatives that we rarely see and also to see some of our family. Dylan would have another party for friends on Sunday afternoon.

We attended worship at Prince of Peace and then ate out before beginning the trip back to Indiana. We got into such heavy rain that I didn't know how David could see the road, but he and the Lord brought us through it safely. I asked to stop at a Chinese Buffet in Goshen when we were about home as I didn't want Morgan and David to have to be hungry all the way back to Indianapolis. That also gave them a little break. I filled Verne's plate to make things easier for him.

When I took Verne to his doctor's appointment on Wednesday, May 22, we asked Dr. Coil why Verne couldn't walk. Dr. Coil didn't know. He did say that the walker was just for balance. Dr. Coil sent us to see Dr. Joan Szynal, a Physitrist, or Doctor of Physical medicine. She said that Verne's muscles were strong but appeared not to be getting messages. She ordered blood tests. She also sent us to see Dr. Neer, a neurologist. He also found that Verne's muscles were strong. After some further testing of the nerves, Dr.Neer said that Verne had Primary Lateral Sclerosis. This would eventually affect all the voluntary muscles, moving up from the legs. It was not supposed to affect non voluntary muscles like the heart. Supposedly the adult form was not a hereditary disease; the childhood form of the disease could be hereditary. In our final appointment with Dr. Szynal in July, she told us that there was nothing she could do and we didn't need to come back. Doctors had no way to help Verne but encouraged him to keep going to therapy to keep muscles moving.

During this summer, our Bethany congregation was interviewing perspective pastors. On June 22, our 56th Wedding Anniversary, members of the Search Committee brought Jim and Linda Vandermark to Greencroft to have lunch in a reserved room at the Groves Caf'e. Bethany Greencroff residents and a few other members living nearby met, ate and questioned the perspective pastor at this one of several small group meetings. The next day Pastor Jim preached and was called to be Bethany's pastor at the congregational business meeting following a carry-in meal.

As summer progressed, so did Verne's weakness. He seemed better on some days than others. Verne often walked bent to the right. I talked with Ron Leer, our former board chair at Wawaka and a chiropractor. He and his wife Gwen came after church on Sunday, July 21st. Ron brought a plywood and a piece of carpet underlayment to use on our bed to adjust Verne's hips and one ankle. I fixed lunch and Verne ate very well

with Ron and Gwen here. Then we iced his lower
back and right hip and he slept in his lift chair.

Monday we were getting ready to go to our hall dinner.
He got up to go, but could barely stand and seemed to
be walking sideways and running into things with the
walker. He made it from his lift chair to his roller
chair near the table and I pushed him on the chair to
the bathroom. We didn't go to the hall party.

On Tuesday Kathy and Caleb came to visit. Verne
stayed awake to ride his motorized scooter and go to
the garden with us. He also rode to show Kathy and
Caleb around inside Manor IV. He ate fairly well at
all three meals. Kathy and Caleb ate lunch and supper
with us.

Friday, July 26, 2019. Verne needed help to do
anything and everything today. Whereas yesterday he
walked a little with me holding his belt in back, today
there was no walking. Yesterday when he tried to
walk he was so wobbly that I cancelled his therapy for
today. He always liked going to therapy – probably
because of the male therapists and their goodness to
him. There are no other men in our wing – only
widows.

My Friday journal entry continues, "God gave me
strength to hold on to him yesterday, and as I told John

last night, 'I didn't drop him!' Today he needed me to tell him how to get up – like where to put his legs, and also to help him get up. I felt like I was getting a hernia today. I am surprised that I can use my back after its compression fractures.

My hair cut was scheduled for 2 p.m. today. Lisa Ensz was coming here to do it. At 1:30 I started getting Verne to the bathroom using the wheelchair. At 2 p.m. Verne was still trying to get off the stool. Finally we got him up and Lisa was a little late. Verne was as far as the bathroom door when I went to let Lisa in. Lisa helped me get Verne moved to his lift chair and transferred into it with the aid of his walker.

After Lisa left I managed to get Verne to bed. He took 'forever' to get up with my help and use the commode and get back to bed. He drank a shake I made late afternoon, but refused to eat anything. He clamped his mouth shut.

He can barely move tonight. He says he doesn't know how to get up. I tell him. I wait and wait. He isn't getting up. I finally change him in bed. I wonder if he has a bowel blockage."

Saturday, July 27, 2019. I got up at 6 a.m. and got myself ready. I made smoothies for both of us. Then I put them in the refrigerator and washed Verne and changed Verne's Depends and pajamas. First I put another blanket down to cover the soaked bed. He was not up all night. He couldn't. That's a first. Still he tossed and turned a lot. I gave him his shake and he drank it. He had a little Shaklee Hydrate and a sip of water earlier. I called 911 sometime after 7:00 a.m."

At the hospital Verne had at least five blood tests and a CAT scan. At 10:00 a.m. a doctor came in to say that Verne had an abscess that would need to be drained. I knew the redness and swelling on one side of his abdomen was not good. At 10:25 Dr. Murphy came in to say that she would be doing the surgery.

About 12:35 Verne went into surgery. It was not a normal day for surgery and the surgical waiting room was fairly dark and eerie with no lights on and no one else around. At about 1:20 p.m. Dr. Murphy came to tell me the abscess was all puss, no bowels. She said the hole was large enough that she could put her fist into it. She said that she went in through a scar area that may be more numb that some areas. She also put some pain medicine into the hole. She would repack the hole in the morning. Verne could have clear liquids. An hour later, at about 2:20 p.m. Verne was taken to a room and given the side next to the windows. Around 3:00 p.m. Verne was able to have beef broth and apple juice. He even had potato soup and pudding in the evening.

Doctors thought that Verne Henry should have a colonoscopy and John agreed. So Verne's Sunday menu consisted of a gallon of "clean me out juice." I was surprised to see Verne have a short walk before lunch (what lunch?) with physical therapists. Seeing him standing was amazing. He always tries so hard to accommodate and keep medical workers happy.

Sunday night's nurse had the job of getting the rest of the Golightly fluid down Verne and getting him on the bedside commode. He had downed about 2/3 of the gallon for me before I left shortly after 8:00 p.m. The colonoscopy was scheduled for about 5 p.m. on Monday. So that meant going another day with no nourishment by mouth. We learned Verne's wound is 8-9 centimeters deep and 8 centimeters wide and gaps open.

Verne is barely moving on Monday. He is exhausted and needs some nutrition. When they finally wheeled him off for what we thought was his colonoscopy, the anesthesiologist refused to work on him until he had a potassium test. At 4:52 he had the potassium test. It was fine and the colonoscopy proceeded. It showed a mass that we need to deal with after we get the biopsy report.

Verne does not complain. But he worries. He said he didn't sleep well Monday night because he was worrying about where he would go when he left the hospital. After I helped Verne with his lunch, John and I went to meet with Delia about getting a place in healthcare for Verne. We agreed to request a double room, window side where Verne wouldn't have to move later when he could no longer do therapy/rehabilitation to qualify to be in the Gables.

Friday, August 2, 2020. I wore a mask and watched the PIC line being put into Verne this morning. Later all other IV ports were removed. Fluids are going in through the PIC line. He cleaned up all of his breakfast and lunch today. That seemed like a good sign. But I was worried because the area around his PIC line was quite bloody. I didn't remember the area around the entrance of our grandson Caleb's PIC line being so bloody.

Verne was moved to the Greencroft Healthcare around 2:30 p.m. and began the rigors of being checked in. He was evaluated by Colleen, the head of occupational therapy.. A nurse gave him a TB test. Sarah, the staff who would manage his wound care, had to redo his vacuum pump set up because the hospital's machine connections didn't match those of Greencroft's portable machine. Sarah never thought to give Verne pain medicine before she dug all the packing gauze out of his huge hole, repacked it and got the wound vac hooked up . That was a bad and painful mistake which they never repeated. Dr. Buller examined Verne. A nurse took all his vital signs. He still had energy to choose his supper and he ate it all at the table in his room.

Verne is able to go to the dining room when a nurse pushes him in his wheelchair. His wound vac goes wherever he goes. He sits at his assigned table and chooses his own food. I purchased some tickets so that I could occasionally eat with Verne. I chose Salmon and he chose Swiss steak at noon on Sunday, August 4th. As long as he can go to the dining room and feed himself I don't have to be as concerned about his every meal. After lunch and a three hour nap, I went back to see Verne. He has been having hiccoughs again.

Monday morning, August 5. I went to see Verne before I volunteered at the Manor IV Gift Shop. While I waited for an aid to get Verne cleaned up and dressed, the night nurse called me over and told me this: "Verne didn't push his call button. Instead he got up, used his night stand as a walker and started toward the bathroom. His vacuum pump fell into the waste basket. He pooped a trail on the carpet. The night nurse cared for everything as best as she could. The carpet will be or has now been spot shampooed.

She heard his racket and found him. He may have taken his "briefs" off. I don't know."

As I ponder what the night nurse shared, I am sad but amazed. Amazed that Verne could get out of bed by himself. Amazed that he could walk. Understanding that it was night and the room was dark or maybe dimly lit and that if he couldn't find his call button, he would try to take care of himself.

After Verne was dressed, we/he went to breakfast. He ate eggs, bacon, toast, milk and juice. Physical therapy was waiting for him so I put his banana in his room.

I received permission to take Shaklee shakes for Verne to have each day and staff promised to give them to him. The shake the healthcare provides is 6% protein and 19% sugar. Shaklee's shakes are 20% protein. The ones I use have stevia and no sugar.

No call today with cancer care recommendations. Verne's family physician's office called to share that Dr. Coil's recommendation is for long term care. That seems like what we are doing.

August 6, 2019. Dr. Diener, the doctor who performed Verne's last hernia surgery and who was in the same medical group as Dr. Murphy phoned me over his lunch break. He said that if Verne would have surgery it "probably wouldn't make him better." I asked if he said "would" or "wouldn't." Dr. Diener said it probably wouldn't because they could take out a bad section, but with his fistulas or perforations the cancer could spread or infection return. Some lymph nodes were also enlarged on CAT scan. This could be because of infection or cancer.

I asked about the bleeding around Verne's PIC line which bothered me so much. The doctor said the bleeding was caused by blood thinners. I didn't know Verne was ever on blood thinners. I learned that the shots Verne got each day at the hospital in his stomach to keep from getting blood clots were blood thinners.

Last of all, Dr. Diener said we may soon want to consider Hospice. As I read this in my journal I wish that I would have taken these words seriously. When I asked the Social Worker, Melissa, at Greencroft about Hospice, she didn't think Verne needed that yet. In retrospect, it may have made him more comfortable. I now realize that Medicare will pay for one or the other – Healthcare or Hospice. I should have considered from whom I was accepting advice.

Friday, August 9, 2019. I was met this morning by Aide Amber who shared that Verne vomited at breakfast. The nurse shared the same. Now again he has the hiccoughs. It looks to me like Verne has the same symptoms he had in April when he got the promethazine shot that cured hiccoughs and made him limp and unable to walk. Dr. Buller, the doctor for Greencroft Healthcare, prescribed medicine for a "stomach bug." More vomiting at night.

Sunday, August 11, 2019. I went to see Verne before I went to church. He was in a wheelchair and they were holding off on his having breakfast because he had just taken a nausea pill. I heard he ate a little applesauce and a couple bites of toast. After Sunday School I hurried back to find Verne at his place in the dining room with noodle soup and applesauce while those around his had a beautiful Sunday dinner. I fed him his applesauce and a few bites of noodle soup and some apple juice. I had to help him hold his head up, he was so weak. This was just less than a week since he had gotten himself out of bed and walked toward the bathroom.

Finally I pushed him to his room because all aides were busy. We waited and waited and waited for someone to help him into bed. Finally he said, "I can't sit up any longer." That scared me so I went for help. When I got out front I said something like, "Verne is so weak. Are you going to wait until he falls out of his wheelchair?" In the short time I was gone, Verne fell forward across the bed. His legs were dangling over the side of the bed. But I did get him some help.

Now I was more a mess than he was. I laid down by him and he said for me to calm down. My chest is uncomfortable this afternoon. A nurse thinks the antibiotic in Verne's PIC line is upsetting his stomach. I'm not so sure, but I hope she's right. That antibiotic will be finished tomorrow.

Verne is not well. I worry. When I went back at 4:00 he had a gown on. Seems he messed his clothes. When they brought his supper he asked to be cleaned up first. He was poopy again. He was too weak to help them get him up, so they got a lift and got him to the bathroom. Three persons worked with holding and cleaning him. I fed him the small amount of mushroom soup they brought him, and his apples and apple juice, but his sandwich was too thick and hard to chew. He asked for a Shaklee shake and I was amazed that they brought it and he drank the full serving. By this time he was all poopy again.

My Sunday evening journal entry reads, "Oh Lord, please give Verne energy, a calm digestive system and a good night's sleep. I thank you for his care. Please calm me as well."

Monday, August 12, 2019. Verne was allowed to sleep in this morning. (That was an answer to prayer.) He was awake when I left him at 8:45 a.m. to go to run the Manor IV Gift Shop. An aide I had never seen before was getting him breakfast. When I returned, Colleen from Occupational Therapy had cared for him, cleaned him or helped him do what he could and dressed him.

For lunch he ate all his tilapia, mashed potatoes and gravy, and the strawberries out of his red jello and drank his grape juice. I fed him. He didn't want asparagus or salad. He sat at the table in his room to eat.

When I arrived at 4:30 Verne was sitting up in bed with soup, applesauce and a peanut butter cookie in front of him. I was upset that Melissa, the Social worker came right then to ask him a barrage of questions while he had his light on to use the bathroom. When aids finally came, he was quite messed. It upset me that Melissa didn't help him get to the bathroom or eat, but rather insisted on questioning him when he had other urgent needs..

12:55 a.m. Tuesday morning, August 13, 2019. I was awakened by a nurse from the Gables calling to say that Verne was dehydrated and they were sending him to the hospital. After phoning both the Goshen Hospital and the Gables I learned he left for the hospital at 1:15 a.m..

Daytime, Tuesday.   Tests show that Verne's diarrhea is not infectious. It is caused by his antibiotics. His bottom is very raw. His current IV is for pneumonia. He is also getting oxygen.

Wednesday, August 14, 2019. Verne has not been out of bed since he arrived at the hospital. The white board in his room say his "activity" is bed rest and bed pan.

Thursday, August 15, 2019. Verne had a swallowing study this morning. He is to eat small meals often, take small bites, put his chin down to swallow and never use a straw. This afternoon Verne left the hospital for Greencroft Healthcare on oxygen and a pureed food diet. He still has his wound vac.

Friday, August 16, 2019. After not being out of bed at any time during his hospital stay, today Verne has swallowing therapy, occupational therapy and physical therapy. That seems to me like too much work for one day on his first day back and first day to be out of bed since Monday.

Verne also had company today. John and family were over from their motel to say "good bye" before they left to take Dylan to Manchester University for his first year there. Morgan came shortly before 10:00 a.m. and missed John's family by less than an hour. She helped me with laundry, cooking, dishes and we worked together at feeding Verne. She fixed meals so I could pay sales tax and do my two Camp Mack Festival agendas.

Thursday, August 22. A grueling day. Schedule was:
    6 a.m. Occupational Therapy
    7:30 a.m. Breakfast
    9:00 a.m. Care Plan meeting – he went with me
    11:00 a.m. Physical therapy
    12:30 p.m. Speech/Swallowing therapy during
lunch
    1:30-4:30 Trip to Wound Center
    5:30 Supper, but too tired to eat

At the Care Plan meeting I was surprised to learn that Verne had an appointment at the Wound Center, a place we had never been. I asked questions: One was, "How will Verne be able to go to the Wound Center Appointment?" My answer was "Verne will have a tall wheelchair that can be laid down and the Greencroft shuttle will take you." He had that tall wheelchair the rest of his time at Healthcare.

When people at the Wound Center said Verne needed to come back, I scheduled our next Wound Center appointment for the morning of Wednesday, August 28, thinking we would not have to wait very long.. Wrong. But that second long wait produced a good diagnosis. Verne got back at lunchtime without the wound vac! Yeah! But there was also a bad diagnosis that day. The doctor working there from the Gerig group – not Dr. Diener – dictated his notes out loud in front of both of us stating "Cancer surgery would kill him."

Thursday, August 29, 2019 Temporary help was pulling Verne up in bed to eat supper. He has to sit erect to eat so that he can tip his head to swallow, so he gets pulled up in bed just before each meal, and no longer goes to the dining room. I usually get his food and bring it to him and feed him after he is pulled up. This night the temporary help banged Verne's head on the wooden headboard moving him up in bed. We both cried. Then he was too upset to eat.

Friday, August 30, 2019. Verne got off his oxygen today. Now if he gets up to go to the bathroom, no equipment is trailing behind – no wound vac and now no portable oxygen. He had been on oxygen since he last left Goshen Hospital on August 15.

Labor Day, September 2, 2019. Barb and Rob came to tell him they were going home. Verne could not hug Barb as he had the last time she visited. His ribs were too painful and he couldn't lift his left arm to put around his daughter. Verne Henry explained, "They grab me around the ribs and squeeze tight and move me. I hate to say anything, but I can hardly take it anymore." He continued, "I can't get up to use the bathroom because they keep squeezing my ribs." He couldn't drink today because he couldn't use his arm.

Wednesday, September 4, 2019 Care Plan Meeting. Verne has high pain level and didn't walk at Physical Therapy yesterday. Dr. Buller says his chest wall may be bruised and has prescribed a pain medicine. This Friday will be his last day on therapy. He will go on private pay on Saturday, September 7. Perhaps rest will give him more strength and help him eat and gain weight. Then he may have a therapy consult and perhaps go back on therapy on October 5th.

According to the Swallowing therapist, Verne is to use a sippy cup (never a straw) and always have water within reach. I enumerated problems about Verne's care to Social Worker, Melissa. I told her that Friday morning, September 6 Verne's bed table with his water in sippy cup was in the next room. The day before Verne's Shaklee shake was on his bed table in a glass glass with a straw. There was no way he could drink it. Sometimes I can't find water anywhere in his room except the water I bring in quart jars sitting on his chest of drawers. I provide plenty of reverse osmosis water for him and often fill sippy cups myself. But I expect the water and shakes to be in sippy cups and not to be moved out of his reach

Friday, September 13, 2019 Verne seems to be getting thin and fragile. Rest seems to be helping. Although he doesn't have therapies, he has some restorative exercise in his room occasionally. Now that his wound is much smaller and he doesn't have the wound vac, the wound still needs to be packed and taped over. My problem is that I have seen this wound cared for both at the hospital and at the wound center. In fact, at the wound center I was trained in case I would have to care for it. The nurse today didn't do it like I was taught, but I held my tongue.

Sunday, September 15, 2019. I have been feeding Verne all three meals each day now with him sitting up in bed. I asked for a staff person to feed Verne the Sunday noon meal so that I could be at the carry-in and farewell for Interim Pastor Musa Manbula and his wife Sarah.

Tuesday, September 17, 2019. Verne's bed is next to a window and when he is able we enjoy seeing squirrels and ducks outside his window. Today Verne said, "I hear a noise outside." Thoughtfully he added, "It sounds like a generator." The male caregiver confirmed that the sound was from a generator. We learned that generators are tested on Tuesdays to be sure there will always be back up power available. Verne was alert this morning. I would not have known what the sound was.

Thursday, September 19, 2019. Verne is eating well. He is not exhausted. He tells me his restorative therapy time is being increased.

Sunday, September 22, 2019. Verne was up for a short walk with a walker. Fernando, a caring staff person, helped him. Then someone (Fernando?) asked Verne if he would like to go to hear a gospel quartet in the meeting room. Verne went. Being out of his room and going to an event was a rare treat.

Wednesday, September 25, 2019. At the Care Meeting today, I mentioned that physical therapy is the only known treatment for Primary Lateral Sclerosis. Verne is getting stronger and may be evaluated to try therapy again on October 5.

Monday, September 30, 2019. Verne couldn't eat breakfast or lunch. He was sick after eating a bite or two both times and didn't keep the food down. His bowels aren't moving. Before supper the nurse gave him two Shaklee Herblax that I had provided. He ate for me at supper and seemed to feel better.

Saturday, October 5, 2019. As Chair of the Camp Mack Festival, I felt obligated to be at the Festival. I asked for a staff to feed Verne lunch. I went after I fed Verne breakfast and returned in time to help him with his evening meal. I left the Festival while the auction was still in process, and this time I didn't care. It was a cold and blustery day and I didn't wear a hat or have my earmuffs with me. I paid the price for leaving my ears uncovered.

The week after the Camp Mack Festival I was not feeling well. I kept trying to care for Verne, but I didn't want to give him my germs. My ears hurt and I was having trouble swallowing. I didn't feel like driving to my doctor at Nappanee, so on Thursday I went to CVS Minute Clinic near my home. The prescription I was given didn't seem to help. I could barely swallow.

I can't remember when I stopped going to feed Verne every meal, but as sick as I was, I don't think I went on Friday, Saturday or Sunday. I kept up to date on his condition by phone. John and Allison attended the Manchester University Homecoming on October 12 and then came to see me. John asked what he could do and I sent him to pick up a prescription for his father. Allison decided to stay with me and help take care of Verne as I couldn't. John went home.

Sunday, October 13, 2019. A Healthcare nurse called me and said they wanted to take Verne to the hospital. I asked to talk with Dr. Buller. I asked him what the hospital could do for Verne. He admitted the hospital couldn't help Verne. I said not to send him to the hospital. I then asked if we could get Verne on hospice. Dr. Buller agreed that Hospice was a good choice and said that meanwhile he would prescribe a strong pain drug for under Verne's tongue. Allison was back and forth caring for Verne, swiping his mouth with water, and helping me try to eat. Verne let Allison know that he didn't want to go to the hospital, and Allison assured him that I wouldn't let them take him there.

Monday, October 14, 2019. I called Dr. Lisa Orn at Nappanee and got an evening appointment. Allison was back and forth caring for both Verne and me all day. When it was nearly time to leave for Nappanee, Allison and I went to tell Verne that Allison was taking me to the doctor. I think he understood.

Doctor Lisa said I had "a cobblestone throat." She said I had been given enough antibiotic for a 300 pound woman; I weighed not quite 100 pounds. I should stop the antibiotic and go home and gargle with apple cider vinegar. Then I should have a smoothie and put ice cream in it as I needed calories and energy. I asked Dr. Lisa if I could go to see Verne tonight. She said to wait until morning. I needed to get my strength back.

When we got home, I gargled with apple cider vinegar and clear lumps came off my throat. I could swallow! Then we fixed our delicious chocolate smoothies, drank them and got ready for bed. I was barely ready for bed when a Healthcare nurse called to say that Verne had passed away about 9:55 or 10:00 p.m.

Allison and I dressed quickly and went to Healthcare. Staff were still getting Verne cleaned up when we arrived. As soon as I was allowed in, I held Verne's still warm hand. I was alone with Verne. Allison may have been calling John. Finally I said I was ready for Yoder-Culp Funeral Home staff to take him. I watched while he was readied for transport. His top cover was a beautiful maroon colored tapestry.

Our earthly days together were over. God worked out precise and glorious details for Verne's passing. Following is what I wrote shortly after the Celebration of Life Service for Verne Henry.

God's Timing and Preparations for Verne H. Leininger's Glorious Homecoming.

The Camp Mack Festival that I chaired was over and I, Phyllis was not feeling well. By Thursday my left ear and left side of neck hurt and I could barely swallow. I found I would need to fill out an application and wait to be accepted, if I was to get a new doctor nearby.

Moreover, some I called were not taking new patients. One told me to go to CVS Minute Clinic. I did and got a strong antibiotic. This was Thursday morning, October 10. I continued going to feed Verne his pureed meals as much as I could get him to eat that day.

Friday I couldn't swallow and couldn't even get a Shaklee shake down. I didn't go to feed Verne from that time on. But I was often in contact with healthcare by phone.

Saturday was Manchester Homecoming. John and Allison attended and came to Greencroft in the early evening. John asked me what errands he could do. I asked him to go to CVS and pick up prescriptions that Healthcare Doctor Buller had given me for Verne. John cared for that. Then because of a Notre Dame home game and no Motel availability, John and Allison slept in my bed and I slept on the couch. That worked well. They were close. John sat with Verne much of Sunday morning. Verne was in a lot of pain which his pain pill seemed to help very little. I was still sick.

While John was sitting with his father, Allison took me to the ER. I got a CAT scan of my head and neck and ER Doctor Ludwig called my doctor and then told me to get an appointment. John went home Sunday evening. Meanwhile, Leah was home on Fall break

540

from High Point with neither parent there to welcome her. Allison stayed with me, cared for me and went back and forth, also caring for Verne.

October 13, 2019 I got a call from Healthcare sometime late on Sunday that they wanted to put Verne in the hospital. I asked them to have Dr. Buller call me about that. When he called I asked what he thought the hospital could do. He said surgery was all they could do. I asked whether or not he thought Verne was up to surgery. He said, "No." So I said, "Then why put him in the hospital? Could you prescribe Hospice for him?" The doctor agreed, said that was a good idea and also said he would give Verne some morphine under his tongue for pain. Allison noted that Verne was very emphatic that he did not want to go to the hospital.

October 14, 2019 Monday morning I called Dr. Lisa Orn, my family physician and got a 6 p.m. appointment. Allison and I stopped on the way to tell Verne where we were going. (Dr. Orn works 7-7 on Mondays and Tuesdays.) She said the CAT scan showed I'd had a broken bone in the past. She said I had a cobblestone throat and sent me home to gargle with Apple Cider Vinegar and then get some nutrition in me. Dr. Lisa said I was too weak to see Verne that night and that I should get some nutrition (like protein shakes) and see him in the morning. She also said I had been given a dose of antibiotics for a 300 pound woman and no wonder my stomach was now upset. (I weigh 97 lbs.) She prayed with us and we left.

As soon as I gargled with the vinegar, my throat let go of gobs of clear yuk – not yellow, not green just a clear lumps. Allison and I enjoyed chocolate Shaklee shakes with ice cream and then got ready for bed. At 10 p.m. the phone rang. Verne was found unresponsive at about 9:50 p.m. We dressed and went right away. Now I had a little energy from nutrition (or adrenalin). We arrived while the staff was still cleaning Verne up. Verne was still warm. I held his hand and we spent time with him. Finally we were ready for Yoder-Culp employees to take him. I watched him being transferred from the bed and then covered with a beautiful tapestry before he was wheeled away. I was not alone. Allison was with me.

Then it was time for text messages and calls. Here are some of the details of Verne's glorious homecoming that God orchestrated – in no specific order:

Leah was already home from High Point, North Carolina and had the week for Fall Break until Sunday when she had a ticket to return.

Morgan had decided to come to visit Grandpa on Tuesday, Oct 15. She left early in the morning, arrived about 10 a.m. and came over to help us clean out Verne's room. Then she represented her mother's family at the funeral home to make arrangements that afternoon.

Verne Edward was on his way to see his father on Monday night, October 14, and planned to stay overnight with his son, Caleb, at Columbus, Ohio. John called Caleb around 10:30 p.m. Caleb said that Verne was a couple minutes away. When Verne Edward arrived John told him about his father's passing. Verne came on Tuesday morning. (He had gotten proctors to monitor exams he was giving at Bridgewater on Tuesday and Wednesday.) He was here to meet at the funeral home to help make arrangements that afternoon.

John also returned Tuesday morning. How glad we were that this was not a week later. John was scheduled to be in Alaska for work on October 28. Also, Allison was between jobs and would begin her new job on October 28. Thus she was available to be so helpful.

Barb was scheduled to see the specialist in Pittsburg, PA again on October 22 and 23 for her head injury. That week wouldn't have worked well for her. She was well enough to travel here and to write and present a beautiful eulogy for her father.

Meanwhile her brothers, Verne Edward and John Henry were able to spend time together working for hours to sort and put together a slide show about their father.

Joslyn, Sean's wife, was expecting in November. So Verne's passing a week later might have been more problematic for her.

With the visitation on Thursday, Funeral Friday and burial on Saturday, Leah was able to keep her appointments in Indy on Wednesday for her class project.

Dylan was able to be at the visitation and funeral and then return to Manchester to travel with his Cross Country Team to Oberlin, Ohio for the event on Saturday where he ran his personal best time.

Because this was during the week and the Notre Dame game was past, I was able to get rooms for each family for Tuesday, Wednesday and Thursday nights at Fairfield Suites. Then we traveled Friday after the funeral to Defiance, Ohio where I got rooms for the night before the burial. It was good to visit together, but I was pretty worn out.

Barb asked the Poplar Ridge church to be open so that we could use restrooms before going to the cemetery. It was not just open, the ladies had prepared a variety of food, coffee and Orange Juice to welcome us. Judy Chase wanted to show me the library. That seemed odd until I got there and discovered that for the month of October, the display in the library was on Verne

Henry. I hadn't even noticed his picture in the Manchester ad in this year's August Messenger where he is shown on a deputation team from years ago.

Is there any doubt that God loved Verne and Verne loved God? What a wonderful homecoming. And besides all that, there was no rain or snow and there were many traveling mercies. God is good!

By the way, my Hospice appointment was to be Tuesday morning at 9:00. Verne was already gone.

A Different Together

Family was together. We planned the service and chose a lovely wood casket as Verne built lovely walnut, oak and cherry furniture during his healthy days. Visitation brought many of our extended family and friends together to share their love and say their farewell to Verne Henry. Verne Henry was continually alive in my memory and my considerations for his memorial service. But I no longer worried about him. Already on Thursday morning prior to visitation that day, I wrote in my journal:

> "I spent many turbulent nights crying: Bemoaning the fact that nurses couldn't do more. Worrying about Verne's large surgery wound and his wound vac connection and if his wound was packed in all the tunnels of his hole. Crying because his PIC line was bloody. Concerned when he couldn't eat. Streaming tears when I played the song, "Go, Silent Friend." Worried when I got really sick on Thursday before he died that I would give him my germs and he would be worse. Missing him so much as it got more difficult to communicate. And then Verne was gone. Life is not the same, but I feel much more at peace. The Bible says, "Weeping may last for a night, but joy comes in the morning." I hope so.

I was scheduled to attend Seasoned Citizens Retreat at Camp Mack from Monday afternoon to Thursday after lunch, beginning on October 21, the Monday following the Saturday we buried Verne Henry. I hoped I could rest there and have some time away, so I went. I took one afternoon away from camp and went to see our former home and visit the young couple who purchased our property. The interior is spaciously opened up with most of the wall gone between the kitchen and living room. New cupboards and some new appliances make a lovely kitchen.

Our living room is now their dining room and Verne's big family table is there. Our computer room is combined with our bedroom, making a large master bedroom.

On the day I went to Camp Mack, October 21, 2019, Joslyn gave birth to Everett Henry David Dickason. Baby Everett had a difficult start to life and was in the hospital an extended time. His mother had a precarious delivery. The baby's grandmother, my daughter, Barb, helped the baby's family in Indianapolis while I was at Camp.

I discovered what anyone knows who has lost a mate – planning the memorial celebration is just the prelude to a lot of responsibilities. My list shows I wrote 38 thank you notes. The Yoder-Culp Funeral Home did the initial notification to Social Security of Verne's death, but I still had to complete the process of receiving Verne's Social Security instead of mine. Every insurance, bank account, credit card, and retirement fund needed to be notified and often have a death certificate sent. John helped me replace Verne Henry's name with his on my bank accounts. He also took me to meet with State Farm when I decided to put Verne's State Farm Insurance money into a State Farm interest bearing checking account. Other accounts I managed by phone and/or mail. I did drive to the Bureau of Motor Vehicles and get the car in my name only.

Barb insisted on staying with me for a couple of weeks after I came home from Camp. I wasn't sure at first that I needed her to do that. But I found myself depending upon her. She took me to the Social Security Office. We went shopping and found some summer sales. I bought a dress with peacock colors for Caleb and Amanda's peacock-themed wedding planned for June. Barb drove and went with me to my Echo-cardiogram. . On Monday, November 11, I had an eye appointment and the Optometrist was worried I might have a rare eye disease because of my long ear ache. I took the eye doctor's blood test order to Anglemyer Clinic when I went the next day to see Dr. Orn That Tuesday, November 12 Barb drove me to Nappanee after clearing about six inches of snow off her vehicle. This was my third appointment for earache and throat problems. Dr. Orn prescribed a nasal spray for allergies. The blood test for the eye disease was negative and my echo cardiogram showed my heart is strong with some signs of aging. That Tuesday afternoon Barb left before the weather could get worse.

I celebrated both my first Thanksgiving and my first Christmas without Verne Henry with my son John's family. At Thanksgiving a number of family members were able to be together. Besides John's family, Barb's family members were all there except for Sean who needed to work. This was the first time I met and got to hold Everett Henry, as I like to call him. John's son, Dylan, home from Manchester University, was a magnet for three-year-old Amelia, Everett's sister, who loved playing with him and didn't want to let Dylan out of her sight.

At Christmas it was just the five of us. Allison was sick and had missed some work. The rest of us went to Christmas Eve service at Prince of Peace Church. On the way home from church, John took his children's annual Christmas picture in front of a big lit tree at a park. This year I was in the picture, too.

Allison surprised me by making a bear out of one of Verne Henry's shirts and pants that I sent at her request with Dylan when he went home at the end of semester finals, a week or so before Christmas. I couldn't go to Ohio with Dylan as my friend, Margaret and I were in charge of the Manor IV Christmas program and I was also playing in a Christmas concert at the Greencroft Community Center. John came to the concert and then we went to his home for the Christmas holidays.

I was especially surprised when I unwrapped the bear because I thought Allison was too sick to be making it. Allison had gotten up early to work on it while she was sick. I call the bear, "Verne Bear" and sleep with the bear every night.

The year 2020 will be remembered for the pandemic of the Covid-19 virus. The virus restrictions began at Greencroft at 7:00 a.m. on March 11. Healthcare closed to all visitors except for end of life situations. I am so thankful that Verne Henry is no longer there. I wouldn't be able to visit or to go three times a day to feed him.

Until March 11, I was busy and active on campus. Early in January Independent Living Chaplain Dan Petry called and asked if I would play the piano for the Manor IV Service of Remembrance on January 16. Some thought I should not have said, "yes." Others commended me for being willing to play for the service. Pastor Dan called back to confirm that I was willing to play when he realized that Verne Henry would be one of the twelve Manor IV residents that died in 2019 who would be remembered during this memorial service.

I played a 15 minute prelude and also accompanied Chaplain Dan who sang "In the Bulb There Is a Flower and "O Love that Wilt not Let Me Go." I know the Spirit of God was with me when I played. I felt a great peace and many afterwards shared that they were touched by the music. When it was time to remember Verne, I was able to read the following:

> We moved into Greencroft, Manor IV, on December 22, 2018. Verne talked about how he would be able to go anywhere on site with his motorized cart. But it was winter. After several hospital stays, his excursions soon were to rehab. He enjoyed talking with persons while he sat on his cart near Manor IV entrance waiting for the shuttle to take him to rehab. He considered Jeff and Loren, his rehab therapists, to be his good friends. They were his main male companions here as he was the only man in our section of hall 2.

> Verne turned 80 years old on April 1st, 2019. He was completely surprised when we celebrated with our children from Ohio, Virginia and Georgia and grandchildren from Indy and Pennsylvania in the Family Game room on the Saturday following his birthday. It

was a wonderful day and that day was the first time he took his cart outside exploring with family members. He enjoyed being outside on his cart about three more times – twice to Martin's Grocery and once to our garden.

He was grateful for all the advantages of being at Greencroft – no maintenance to worry about, the hospital a mile away, and Healthcare close by. Verne passed away in the Gables Healthcare on October 14, 2019. He experienced Greencroft for less than ten months.

The next day, January 17, I accompanied Dan Steiner who played Ave Maria on the violin for the Talent Show in Jennings Auditorium at the Community Center. I felt it went well.

I enjoyed attending Thrive Meetings on various health topics. At the February meeting I learned how emotions have an effect on the heart and also on skin and kidneys. I will try to stay calm, be kind, be active, and eat well. Laughter is an amazing medicine. I'll try to keep a positive attitude and foster a large social network.

My social network included a Goshen College Junior named Brooke. She was a nursing student and I was her older adult for a series of interviews and assessments. Brooke and I became good friends. She hurried to my apartment (Greencroft is close to Goshen College) when she got off work at about noon and I would have lunch ready. Lunch was not part of the agreement and Brooke always said I didn't need to fix lunch, but she always seemed to enjoy eating with me and I looked forward to eating with her and sharing good conversation. She always had to take my blood pressure and pulse before she left.

My big job during early 2020 was doing my Federal and State taxes. I sent them off to Beverly Worth at Winona Lake, Indiana to be checked and electronically filed. Beverly called me at 9:45 p.m. one night early in March to talk about my estimated taxes for next year. She is so caring. She explained how much higher my taxes will be in 2020 without Verne's ministerial housing allowance. My taxes came back completed on March 11, just as the Corona virus was closing things down here.

The Covid-19 pandemic shut down most activities and closed schools, colleges, and churches. I kept busy practicing the piano accompaniment for concertos that Sarah and I hoped to play at Caleb and Amanda's June wedding. I also spent much time writing. On March 17, 2020 I was typing the beginning of my Camp Mack memories and, if the doorbell rang, I didn't hear it. When I realized that someone was at my door, I went and found Anita, the Manor IV Facility Manager, handing me a bouquet of orange/salmon colored carnations from my student nurse, Brooke. There was also a pint of raw honey from Brooke. What a surprise! She had to go home that day and she didn't want to take any chance of transmitting the virus to me. Goshen College closed. While I was accepting the flowers, my piano pupil, Kendra, arrived for her lesson. This would be her last lesson until the pandemic is under control. As I write this on October 30, 2020, it has been over seven months since I've taught a piano lesson.

Before the virus, Margaret and I often met at 10:00 a.m. on Wednesdays to play duets. That is just a memory now. Months ago I was asked to serve on the Manor IV Vesper Committee. But since we cannot have groups meetings, we cannot have vespers. I have never had a Vesper Committee meeting.

He is there with you.

March 28, 2020. Corona Virus is keeping most of us inside. I can go out for essentials – groceries and medicines, it I need any. If I go out, I must stay six feet apart from anyone else; it's called "Social Distancing." All churches, libraries, schools and non-essential businesses are closed. Those who are able are working from home.

Yesterday morning, March 27, 2020, during my devotional time a song started playing in my head. The words I was hearing were: "He is there with you,

He is there with you; He is with you all the time." I knew there was a song with those words in our hymnal. I got my Blue Hymnal out, found it on page 585, and read all the words to this short hymn.

In your sickness, your suff'rings, your trials, and pains,   He is with you all the time.
Persecution, temptations, and loneliness,

He is with you all the time.

He is there with you, He is there with you,
He is with you all the time.
He is there with you. He is there with you,
He is with you all the time.[1]

It really does feel like Jesus, God, the Holy Spirit and maybe even Verne are with me. Let me share some things that seem miraculous to me.

On Tuesday, March 17, my Goshen College Student nurse, Brooke, for whom I had been her geriatric patient for a class assignment, had to leave college and go home to Ohio to study on line because of the Corona virus. At this writing, that was eleven days ago. Brooke had a beautiful bright orange/salmon colored bouquet of carnations delivered to me. Each

morning I add enough water to fill the quart jar the
flowers are in level full and each morning I look with
awe at the bouquet that is as fresh looking as the day it
was delivered. The water in the jar is not even cloudy.
But most surprising is the fact that day by day I have
watched unopened buds swell, then open part way,
then burst into full flower. Not just once; but this
miracle continues.

There are more miracles here. Almost a year ago
when I knew I was going to enjoy visiting
Greenhouses with a Greencroft excursion, I wanted
Verne to have a flower in his window. So I bought
him an African violet at Martins shortly before my
Greenhouse tour. It lived well in his window. It
probably didn't get watered too often. And then I
brought it home to my north window (my apartment's
windows are all on the north side) where my plants get
little direct sunlight. This winter I picked off droopy,
dying leaves. I was sure the plant was dying as Verne
had. Then I noticed that it came in a colorful pot with
no holes in the bottom. I repotted the plant, putting a
coffee filter in the bottom of the new pot covering
holes to keep the dirt from sifting out. It didn't look
too promising. But one day I noticed tiny leaves
emerging in the center of the forlorn African violet.
They continue to grow and more new leaves are
showing up. That reminds me of the new life that
Verne is experiencing.

My north window has not benefited my Christmas cactus which hasn't bloomed since we moved here. My aloe vera just don't want to grow. And so it has been with some other plants. They don't seem happy at my north window. In the past, Verne and I would set up grow light bulbs and make sure my sweet potato plants that I started each year had plenty of light. And in the past I would put about six or seven sweet potatoes in jars of water to sprout. This year I only put one orange sweet potato supported with nails stuck in at intervals to start in a quart jar of water. Today I have a window box full of 19 sweet potato starts off that one potato and it is still putting out more. This feels miraculous to me.

And then there is my strange dream and my great joy as today (Saturday) I received a Registered Retail Merchant Certificate with only my name on it. It was a rough week but it turned out – yes that word again – miraculously! First of all, the dream. There was a long line of traffic basically stopped. Verne took me around behind a building. We went inside. It was packed with clutter and large junk items. He started moving them out of the way until there was only a barbed wire thing-a-ma-jig sticking up about five feet. He was going to pull that out. Then there was a big overhead door that I could go through.

Indiana Registered Retail Certificates are good for two years. Ours, with both our names on it, was automatically renewed, but receiving it did me no good. Our certificate expires on March 31, 2020 and Shaklee must receive a current one by that time. Since Verne's name is no longer on our Shaklee account, Shaklee cannot and will not accept a certificate with both our names. I started working in February to solve this problem. I sent a letter, a death certificate, an email and then I thought I had passed the final hurdle when I filed form ROC-1 taking Verne's name off as an officer of our company. That didn't work –they said maybe I was going to add an officer – really?

So I spent Tuesday on the phone mostly on hold and then being transferred elsewhere. In the morning I was the 40th caller in line. But, of course I didn't get what I needed when the call was answered. I was told to call the Secretary of State to dissolve my partnership. But when I got through, after a shorter wait, I was told that the Secretary of State does not record General Partnerships, which apparently ours was as they found no record of it. Mid afternoon I was calling the number I was told could help me, but I was the 43rd caller in line. After 38 minutes I was the sixth caller in line – almost there. I bumped my phone, lost my place in line and the call would not go though any more that afternoon.

Wednesday morning at 10 a.m. I had a zoom call with Todd at Camp Mack (who of course was working from home during the Corona virus) talking about my memories of camp during my 25 years working there. As soon as the zoom call was finished, I called the number I hoped could help me and was only the 9th caller in line. While I was on hold, I called Margaret Weybright on the house phone to cancel our duet time this morning because of the social distancing (6 feet apart) virus restrictions.

A kind lady, Tonya, answered the phone and said she would explain the situation to her supervisor and be back to me no later than tomorrow. I felt encouraged, remembering my dream. I felt like the way would be cleared for me today. At nearly 2 p.m. on that same day, Wednesday, Tonya called me to say that the only way for me to get a registered retail merchant certificate in my name was to start a new business. Later I could cancel the current one. She also shared that her friend, Lois, was much better at navigating the IN/biz website than she, Tonya, was, and would I be willing to let Lois help me. Of course I said yes and was soon transferred to Lois.

Lois and I were on the phone together for three hours. Sometimes circles wouldn't fill in when I tried and I would have to go out and try again. Several times autofill would fill in my address and include commas.

The program we were working in would not accept any punctuation in addresses. I fought with that autofill problem several times. Other times all kinds of addresses came up – it looked to me like all my Shaklee addresses for persons I send Shaklee to, appeared. And then I would go out and come in again. Lois was so kind and so positive. I felt sorry for her having to work with me, but she said we are going to succeed. At the end, after I paid the registration fee for my new business, I thanked Lois repeatedly and said it was probably time for her to go home. It was about 5:00 p.m. That's when I learned she was at home. Lois said I did a good job because I didn't get upset or give up. I really felt positive about the experience. Now, it's Saturday – three days later - and I have the certificate. Thank you, God. Since it has to be mailed and not faxed, how am I going to get it to California by Tuesday? I wonder if I can overnight it from Manor IV.

[1]Text and Music copyright ©Asempa Publishers

God is Good – Life is Good!

Throughout the spring and summer I enjoyed my 20 by 20 foot garden and my small 10 x 10 foot plot. I missed not being able to show Verne the peas or beans I picked and shell or snap them in Verne's healthcare room as I had during the previous summer. On the other hand, I could come and go and stay at the garden as long as I wished without needing to hurry back to feed Verne. Life was different. I often would be in the garden and remember how Verne would have done something – like which way up he said lima bean seeds should be planted.

From mid-March on I did not go to church. For a time, my Bethany Church of the Brethren was only on Facebook. Then, long before most churches reopened, (At this October 31, 2020 writing many churches still hold services only on line for the safety of their parishioners.) Bethany began holding in-person services as well as on line. I decided I wanted to go to church on my 77th birthday on Sunday, September 20, 2020. I played the piano, entering and leaving without relating to others. There were four "praise team members/song leaders" without masks on stage, not far from where I was playing the piano.

On Tuesday, September 22, I went to see Dr. Lisa Orn at Nappanee. I shared with Dr. Lisa that I had gone to church and that most persons there were not wearing masks. She said that I should not go back to church until spring when hopefully persons would be vaccinated.

During the summer I was asked to serve on the Manor IV Council as secretary. We meet monthly, spread out in the dining room with one council member per table.

My first meeting was in August. We use a microphone to hear across the room and wear gloves as well as masks. At the end of the September meeting I moved that we consider having the Manor IV Christmas Program taped and shown on Greencroft's Channel 13.

The Council's hour of meeting time was basically over and my motion was passed quickly Karon A. spoke up and said that she would help me. I didn't know I had agreed to plan it; I had planned last year's Christmas program with Margaret. Anyway, the council had the Christmas Program Committee and the meeting ended.

At that September Council meeting it was noted that some activities on campus have begun meeting again, with masks and socially distanced. It was requested that our Manor IV staff ask permission from Greencroft's Resident Director for residents to resume playing games. Permission was granted and my Rummikub group resumed meeting. After playing, my friend Faye and I usually walk the halls. Walking all of Manor IV halls is walking a mile. I shared my dream with Faye. I said that I had a wild idea that I would like to have a back drop of a stable and animals painted on an opened out refrigerator box for the Christmas program.

The next day I called Sara Zook, a Manor IV resident whom I knew was an artist and told her that the Manor

IV Christmas program would be aired on Chanel 13 because we couldn't have a live audience. I then shared my "wild idea" with Sara. Her response to me about "blew me away." She said, "Oh, I've done that before. I know what you are talking about. I can do that!"

She had previously blown up a picture out of a child's Christmas coloring book. She didn't have the coloring book and so I went on line and printed coloring pictures of a donkey, cow, and lamb and dove. Karon and I approached our Manor IV staff member about perhaps getting a refrigerator box from the maintenance department. Anita said that her sister owned an appliance store and she, Anita, would bring us a couple of refrigerator boxes. Sara's stable and animals are nearly life size and look like they could walk into the room. She had to tape an extra section of box onto the original refrigerator box to have room to paint the entire scene.

Meanwhile every resident whom we asked to be in the Christmas program said "yes," without hesitation. One of our residents built a folding manger in the Greencroft wood-working shop. Our plan was to keep persons outside the dining room until time for them to perform and to keep them socially distanced when they perform. December 10, 2020 was set as the date of the filming of this year's Manor IV Christmas program. I wish that Verne Henry could see the end result of this labor. The Manor IV Christmas Program was shown four times on our Greencroft Channel 13 during the 2020 Christmas season, with the last time being at 10:00 a.m. on Christmas Day.

I don't know what next year will bring, but God has blessed me in the midst of this Pandemic year. I hope I can be a blessing to others.

My Epiphany

The book was nearly written. I still had to complete the Love Letter chapter. I was doing my lunch dishes. Suddenly I had an "a ha!" moment. I realized that all the opportunities and blessings that I so enjoyed as a child and youth, were an introduction and a preparation for what my life would be. I rushed to write this down.

I remembered how I enjoyed Sunday School and Bible School classes, and playing the piano for Sunday School and Worship at the Bristolville (Ohio) Church of the Brethren. I recalled times in Youth Fellowship and going to District Youth Retreats whenever possible.

I thought about how special being a camper at our Northeastern Ohio Church of the Brethren Camp every summer beginning at age nine was to me, and then how thrilled I was to be asked to be a Junior Leader. I thought how unusual it was for me to be chosen to serve as a deaconess to help prepare the Youth Camp Love Feast. This was my first year at Youth Camp. I was one of the youngest youth campers. The following summers I was working. This was the only time I could have served in that role.

I was often asked to share my musical gifts. I remember playing special music for a Mother/Daughter dinner at the Bristolville Methodist Church. I accompanied soloists at contests. I played at numerous school events. I even taught private piano lessons in my later high school years and directed my home church's choir.

Once when asked in a high school class to write about what I wanted to be, I wrote that I wanted to be a minister's wife, but that I would probably just end up teaching English. Even that life desire was already planted in my heart.

If you have read this far in the book, you know that God blessed me with joys as a Pastor's wife, and also as a mother, a camp leader, a camp office manager, a piano teacher and a teacher at church and in public school. Hopefully I am fulfilling God's plan for my life.

Praise and Thanks be to God!

Phyllis E. Leininger
December, 2020

Made in the USA
Monee, IL
03 February 2021

59575960R00312